D1108413

Plate I.—(Frontispiece)

St. Patrick's Cathedral, New York City. This is considered one of the most beautiful organ cases in America, and was designed by Robert J. Reilly. All of the organs in the Cathedral were built by Geo. Kilgen & Sons, St. Louis.

The
Contemporary American Organ

Its Evolution, Design and Construction

---

by

WILLIAM HARRISON BARNES 1892–

Mus. D.
Organ Architect
A.B., Harvard University

Profusely Illustrated

J. FISCHER & BRO.
119 W. 40th St., New York
1956

Lithography by EDWARD KEOGH PRINTING CO., Chicago, U.S.A.

Coxhead DSJ Composition by COMPREHENSIVE COPY SERVICE, Chicago, U.S.A.

To my wife,

Edith McMillan Barnes:

In grateful recognition of her encouragement and assistance.

"If this work finds favor, hers the honor; if it fails, mine the blame."

The author at the console of the organ in his home, 1510 Forest Ave., in Evanston, Illinois

TABLE OF CONTENTS

pedal chest
165

LIST OF ILLUSTRATIONS

EXAMPLES OF ARTISTIC ORGAN CASES

EXAMPLES OF LARGE ORGAN CONSOLES

INTERIORS OF ORGANS AND ORGAN FACTORIES

ILLUSTRATIONS OF THE VARIOUS PORTIONS OF AN ORGAN

(HISTORICAL AND DESCRIPTIVE)

The chief purpose of this work is to acquaint the reader with the details of present day organ building, as practiced by the leading builders of America, both with regard to the mechanisms and the tonal architecture in current use.

The author still believes, after twenty-two years, since the first edition appeared, that there is a place for such a work not filled by any other book dealing with this subject.

As an introduction to those chapters dealing specifically with mechanical and tonal matters, historical chapters precede. They are: "History of the Organ Action", "History of the Organ Console", and a completely new chapter on the "History of Tonal Design", which should be of particular interest to present day students of the organ.

The author is satisfied that we have progressed a good way along the road in both mechanical and tonal improvements since those monumental works on the organ were written in English, to wit: "The Organ" by Hopkins & Rimbault (1855) and "The Art of Organ Building" by George Ashdown Audsley (1904). Not to mention the great French Bible of organ building "L'Art du Facteur d' Orgues" by Dom Bedos de Celles (1767). Since the first edition of this book in 1930, several excellent works on organ building have appeared in England. "The Modern British Organ" by Noel Bonavia-Hunt, "The Electric Organ" by Reginald Whitworth, and "The Organ" by Clutton & Dixon. Even so, the emphasis of all three of these works is centered on English organ building, while we are concerned primarily with American, as the title of the book suggests.

Because American organ building is more thoroughly covered herein, than in any other available work, it appears that no apology is necessary to keep publishing edition after edition, each one attempting to record the improvements in the art of organ building.

The chapters on the History of Tonal Design, and the later chapters on Specific Examples of Good Tonal Design have caused the author more worry and concentrated thought than any others. He has been accused of being "middle of the road" in his tonal ideas. There is even something to be said in justification of this position — by driving in the middle of the road, he avoids the ditches on either side. The author certainly has tried to be impartial and to give the ideas of the extremists a fair hearing also. An article on Baroque organs and organ playing, which he wrote a year ago for "The Diapason" may have generated more heat than light, but it certainly left no doubt of the keen interest in this subject. The "History of Tonal Design" chapter was written primarily to give as much factual information as possible, with a minimum statement of opinion. In this way, perhaps more light than heat may be thrown on this highly interesting, if controversial subject. Surely good should come from making easily available this knowledge of the tonal concepts of organs of the 17th, 18th, and 19th centuries in various European countries. A knowledge of the past, should precede an intelligent appraisal of the present. Our problems are of the present, but we can solve them better with some historical background.

This book is written, first, for the beginning student of the organ to whom the modern organ is more or less a mystery, and second, for organ builders and advanced students of organ construction who are interested in knowing precisely the type of action and the tonal ideas which their contemporaries employ.

It has been a source of great satisfaction that numerous organ builders have cooperated heartily in the preparation of this work. The very fact that such co-operation has been given so freely, indicates that there has been a remarkable change in attitude of organ builders toward each other. It is gratifying to know that the day in which each builder was suspicious of his contemporary and afraid that the other might learn his secrets of construction seems to have passed in America. Certainly only good can come when a wider dissemination of knowledge is available to all.

Though the modern organ is a highly ingenious and complicated mechanism, (the product of many inventive minds over a period of many centuries) yet there should be no mystery about it. Even in its present high state of development, every mechanical part of it, although more difficult to explain than the earlier types of organ action, may still be clearly understood by referring to the plates, drawings and diagrams.

This book does not include specific drawings and complete information about the work of every American organ builder. That would manifestly take more space than is at the author's disposal, and would be quite unprofitable from the standpoint of information. The work of many of the important builders is given in some detail. All general types of action usually employed by American organ builders are shown, also some highly specialized and unique types, where the builder has done enough important work to justify such consideration, or if the builder's work is alone in its class, such as direct electric action. The writer has necessarily reserved the privilege of including the information that in his judgment will best satisfy the two classes of readers referred to.

Acknowledgements and heartiest thanks are due to all builders who have so kindly permitted the writer the use of their shop drawings from which the reproductions in this book are made. The origin of each drawing is credited in the text, with the name of the builder. A work of this dimension could not attempt to make original drawings of the many actions illustrated.

The drawings which are used in connection with the description of older actions, and some of the drawings of organ pipes have been reproduced from various works on the organ, acknowledgement being accorded in each case.

INTRODUCTION

The writer is indebted to Mr. T. Scott Buhrman, editor of the "American Organist", for permission to use many half-tones of organ cases and consoles that have previously appeared in that journal. He has also granted permission to quote from some of the author's articles in the "American Organist", and from other articles in that magazine. Also to Mr. S. E. Gruenstein, editor of "The Diapason" for permission to quote.

Acknowledgements and thanks are due to that great authority on organ tonal matters, the Rev. Noel Bonavia-Hunt for his kind permission to quote freely from his works "The Modern British Organ" and "The Church Organ."

It is a pleasure to acknowledge the great interest and many suggestions and ideas offered by Mr. Edward B. Gammons of Groton School, in preparing this revision of the work.

Finally, to all others who have either given permission to quote, or in other ways have assisted in the preparation of this work, the author wishes to convey his thanks.

Evanston, Ill., July 29, 1952

CHAPTER I

A BRIEF HISTORY *of the* ORGAN

The origin of the organ dates back to great antiquity. The flute, which is a component part of the organ, is one of the most ancient of musical instruments. It is pictured on the walls of early Egyptian tombs; specimens of it still in playable condition have been unearthed and can be seen in our museums. The Pipes of Pan are sometimes considered to be the original source of the organ. Frequent allusion is made to the organ in the Bible, though it is not at all clear that this refers to even the ancient type of organ. The ancient Greeks had no particular musical instrument called an organ, but the word with them was a general name for an instrument, work, or an implement of any kind. Confusion may have arisen concerning this term by the translators of the Bible from the Greek. The Greek musical theorists applied the word "organic," as a general term, to instrumental music.

About 284-246, B.C. a man named Ctesibius, who followed his father's trade of barber, being of a mechanical turn of mind, noticed that the counter-weight of a movable mirror used for the purposes of his trade, produced a musical sound by the force with which it drove the air out of the tube in which it moved. By experimenting he succeeded in making a machine containing only a single vase, inverted, with an opening at the top to which was attached a trumpet. When water was pumped into the base of the vase, the air was driven forcibly through the trumpet, producing a very powerful sound. This machine caused so much admiration it was consecrated to the temple of Venus.

The principle involved may be illustrated by the modern fire engine, which is practically the Ctesibian vase reversed. In the ancient instruments, water was used to force air in a steady flow through an opening in the top of a hemisphere. In the modern fire engine, air confined in the top of a hemisphere forces the water in a steady stream through an opening in the bottom.

Later research has cast some doubt on the authenticity of the Ctesibius legend. The ancient Mesopotamians and Egyptians, even before the Greeks, had instruments which bore some rudimentary resemblance to an organ. The hydraulus appears to have been invented about the fourth century, B.C. but the name of the inventor is by no means certain.

A pupil of Ctesibius, named Hero, an engineer, wrote a work called "De Pneumaticis," in which he described many mechanical applications of steam, water and air. He also gave a description of a musical instrument developed from the old Ctesibius trumpet in which the air was conveyed from the vase to a row of pipes arranged in the order of a musical scale, any one of which could be caused to sound at will, the motive power being supplied by water. The instrument was called the "Hydrau-

Plate II.
Cathedral of St. John the Divine, New York City. Skinner Organ Company,
builders of the organ.

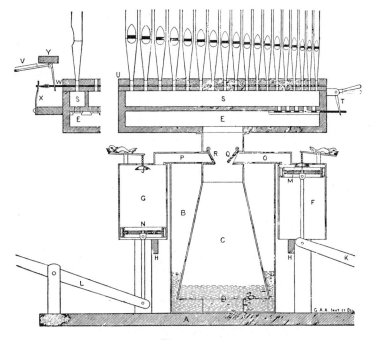

Figure 1.

Ancient Hydraulic Organ. Invented by Ctesibius about 200
B.C. Drawn by G. A. Audsley from photograph of terra cotta
models by Rev. Père Delatre. Models found at Carthage. When
the piston N, was forced up in the cylinder, G, air was directed
though P into the inverted vase, C. The pressure of air in this vase
against the water, D, drives the water up on either side into B.
When the cylinders are not supplying air, the valves R Q close,
preventing the escape of air. The weight of the displaced water
forces the air in a more or less steady stream into the pipes. The
water in the early organ took the place of a reservoir for producing more even pressure on the wind. The two cylinders, with their
pistons were later supplanted by feeders.

lus" and appears to have been a predecessor of our organ, more directly
than the ancient flute.

The Hydraulus became exceedingly popular, and was for centuries
a source of admiration and astonishment to the unlearned. "The powerful
sound, the mysterious pumping of the water, the exertions of the slaves
who were obliged to pump with all their might to supply air of sufficient
quantity, all combined to attract attention to it." This instrument was
used for contests, public games, feasts, and even in homes of the wealthy.

In the British Museum are ancient Roman coins of the time of Nero
that depict the Hydraulus quite clearly. A piece of pottery recently found
at Carthage represents a performer seated between the two cylinders
described by Vitruvius. The Emperor Nero was particularly attracted by
the Hydraulus.

HISTORY

Tertullian, speaking of Ctesibius as the inventor and Archimedes as the improver of the Hydraulus, says: "Observe the extraordinary genius of Archimedes. I speak of the Hydraulus. What members, what parts, what joinings, what rows of pipes, what a compendium of tibiae, and all composing one great whole! That spirit, which breathes from the trouble of the waters, is administered through the parts, is solid in substance, divided in operation."

The compass of the Hydraulus must have embraced about three octaves at about 100 A.D. The pipes were tuned to the ancient Greek modes. The use of water in the Hydraulus was to steady the pressure of wind. An organ pipe will rise in pitch if the pressure is slightly increased. It has been the object of organ builders in all ages to supply wind to the pipes at an even pressure. Immense difficulties have had to be overcome to finally accomplish this. When water was no longer employed to steady the wind, organs built with regular bellows were called by ancient historians, "pneumatic" organs to distinguish them from the Hydraulus. In the Hydraulus the pipes were made to sound by opening valves admitting air, played by keys, somewhat like the modern organ.

St. Augustine applied the word "organum" to any musical instrument, but particularly to any which was blown by bellows, in which connection he used the word in the plural. The Talmud mentions an organ of ten pipes played by a key-board as being in existence in the second century.

In about the tenth century began the rise of contrapuntal experimentation in combining voices which led to the great eras of polyphony, and later, harmonic writing. Through the ninth century all music had been in unison or octaves and the vast companies of musicians described in the Bible play in unison or alternating groups sounding monophonic music.

Sir John Stainer says, "The large pipes of every key of the old organ stood in the front. The whole instrument sounded and shrieked in a harsh, loud manner. The key-board had eleven to thirteen keys in a diatonic succession without semitones. It was impossible to get anything except a choral melody for one voice on such an organ. The width of a single key amounted to three inches and even as much as five to six inches. The valves to the keys and the whole mechanism being clumsy, playing with the finger was not to be thought of, but the organist was obliged to strike with the clenched fist and the organist was often called an 'organ beater'."

Gradually the keys were reduced in size and semi-tones were added. Before the year 1500 the keys had approximately reached their present normal proportions. The invention of the pedal key-board is credited to the German, Bernhard, a skillful musician of Venice, about the year 1470. Hopkins & Rimbault think that it was certainly earlier than this. A study of the organ compositions of Frescobaldi, the celebrated Italian organist,

12

who lived in the early part of the seventeenth century, indicates that the organ was then playable by fingers and pedal keys, as at present.

From about the beginning of the sixteenth century until the early part of the nineteenth there does not appear to have been any great improvement made in organ building, except a gradual improvement of the pipe work.

The organ was from very early time used in connection with the music of the Church, though in the thirteenth century the Priests of both the Greek and Roman church thought the use of organs in divine service to be "scandalous and profane." Even to this day the Greek church does not tolerate the use of organs in its services. In spite of this, largely due to the fact that education of any sort was generally confined to monasteries and castles, the use of the organ and other musical instruments became general not only in great churches, but in monasteries and convents. The historians of this period make much of several monks distinguished for their art of playing the organ and other musical abilities.

The *Regal* was a portable organ, having one row of pipes sounding the treble notes, that was used in processions, carried by one person and played upon by another. In contrast to the Regal or portable organ, there was the *Positive* organ from the Latin word *ponere,* "to set down." This instrument was provided with a key-board of full compass and was played upon with both hands. The portable organ was used principally to assist the voice and to play the melody of the plain song.

Sir John Hawkins states, "The Positive is the noble instrument to the harmony whereof the choral service has, ever since its inception, been sung. The Regal, or portative, on account of its smallness and the simplicity of its construction, was so-called."

Hopkins & Rimbault, in their history of the organ, explain the term which is frequently found in medieval manuscripts concerning organs in which an organ is nearly always referred to as a "pair of organs." They state, "The truth is that a pair of organs meant simply an organ with more pipes than one, similar to the way we frequently refer to a flight of stairs, as a pair of stairs."

Numerous examples of old organs, of various types and some very beautifully finished, are to be seen at the Metropolitan Museum of Art in New York and also at the George F. Harding Museum in Chicago.

A large organ existed in the Winchester Cathedral, England, in the tenth century, which caused widespread attention and comment from the medieval writers.

Nearly all early organ builders were ecclesiastics, usually monks of a mechanical turn of mind. It was not until about the fifteenth century that organ building became a profession. For many centuries it appears that organ building was developing in various parts of Europe, but more especially in Germany, France and England. These latter countries possessed distinct schools of organ building until nearly the beginning of the nineteenth century.

Perhaps the most important school of organ building from about 1359 until 1780 was the German—Saxony in particular. Over two hundred organ builders can be counted in Saxony alone as having flourished during this period, including such masters as the Silbermanns, Hildebrand, Gabler, Sommer and Herbst. The great Bach played upon organs of Silbermann.

Since the time of Luther, the German worshippers have been devotional and almost always possessed of strong musical voices. To support this hearty and enthusiastic congregational singing, organs of considerable magnitude were required. The building of large organs, until the invention of the pneumatic lever, was beset with great difficulties. The touch or resistance of the keys became so heavy that it put a practical limit to the size of the organ.

The only measures then known to combat this unsatisfactory state of things were:

1. To retain a moderate wind pressure, but to make the windchest pallets small, only capable of supplying a few stops at one time. This allowed every stop to be used individually and a fair number together, but virtually reduced a large organ to a small one. For example, an organ of forty stops was furnished with pallets only sufficiently large to permit the use of half this number at any one time. These could be chosen in successive groups according to the taste of the organist, but it was impossible to play "full" organ.

2. To reduce the wind pressure somewhat, thereby largely spoiling the effectiveness of the reed stops and the upper portions of the flue work. The French school usually chose the former method, while the German school of builders employed the latter.

Dom Bedos, in his great work (written 1766-1768) "L'Art de Facteur d'Orgues," has a long chapter on what he considers "usual and desirable" stop combinations. He says, for example, "No Flue Work is ever to be used with the pedal reeds." Some of the combinations he suggested seem weird to a modern organist, but they were necessary because of the fact that the whole or "full" organ could not be used at the same moment.

The organ in France had seldom to sustain large masses of congregational singing, so that it came to be treated merely as a kind of orchestra, intended to embellish the services of the Roman Catholic Church. It was customary, and still is, in the large churches of France, to have two organs, a small one in the chancel to accompany the choir, and a much larger organ in the gallery at the west end of the church, whereby brilliant technical displays are possible at intervals during the service.

The German system of employing low wind pressures was unfavorable to good reed tone, so this latter was largely neglected. They invented as a substitute, that lovely family of organ tone, known under the general name of "Gamba."

The English school was greatly influenced by the German, as several important German builders did much work in England, e.g., Father Smith, Schulze, and Snetzler. The influence of these men was very great on English organ building. As the English did not require such large organs, they ordinarily employed slightly higher pressures and made many improvements of their own.

Later pages will mention more specifically the inventions of three Englishmen that greatly improved the organ. They were as follows:

Jordan's Swell, rendering the organ capable of expression;

The invention by Flight of inverted ribs in the bellows reservoir, affording much steadier wind pressure;

Barker's pneumatic lever, permitting organs to be built of any size, and still be capable of being played "full" organ, as the resistance to opening large pallets was overcome pneumatically.

These various discoveries and inventions enabled the modern builder to develop these ideas and to combine effects hitherto only attained in different countries under conditions special to each.

The two greatest organ builders of 19th century England and France "Father" Willis and Aristide Cavaille-Coll will be more specifically mentioned in our chapters on the Construction of Organ Pipes, and the Development of the Pneumatic Action. Even though the organ has such great antiquity and a more or less constant evolution, it is perhaps not too much to say that there have been as many improvements made in it both tonally and mechanically in the past thirty to fifty years as in the many centuries previous. These later improvements we shall examine in some detail in the following pages.

From the foregoing brief account of the early history and development of the organ, it appears evident that the organ is in truth one of the most ancient of musical instruments and has had continuous evolution bringing it to its present state of high musical efficiency.

Chapter 15 contains the History of the organ with special reference to its Tonal Design, during the classic period (1600-1750) and the 19th century.

Plate III.

First Methodist Church, Evanston, Illinois. Austin Organs, Inc., Builders.

CHAPTER II

THE WIND SUPPLY *of the* ORGAN

The organ is, as everyone knows, primarily a wind instrument. It is of the greatest importance that it be supplied with an adequate amount of wind at a steady pressure, which is determined at the time the pipes are originally voiced.

The earliest devices for supplying wind to the organ were crude affairs. They resembled the bellows formerly to be seen in every blacksmith's shop. These have been superseded of late years by a rotary blower, known as a forge blower, as is the case with the organ bellows.

In order to overcome the violent unsteadiness of wind inevitable when an organ was supplied directly from a bellows of this type, a reservoir was added above the simple wind collecting apparatus, into which the compressed air or wind was fed from the feeders. Figure 2 shows such a reservoir with the feeders below.

The reservoir itself consisted of a double set of folds or ribs, the upper set folding towards the outside of the reservoir, and the lower set folding inside. Air is admitted into the feeders by a series of holes cut in the bottom boards, covered with a set of valves on top. The bottom of the reservoir has another set of holes covered also by valves, both sets of valves opening upwards. In its normal position one of the feeders hangs down, so that it can be opened to its fullest extent and filled with air. On raising this feeder, the valves in the bottom board are driven shut and the air within it is driven into the reservoir. On allowing the feeder again to descend, the valves in the reservoir close and prevent the return of the air, while at the same time the valves of the feeder open and admit the air which is driven into the reservoir at the next upstroke of the feeders. A safety valve is provided at the top of the reservoir, which will allow air to escape in case the reservoir is raised beyond a certain point, thus preventing any danger of its bursting. It was considered that the two sets of folds or ribs of the reservoir closing in opposite directions caused the pressure to remain steady, no matter whether the reservoir was widely open or nearly closed. If there was only one set of ribs, it was found the pressure would be constantly varying. As a matter of fact, the pressure was constantly varying anyway with this type of reservoir fed by feeders, as everyone knows who is familiar with the hand-pumped or water-motor driven organ of many years ago. No doubt the double system of folds was a valuable improvement. This is the type of bellows which supplied wind to most of the organs in the United States up to within recent years. In fact, some surprisingly large organs were blown by hand in the old days.*

To this same type of bellows was applied later a water motor, whose function was that which had been the duty of the bellows boy. The water motor moved the feeders up and down at a rate of speed sufficient to keep

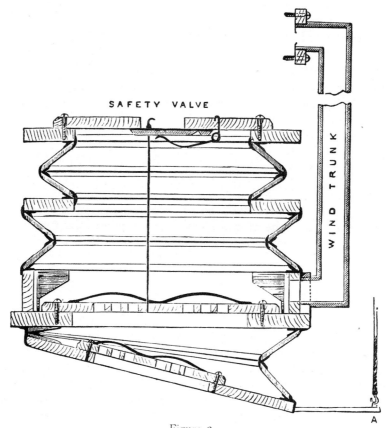

Figure 2.
Cross section of an organ bellows, showing reservoir with double folds and feeder below.

the top of the reservoir at a given height. This was accomplished by a counter-weight on the top of the bellows which was connected by a chain and pulleys to a valve in the water motor, and as the top of the reservoir was raised the counter-weight was raised with it, and allowed the valve that admitted the water to the water motor to close, thereby stopping the operation of the feeders. As soon as the organ was played and the wind

*There was an interesting club, under the leadership of the late Mr. Chet Shaefer, who termed himself "Grand Diapason" and whose organization was called the "Guild of Former Pipe Organ Pumpers." It is termed a non-essential, non-profitable organization, its motto is "Pump for the Wind is Fleeting," and the primary purpose of the organization appears to be to prove that not all successful business men started in life as newsboys. Some of the most successful have started by pumping the organ in the village church.

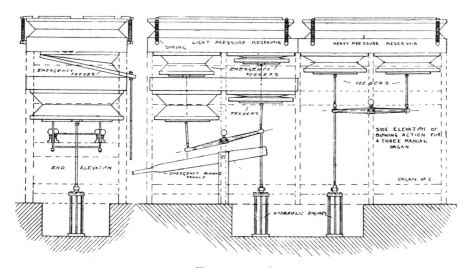

Figure 3.
Showing application of water motors to the operation of feeders.
(W. & T. Lewis, "Modern Organ Building")

started to leave the reservoir, allowing the top to go down, the counter-weight went down with it and pulled open the valve admitting water to the motor which started pumping.

These water motors were quite popular with churches, because most churches pay no water taxes (or any other taxes) and they, therefore, had the organ pumped at no expense. In consequence, even though the introduction of the rotary electric fan blower caused a great improvement in wind supply, many churches were slow to adopt it because they would have to pay for the electricity consumed. They were content to run along with an unsatisfactory, unsteady, and (usually) noisy wind supply which was the best the water motor could furnish.

An intermediate form of blowing mechanism is shown in our Figure 4. An electric motor adapted to operating the feeders by the introduction of pulleys and crank was used. The motor required direct current, so that a resistance or rheostat could be provided for regulating its speed for the varying requirements of the wind needed. There were comparatively few organs built with this type of supply. Gas and petrol engines were used in England for blowing organs many years ago, but they were seldom employed here.

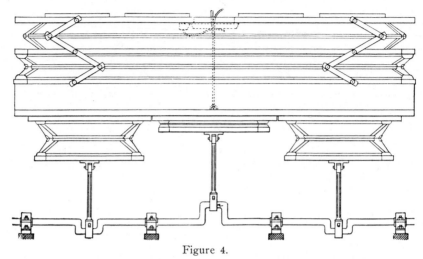

Figure 4.

The best type of three-feeder bellows. The left feeder has opened most of its distance and the right has closed part way, while the center is at the point of beginning to open. This gives an uninterrupted and jerk-less feeding of air. Note the safety valve. Drawing made by Mr. G. A. Audsley.

From either the bellows boy or water motor many churches graduated immediately to the electric fan blower. All of their blowing troubles were solved by this means and a steady supply of wind was at once made available without the noise occasioned by squeaky feeders or other moving parts in the organ itself.

Many of the younger generation of organists do not realize the difficulties that organists of twenty-five or more years ago had with the matter of an adequate wind supply. The organist had to find the bellows boy when he wanted to practice and this functionary sometimes allowed the wind to run out at inopportune times, else dependence had to be placed on the uncertainties of the water motor, with fluctuating water pressure.

The organist of the present day merely presses a button and starts to play, without giving much consideration to what happens when he does so, except that he counts on an ample supply of wind. Figures 7 and 8 show sections of modern fan blowers. It should be noticed that the fans rotate at a constant speed, usually at the speed of the motor which is directly attached to the fans on the same shaft. The supply of air that the blower furnishes to the reservoir is regulated by a valve of some sort, as for example that shown in Figure 5. When the top of the reservoir is raised, it shuts off further air from the blower. The fans then merely churn up the air inside the blower and suck in very little air from the outside. As soon as air is used in the organ, the reservoir top goes down, and

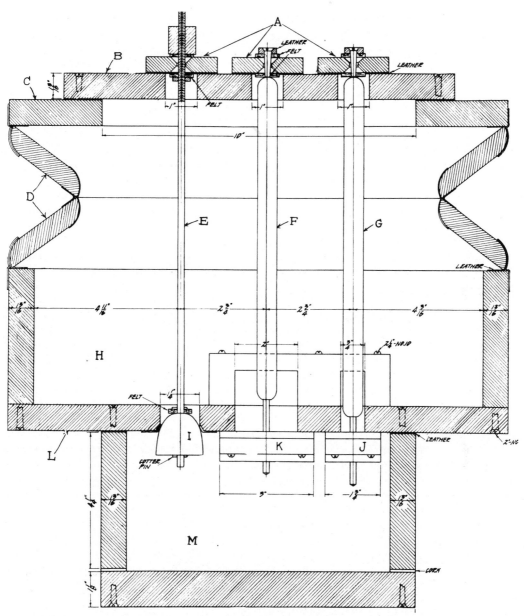

Figure 5.

High pressure reservoir used by the W. W. Kimball Co. Three control valves are used for admitting air to the reservoir from the blower, graduating in size from very small to large. The purpose of the three valves is to steady the pressure. If only one large valve is used the resistance of the high pressure wind against the valve is so great that it is difficult to draw the valve from its seat. As the top of the reservoir B, falls, the first valve to be opened to admit more wind is the cone valve I, which can be readily opened, because of its small area. As the top falls further, the pallet valve J is pushed open by the rod G. Further falling of the top board will cause the large pallet valve K to open, admitting a large flood of wind to the reservoir, sufficient for the greatest demands. This arrangement materially assists in maintaining steady pressure at all times.

more air is allowed to pass from the blower to the reservoir. In reality, the term "reservoir" is not an accurate description of the operating part that is left of the old bellows in the modern organ. This reservoir is merely a regulator of the pressure that the blower is capable of supplying constantly. Feeders are discarded entirely. Therefore, no such thing as an actual reservoir is required, as in the old organ where a large amount of air had to be in reserve for sudden demands made upon the wind supply, in striking or holding big chords. The modern bellows need simply to respond to the varying demands for wind by serving as a regulator to cut down the maximum supply of air that is capable of being furnished by the blower to the particular requirements of the moment.

The old type of reservoir created the proper pressure of air by having weights placed on top of the bellows. Owing to the inertia or slowness of action of these weights, the top of the reservoir could not be set into motion rapidly. When a staccato chord was played on one of these early organs with all its stops drawn, little or no response was obtained from the pipes. The air in the windchest was instantly exhausted, and no time was allowed for the inert bellows weights to fall and so to force a fresh supply of air into the windchest.

Mr. Robert Hope-Jones seems to have been the first to replace weights with springs. The use of the latter for obtaining the proper pressure has had a far-reaching effect upon organ building. It has made it possible to remove the unsteadiness of wind, from which all organs of the time suffered in greater or less degree. It has quickened the attack of the action and the speech of the pipes to a remarkable degree and has opened a new and wider field to the king of instruments. There is no inertia to be overcome when springs are used on a reservoir. The same reservoir, with the same demands for wind, will be perfectly steady when springs are used and very unsteady with weights.

MEASURING OF WIND PRESSURE

The subject of wind pressure may now be discussed profitably in some detail. Reference has been made to the fact that some surprisingly large organs were capable of being blown by hand. These were practically all of the tracker type, which, of course, require no wind for the action, but only for the Speaking Pipes. In the case of nearly all of these organs the wind pressure did not exceed three or at the most four inches. This pressure is measured by means of a wind gauge or anemometer. It is a glass tube approximately one-half inch in diameter bent in the form of a very much widened S. One end of the S tube is connected with the wind supply of the organ at a point on the windchest, usually by taking out a pipe from the top of the chest. Then, when one holds the valve below open, the pressure of air that is actually delivered to the pipes flows into the bent glass tube. The lower curve of the tube is filled with water, which, when no pressure is exerted, stands at equal level in both arms of the tube. As soon as pressure is exerted by the compressed air of the chest, the water is displaced downwards in the side of the tube that has the air pressure against it, and the water in the other side of the tube is raised a corresponding amount, as the other side is open to the atmosphere. The difference in the level of the water in the arms of the glass tube measured in inches is the wind pressure. This is the method of measuring wind pressure ordinarily employed in organ building practice.

Contrary to what might be supposed, to double the wind pressure, e.g., from three inches to six inches, requires materially more than double the amount of energy from the blowing apparatus. Consequently, organs of the tracker type that contained as many as forty stops on three inch pressure might be easily blown by a one-horse power or at most two-horse power motor, whereas an organ of this number of stops on seven and one-half inch pressure (very common for the modern organ) will require a motor of from seven and one-half to ten horse power.

Nearly all large organs have more than one pressure, some as many as ten or twelve. Two pressures are frequently introduced and the fan blowers are so built that wind of various pressures can be tapped off them for the various requirements of the organ.

Let us assume a battery of four fans (see Figures 7 and 8). The first fan receives the air current, raises the pressure from normal to three inches and delivers the air-stream to the second fan at this pressure. The second, third, and fourth fans, repeating the process, raise the pressure to six, nine and twelve inches respectively. Thus, by adding fans, pressures up to 50" may be obtained.

In many moderate sized organs all of the stops are on one pressure. This has been standardized by several of our leading builders between six and seven and one-half inches. Such a pressure has been determined primarily from consideration of the needs of the action rather than the pipe work, the latter other than the Reeds seldom needing more than four or five inch pressure except in very large buildings.

There is much to be said in favor of moderate pressures, those between four and five inches for Diapasons particularly, in any but the very largest organs. The greatest advantage that has accrued tonally to the organ by means of increased pressure has been with the Reeds, the Chorus Reeds especially, which tone undoubtedly can be made very much more smooth, prompt, and musical, by increase of pressure. This will be discussed later in our chapter on the Reeds in the Organ.

Increase in pressure does not necessarily mean increase in volume of sound.

Large organs in the past had to be blown by one or several men. Such was, until recently, the case with the organ at Notre Dame Cathedral

Figure 6.
40 H.P. with 2 H.P. step-up "Orgoblos" for a large organ.

Figure 7.
Phantom view of an "Orgoblo" showing the progress and direction of the wind through two fans, with baffle plate between.

in Paris. These organs had necessarily to be blown on quite low pressure in order to make it possible to work them at all. To get a sufficient volume of tone without excessive demands on the wind supply it was necessary to have a large number of Reed stops on very low pressure. These were voiced absolutely "freely" to produce the maximum amount of tone on the pressure available. The Reeds in any organ take much less wind in proportion to the volume of sound they emit than do the Diapasons and large Flutes. Old organs, therefore, had few, if any, large Flutes and mostly small scaled, lightly winded Diapasons. This had to be done to conserve the wind supply, which was a very considerable problem in the case of a large organ.

Another of the great advantages of the fan blower, in addition to doing away with the feeders entirely, is that the reservoir may be of moderate dimensions as compared with what was imperatively needed when the organ was supplied by feeders. Old organs usually had one large reservoir, in some cases as large as eight by fifteen feet or even larger, to supply the requirements of the entire organ. This function is now performed by a small reservoir not necessarily more than three feet square for each division of the organ, and with a separate reservoir for the large Pedal Stops. Pedal pipes, being of large size, require much more wind and would be likely, if on the same regulator as the Manual pipes, to cause unsteadiness. It is customary at present with most of our best builders to set off the basses (or the eight foot octave), of all the heavily winded Manual stops on a separate bass chest. This causes the wind pressure on the main chest to remain more steady when heavy chords are played in the bass octave on the Manual key board. All of these devices and expedients have served to allow the modern organ to maintain a wind pressure of remarkable steadiness. This is one of the foremost requirements for the proper intonation of the pipes.

The wind is distributed from the reservoirs to the various windchests on which the pipes are planted by rectangular wooden conveyances, or frequently, in modern work, by round galvanized sheet iron pipes of the proper diameter to insure an adequate supply.

When there is a very long distance between the reservoir and the chest, as is sometimes unavoidable (though great distances are always undesirable), the pressure is apt to become unsteady because of the long column of elastic air in the conductor pipe. This unsteadiness is frequently avoided by the addition of a small bellows placed on the outside of the conductor with springs adjusting the motion of the top board of this so-called "concussion" bellows, so that when there is no disturbance in the wind supply the bellows remains about half way open. As soon as a sudden demand is made on the wind, this bellows collapses momentarily and then rebounds absorbing the greater part of the shock to the air column and steadying the wind pressure at the mouths of the pipes. This is

25

Figure 8.

The Kinetic organ blower, as manufactured by M. P. Moller, Inc. The motor shaft and fan shaft are firmly coupled together, so that no belts or pulleys are required. Any standard motor or generator may be used. The generator is mounted on the opposite side of the blower from the motor, ordinarily, though in some cases the generator is driven by a belt from the main shaft.

a very ancient expedient that was resorted to in the days of hand blown organs, and it seems that it should not be necessary in the modern organ. Yet I have observed numerous instances where it was imperatively required to steady the wind, particularly on a large swell chest that was far removed from its reservoir.

The Austin system of building organs, where the entire air chest is made into an immense reservoir, is described in our chapter on Types of Windchests. This is no doubt the ultimate system for absolutely steady wind pressure. Its advantages and disadvantages are there explained.

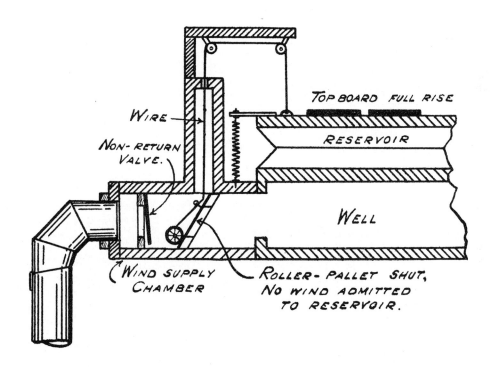

Figure 9.

Curtain Valve, for regulating the supply of wind furnished by blower. Instead of a wire passing over pulleys, as shown above, controlling the rise and fall of the curtain valve as the reservoir top rises and falls, a ¼" rod may be directly connected to the curtain valve and top of reservoir, thus avoiding any chance for "shimmy" or unsteady wind. The curtain valve may also be placed within the bottom of the reservoir itself, as done by M. P. Moller, Inc., in all of their reservoirs. This is, in my opinion, the best type of wind supply control.

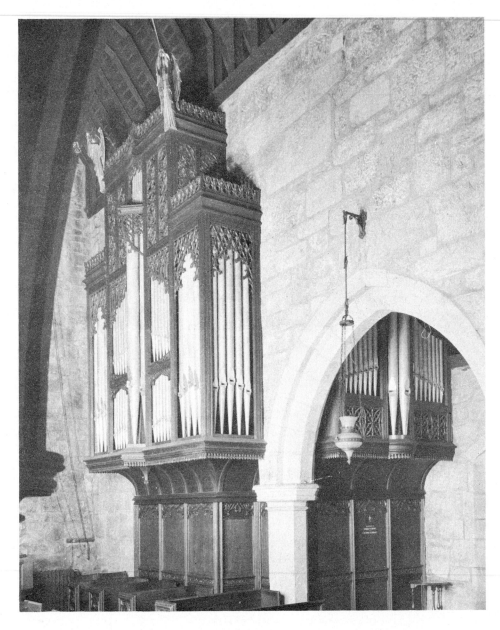

Plate IV.

"A thing of beauty—is a joy forever." Though homeliness in case-building may be only case-deep, the frailty of man still desires the element of beauty and rebels at the thought of having to use a tomahawk in generous sweeps in order to make the sight more lovely. Case-building is not a lost art and never was. If there is a lost art it is the gentle art of case-buying. Organs are made to be heard first and seen second, as a general rule. A builder who tries to paint a picture in pipes before finishing his picture in tone is no friend of the future of the organ. Yet when the buyer has the soul of an artist and the pocketbook of a banker, the organ builder finds the situation ideal and Hillgreen, Lane & Co. met the situation by building for the church of St. James the Less, Philadelphia, Pa., a small organ of such merit as to make us all pause a moment in complimentary contemplation.

(From "The American Organist")

28

CHAPTER 3

THE SOUND PRODUCING PORTIONS *of the* ORGAN

In the heading of this chapter, use is made of the terminology employed by Hopkins and Rimbault in their monumental work entitled "The Organ." This work, for its day, was one of the greatest contributions ever made to the literature of organ building. Much of its material is now interesting from a historical viewpoint only, particularly the descriptions of mechanical construction. However, some of the ideas expressed in this work on tonal structure are just as sound today as they were when first put down.

Some of our present day American builders and organists seem to think that the joint use of a complete Diapason chorus on the great organ and Reed chorus on the swell organ is a new departure. It is for many American builders and many organists. It is a fact that, due to the influence of Hope-Jones and others, during the past thirty or forty years many American builders have been building, and organists have been playing, organs that were designed with very small regard for tonal build-up—but more of this in our chapter on The Tonal Structure of the Organ.

First we propose to describe the construction of those parts of the organ which have to do primarily with its tone. In later chapters the matters pertaining to tonal build-up and ensemble will be considered particularly. We will now discuss the construction of the pipes themselves, which fall into three distinct classes, viz: 1. Flue Pipes, 2. Reed Pipes, 3. Diaphones. Their shape may be either round or rectangular, long or short, broad or narrow, according to circumstances. The materials from which organ pipes are made are tin, lead, a mixture of the two with antimony metal, zinc, and wood of various kinds.

CONSTRUCTION OF METAL FLUE PIPES

Of all the materials used in the construction of organ pipes, that which ranks first in point of excellence is pure tin. It is almost indispensable in the production of the keener string-toned stops. For duller toned pipes such as Metal Flutes and the Phonon type of Diapason (not used now) a very large percentage of lead is introduced. Pipe metal is made in a great variety of proportions of tin and lead melted together. Ordinary pipe metal, such as is used for Diapasons, contains about twenty per cent tin and the balance lead, with possibly some antimony for stiffening. This is the minimum amount of tin that may be used satisfactorily in pipe making, for, if a larger proportion than eighty per cent of lead is used, there will not be sufficient stiffness and the pipes will crumple upon themselves from their own weight. For ordinary pipe metal about one-third tin and two-thirds lead is used, although a better quality is forty-five per cent tin and fifty-five per cent lead.

When this much tin is used it causes spots to appear in the metal and makes what is termed "spotted" metal. These spots rise to the surface when the metal is cooling after being cast, and when the pipes are polished up they look as if they were marked all over with ink stains which had been partially cleaned off. If the proportion of tin runs high, the spots run closely together; indeed spotted metal proclaims its quality by its appearance. If the spots are very widely separated, the quantity of tin is small. Such pipes give good round tones and are very satisfactory for all metal stops where a reasonable amount of harmonic development is required, but when an excessive amount is necessary as in keen String tone, ninety per cent tin is the best metal to employ. The thickness of the metal has also much to do with the development of harmonics, or the reverse. Thick metal causes the tone of pipes made with it to be more foundational. Pipes made with thin walls have greater harmonic development.

It is a curious circumstance in connection with modern organ building, that in the production of metal pipes from the very first processes of casting the metal, through to practically the finished product, there have been scarcely any changes or improvements made in the *modus operandi* for hundreds of years.

Dom Bedos, in his great work on organ building, written nearly two hundred years ago, shows a wood cut of a metal pipe shop in those days. The tools and appliances used then, look very similar to what we see in a modern American pipe shop. The casting bench and soldering irons, the mandrels and all of the appliances used are there shown; the only difference appearing in the dress of the pipe maker, for he apparently wore a wig and ruffles on his shirt sleeves, while today he is more apt to wear an apron. Even writers of the 10th century describe pipe making much as it is done in our modern day.

After the proportions of tin and lead have been decided upon, they are weighed out and placed in a large iron pot and the metal brought to a proper temperature for casting. The casting process is accomplished on a long wooden table or horizontal slab, usually about three feet wide and fifteen feet long. The top of this table is covered with a canvas or moleskin cloth which is stretched very tightly and smoothly over the entire top surface. The table top presents almost the appearance of an artist's canvas stretched ready to paint upon. A box is provided to run in grooves from one end to the other of the length of the table with one side of the box capable of being raised or lowered a small distance from the top of the table.

The molten metal is placed in this casting box and the thickness of the metal to be cast is determined by the width of the opening between the movable side of the box and the top of the bench. The box is then dragged from one end of the bench to the other, leaving a sheet of metal behind that has flowed out from the back of the box as it was pulled along the bench. Metal of any thickness required in pipe making can be cast in this manner. As soon as the sheet has cooled sufficiently, it may be removed and another sheet cast.

These sheets are then planed to make them smooth and this is done by planing away from the point where the sheet of metal is secured to the bench. The plane used is like an ordinary carpenter's plane only the blade is set more nearly vertically. A flat steel scraper is used for finishing and to make the metal of the required uniform thickness. It certainly seems strange that after the hundreds of years that pipes have been made for organs, that no more modern means of preparing the metal to be made up into pipes has yet been devised by any builder than to plane down the cast sheets of metal by hand. Usually the heavy Diapason metal is planed down on only one side, leaving the marks of the canvas on the opposite side, just as it comes from the casting bench, the idea being that as weight of metal is particularly desired in these pipes, it is useless to plane the sheets thinner.

Having now a sufficient quantity of pipe metal sheets cast, they are cut to the exact size and shape required for the particular scale of stop that is being built. Organ pipe shops have complete patterns of all the scales generally used, and simply cut the sheets from the patterns, both the body of the pipes and the feet.

Before going further, a few definitions should perhaps be given concerning the various portions of the pipes. Let us refer to Figure 10.

An open metal Flue pipe is composed of three distinct parts, called the body, the foot and the languid. The larger metal Flue pipes have in addition two other parts that are soldered on separately, viz., the upper and lower lips. The body is that part of the pipe that commences at the mouth of the pipe and extends to the top. It is formed by rolling a sheet of metal of the required dimensions around a smooth cylindrical column called a mandrel, and uniting the edges together with solder. The joint thus formed is called a seam, and occurs at the back of the pipe. The body of the pipe, on the opposite side of the seam near the lower end, is flattened by burnishing, forming the upper lip or leaf of the pipe. A portion of this flattened part is cut away from the body leaving a broad opening. The edge that is left immediately above this opening is called the upper lip.

The foot is that part of the pipe of an inverted conical shape which extends from the mouth downwards. It is made in a similar manner to the body, that is, with the seam running vertically up the center of the

31

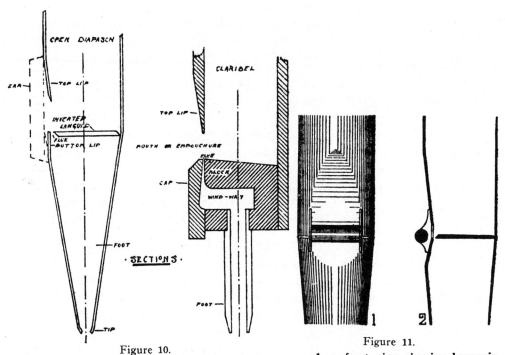

Figure 10.

Left, a section of a metal pipe. Right, a section of a wood pipe.

Figure 11.

1, a front view showing harmonic bridge applied to the mouth. 2, a side view of the same pipe.

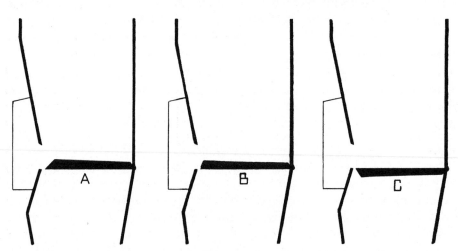

Figure 12.

A shows the normal shape of the languid in Diapason pipes. B is a languid with a more obtuse bevel, used in early English examples of the stop. C is the inverted languid.

(From Audsley, "The Art of Organ Building")

Figure 13.

Construction of metal pipes. A series of pipe bodies are here shown that have been formed around a mandrel, having previously had a portion of the lower part of the body cut away. The upper lips will be soldered onto these cuts in the body. The feet are also shown with the lower lips soldered in place. The next operation will be to solder on the languid, and then to solder the feet onto the body of the pipes. The pipes will then be ready for the voicer. Note the series of patterns in the lower left from which the upper lips are cut. The smaller metal pipes have their upper and lower lips burnished flat, avoiding the necessity for soldering on flat pieces of metal at these points. The large metal pipes are nearly always made of zinc, which requires the treatment shown above.

back and an indentation in the front, though in this instance it is the upper part of the foot that is flattened, corresponding with that in the body of the pipe. This flattened portion of the foot of the pipe forms the lower lip.

The function of the foot is to serve as a conductor of wind from the windchest to the mouth of the pipe. Hence in the apex of the conical foot a hole is made for the entrance of the wind. The foot also serves as a support for the pipe. It is, therefore, nearly always made of zinc for the larger pipes as it has to support considerable weight, especially if the pipes are made of heavy pipe metal. Metal pipes longer than four feet are nearly always made of zinc. The common American practice is to make these pipes of annealed or softened zinc, which is much more readily worked than the unannealed or hard metal. The latter is considered better and is usually employed by the English builders. If the feet of heavy metal pipes were made of the same material as the bodies, the pipes would be apt to collapse of their own weight, as sometimes happened in old organs.

The languid is the flat plate of metal that lies horizontally on the top of the foot just inside of the mouth. It is made of much thicker material than any other part of the pipe because it is entirely unsupported, except at the sides and back. In front it presents a straight edge corresponding with the lips of the body and foot, but slightly behind that of the latter, leaving a narrow slit or windway between. The front edge of the languid is usually bevelled inwards and upwards, though certain pipes are made with what is known as inverted languids bevelled in the opposite direction. Figure 11 illustrates these two types. The languid is made strong and thick so that it will not sink of its own weight where it is unsupported in front or in the middle, in which case the sheet of wind passing from the windway would miss the upper lip and so render the speech of the pipe defective.

The mouth, as already indicated, is the hollow cut, or opening, that occurs at the junction of the body and feet of the pipe. The separate parts of an open Flue pipe are joined together in the following manner: The straight edges of the languid and the foot are first arranged parallel and then the back and sides of the two are soldered together, the narrow slit in front being left open so as to form a passage, or windway, for the current of air that enters at the foot of the pipe. In the next place, the upper lip of the body and the lower lip of the foot are put precisely opposite each other and the body and foot are then soldered together all around. The languid is thus entirely enclosed within the finished pipe.

In making the various joints or seams, the solder is prevented from spreading to more of the surface of the pipe than is desired, by coating

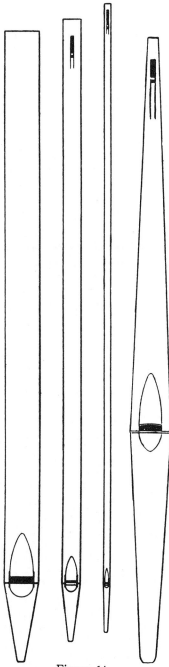

Figure 14.

From left to right, the pipes are Diapason, Dulciana. Viole d'Orchestre, and Spitz Flute.
(From Audsley, "The Art of Organ Building")

Figure 15.
LUDWIGTONE

Perfected by H. H. Holtkamp and A. G. Sparling and first used in the year 1925 at either 8' or 4' pitch. One side of pipe is tuned slightly flat of unison and the other slightly sharp of unison. In addition to the beat caused by the difference in pitch, there is an undulation in the tone. This undulation is much slower than the pitch beat and hence you have a beat within an undulation. It is this compound tone curve which gives the tone its peculiar charm. Each side of the pipe is dependent upon the other for its speech. Neither side is tonally good alone. Besides the normal uses of an undulating organ tone, Ludwigtone is ideal for the accompaniment of Plain Chant and provides a perfect carpet of tone for the singers.

the pipes with whiting before they are soldered. This is easily washed off after the pipes are finished. The joints to be soldered are then slightly bevelled and scraped so that they are entirely free from whiting or grease. Candle wax has been employed as a flux for this soldering since time immemorial. This doubtless furnishes a use for the burnt down stubs of altar candles. Nearly all larger pipes or those longer than eight or ten inches have ears or pieces of metal soldered on each side of the mouth to help guide the wind sheet.

Having described in some detail how metal pipes are constructed, I should perhaps explain what causes them to sound a note after they are formed as described. In order to understand the production of sound in an organ pipe, we shall make a short study of some of the acoustical matters involved. The flute as a musical instrument dates back to extreme antiquity. The tone of the flute is produced by blowing across a hole punched in its side. In other words, it is possible to produce a tone by a stream of wind striking upon a cutting edge. In this way, by blowing across the end of any tube made of any material, such as glass, iron, rubber or cane, a tone can be produced.

The primitive flutes found in the Egyptian tombs and also depicted in the ancient hieroglyphics were made of reed or cane about fourteen inches long, possessing the usual six finger holes. When the six holes are closed by the fingers, the ground tone of the tube is produced. By lifting the fingers in successive order from the bottom end the seven notes of the major scale are obtained. By closing the holes again and blowing harder, we obtain the same scale an octave higher, by blowing still harder, we may obtain two octaves higher. In other words, we are producing harmonics. It is possible to produce a complete series of harmonics from a plain tube without finger holes or valves such as the old type of French horn by tightening the lips and increasing the pressure of the player's breath. We learn from this that the pitch of the sound depends on the length of the tube and further that the pitch of the sound also depends on the amount of wind pressure. Therefore it is obviously important that the pressure of wind in an organ should be steady and uniform, otherwise the pipes will speak a harmonic instead of the sound intended.

When a stop is labelled eight feet it simply means that the longest pipe of the stop, known as CC, is eight feet long and the pitch will be the unison or normal. That is, middle C on the organ keyboard will correspond with the middle C of the piano key-board. A sixteen foot stop will sound an octave lower, a four foot stop will sound an octave higher. These measures refer to pipes which are open at the top and are only approximately correct for very narrow pipes such as Salicionals and Dulcianas. Large scaled pipes do not have to be so long to produce the same pitch.

36

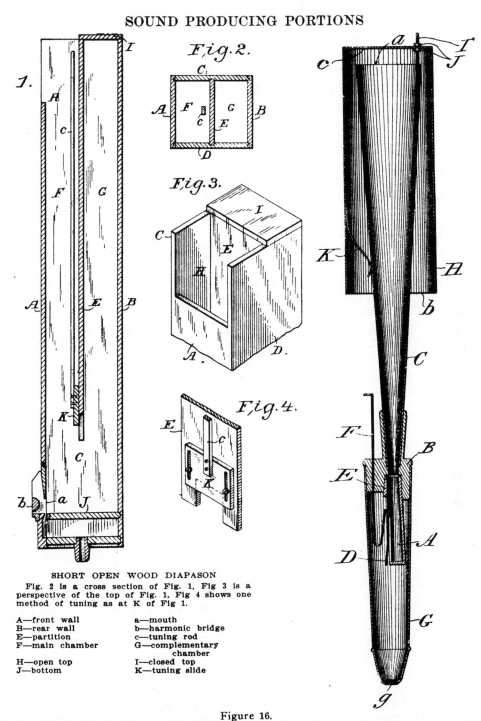

SHORT OPEN WOOD DIAPASON

Fig. 2 is a cross section of Fig. 1, Fig 3 is a perspective of the top of Fig. 1, Fig 4 shows one method of tuning as at K of Fig 1.

A—front wall
B—rear wall
E—partition
F—main chamber
H—open top
J—bottom

a—mouth
b—harmonic bridge
c—tuning rod
G—complementary chamber
I—closed top
K—tuning slide

Figure 16.

Examples of Mr. William E. Haskell's short length pipes used by the Estey Organ Co.

If a tube open at both ends be blown across at one end with a normal amount of wind pressure, the fundamental tone of the tube will be sounded as already pointed out. But, if the hand be placed at one end of the tube so as to effectively close it and the open end be blown across as before, a sound will be heard exactly one octave below that which was heard when blown into with the top open. One of these pipes is an open pipe, the other a stopped pipe. The difference between the two is that which constitutes the two great classes into which Flue pipes of organs are divided. It is, therefore, seen that by stopping up the end of an organ pipe it is possible to obtain eight foot tone from a pipe only four feet long, and sixteen foot tone from a pipe eight feet long, but with some loss of power and volume. The harmonic series produced from stopped pipes is entirely different from that of open pipes. The latter harmonic series is produced by vibration rates per second which are in the ratio of 1-2-3-4, etc., while those of the stopped pipes have vibration rates per second which are 1-3-5-7, etc. Only the odd numbered harmonics can be produced from closed or stopped pipes.

The Estey Organ Company appear to have discovered a new principle in acoustics in their open bass pipes shown in Figure 16. The late Mr. William E. Haskell is the inventor of this ingenious type of pipe. He states, "The inserted tube or complementing chamber in the pipe is such in length as to complete the full length of the pipe. It is, as will be noticed, smaller in scale than the outside pipe. The effect is to produce a vibration that would be obtained with a full length pipe and in no way does it interfere with the quality of tone. In fact, it assists the pipe materially in its speech," according to the statement of the builders. The Estey Organ Company state that they have worked out this type of pipe for all classes of tone, Strings, Flutes and Diapasons and the law holds good in every instance.

Helmholz was the first to demonstrate that the quality of all musical tones depends entirely upon the presence or absence of their upper partials. Thus a large scaled Flute pipe has practically no harmonics present, and its tone is practically all ground tone. This is also true of the large scaled, high, narrow mouthed Diapason: The clanging tone of the trumpet has very many of the high partial tones present and an intrument like the cymbal gives us the whole of the upper partial tone series.

It will be seen from this that different qualities of tone in organ pipes are produced; first, by the thickness of the material of which the pipe is made, as well as the material itself (although this is not of so much importance as has formerly been thought); second, by the scale of the pipe; third, by the amount of wind pressure; fourth, by the shape and size of the mouth, the relation of the lip to the stream of wind impinging on it from the narrow slit, and the shape and thickness of the lip itself.

Figure 17.

The lowest eight pipes of the Metal 32′ Diapason in the Atlantic City Auditorium Organ. The Low CCCC weighs 2200 pounds and this is said to be the largest and heaviest metal Diapason ever made. Midmer-Losh, Builders.

This manipulation of the mouth and lip to produce the tone desired is called voicing, which will be treated in a later chapter.

Returning now to the construction of pipes themselves, we shall consider the construction of wood pipes.

CONSTRUCTION OF WOOD FLUE PIPES

The wood pipes offer a more limited range of tone than is obtainable from metal pipes. The characteristic tone of nearly all wood pipes is some type of Flute tone. Wood pipes are rather more simple to build and voice than any other pipes in the organ and have frequently been made with good results by amateurs. A scale is required from which the various dimensions of the pipes can be obtained, as they graduate in size from top to bottom. Wood stops may be made from almost any wood, preferably maple, mahogany or even oak; but more usually from spruce or white pine. In any event, the lumber should be well seasoned and dry, and free from knots, sap and shakes.

The first requirement in making wood pipes is the block, which will form the equivalent of the languid in the metal pipe. Having made a series of blocks of the proper dimensions (that is, the inside measurements of the stop that is being built), the blocks are shaped in any one of various ways as shown, e.g., in Figure 10. A gap is cut with a tenon saw through the mahogany or other hard wood facing, that has previously been glued on the front edge of the block, keeping the same proportion for each block. See Figures 10 and 19. Also Figures 22 to 24.

The opening at the bottom of the block is a round hole which is bored after the pipe is put together and in this the foot is inserted. The sides of the pipes are next glued to the blocks. The pieces that are cut out of the blocks are used as a guide for the sides when they are being glued on. The backs and fronts of the pipes are then glued on. The front only extends down to the top of the block and has a chamfer cut for the upper lip, and an opening for the mouth, as shown in Figures 10 and 19. The bevel is ordinarily cut about as high as it is wide, the final height of the mouth being regulated when the pipes are voiced.

The caps are pieces of wood which cover the gaps in the front of the blocks. These are usually made of mahogany or other hard wood and in the case of many Flute pipes are simply flat pieces of the same thickness as the fronts of the pipe. The windway is cut in the top of the cap before it is attached to the block and is made with a flat file. This is finally adjusted in the voicing of the wood pipes. Our illustrations show various types of Flutes and Bourdons, some with the cap hollowed out and some with the upper lip bevelled inwards, as is done in the case of

Figure 18.

The 32' Pedal-Diapason. The largest pipe is 31-13/16"
x 28-1/16" x 33' long, made of sugar pine 3" thick.
(There are five 32' Pedal stops in this Organ.) Pierre
S. duPont organ. Aeolian Company, Builders.

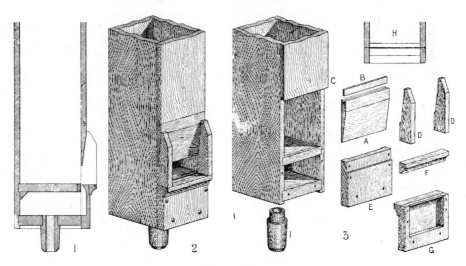

Figure 19.

Parts of a Pedal Bourdon. 1, cross section. 2, completed pipe. 3, separate parts
of the pipe, as for example at A the upper lip with B the tongue grooving the lip
to the body of the pipe at C. DD represent the two ears, F the beard. E and G are
front and back views of the cap or lower lip.

the Melodia. In modern organ factories, some labor saving methods have been introduced in making wood pipes. There are large sanding machines into which the pipes may be fed and have their sides smoothed down with a great deal less labor than by planing them down by hand. There is special machinery provided for bevelling the upper lip and for jointing the sides and fronts of the pipes before gluing so that wood pipes can now be produced more economically from a labor standpoint than was possible before the introduction of wood working machinery. No such improvements seem to have been accomplished in the manufacture of metal pipes. The best practice in the making of the larger wood pipes, such as Pedal Diapasons, etc., is to tongue and groove the joints that are glued. It is a matter of great importance to the tone of any pipe that the body be tight. If the joints of wood pipes become loose, or come open, the tone is usually ruined. It is well, therefore, to take all precautions against this.

Figure 20.

Wood pipe making. The unfinished pipes shown at the right are secured in a clamp while the back and fronts are being glued onto the sides. The pipes shown on the truck have merely their sides glued on to the blocks. The backs and sides are next glued on. Wood pipes are made in nearly all factories in groups of a dozen or so stops of the same kind. This is a convenience in manufacturing.

SOUND PRODUCING PORTIONS

Wood pipes have a coating of glue given to their interior surfaces to counteract somewhat the effects of moisture. They are usually varnished or shellacked on their outer surfaces. Paint is sometimes used, but, as this is only done to hide defects in the lumber, pipes are seldom painted by our best builders. Builders who have used good lumber want to show that they have done so by not covering the wood portions of the organ with paint or other finish that will hide the lumber. The Aeolian Company is an exception. They use the finest lumber obtainable for organ building, and then cover it with a yellow ochre compound that completely hides the wood, yet they have nothing to hide and should be proud to show any lumber they use in organ building. They consider this covering to be more waterproof than ordinary varnish or shellac.

CLASSIFICATION OF FLUE PIPES

Having outlined the general construction of both metal and wood pipes of the type known as Flue pipes, we shall give a brief account of the classifications into which Flue pipes are divided: 1. Diapasons, 2. Flutes, 3. Strings, 4. Echos, or miniatures of the first three groups. This fourth classification is suggested by Mr. Hunt in his work on the "Church Organ," and seems a very logical way of classifying the softer organ tones. I do not recall that this classification has been used by anyone before Mr. Hunt.

DIAPASON TONE

The Diapason has prominence historically, also from its importance as the essential factor in the tonal design of the organ. An organ without a Diapason is not an organ at all, consequently the Diapason may very properly be called the foundation tone of the organ and as such deserves more attention than is generally given to it. There are probably as many ideas of good Diapason tone as there are builders of organs and, I was going to say, almost as there are organists, but this would probably be an exaggeration. The fact is, that the tone of the Diapason is perhaps more affected by bad or advantageous acoustical conditions than any other type of tone in the organ.

Therefore, the same builder may make two Diapasons with precisely the same characteristics and as nearly alike as two Diapasons can be. If the first one be placed in an organ where good acoustical conditions exist, organists will pronounce the tone beautiful, "an ideal Diapason tone." If the duplicate Diapason be placed in an organ where the acoustical conditions are bad, organists will consider this stop as either hard, tubby, or otherwise unsatisfactory. This obviously adds to the problem of

FIGURE 21

Metal pipe voicing. With a pair of proportional dividers, the height of the upper lip is marked off. This height maybe anything from ¼ to ½ the mouth width, depending on wind pressure, quality of tone desired, and other factors described in the text. It is important that whatever cutup is decided on shall be uniform with all pipes in the same stop.

obtaining the best type of Diapason for any given organ. Diapasons suffer greatly from bad acoustics.

The Rev. Noel Bonavia-Hunt, in his very interesting and instructive treatise on the "Church Organ" (a work so undoubtedly sound, that I shall refer to it frequently in the course of this chapter and others), states that the type of Diapason known as the early English Diapason is represented by numerous examples still to be found in England in old organs of Father Smith, Renatus, Harris, Green, England, Knight (of Chichester), Snetzler, Avery, Bridge, Byfield, Jordan, Griffin, Gray, and others. Mr. Hunt states that, although all of these old examples show various standards of excellence, generally speaking they all possess the charm of tone that is characteristic of the type. He describes the tone as one of old world peacefulness, a quality which is only obtainable from pipes of the same construction and on a light wind pressure. He states, "The secret of this lies in the form of languid employed," which is shown in our Figure 11.

The tone is smooth, round, and velvety, the speech being perfectly natural and unforced. "Quality before power" must be the ruling motto adopted by the voicer of this type of Diapason. The scales are not excessive. The mouth may be 2/9 or 1/4 of the circumference and cut up 1/3 of its width. Wind pressure should not exceed 3¾ inches and lower pressure is doubtless preferable such as 2½ or three inches.

A later type of Diapason known as the Schulze Diapason was introduced in England, about 1851, by the firm of J. F. Schulze & Sons of Paulinzelle, Germany, who sent a small two manual instrument to the Great Exhibition. This led to Schulze's receiving a number of orders for larger organs, the most notable of which are those at Doncaster, Armley, Tyne Dock and Hindley. The Diapasons built by Schulze for the organs at Armley and Tyne Dock are the ones that are quoted as the finest examples of Diapason tone in England by Dr. Audsley in his works on the organ. The tone is characterized as being both brighter, more vigorous and more assertive than that of the earlier English examples. Apparently at Tyne Dock, Schulze showed what he could do in the production of power and majesty of tone when it was required for a special purpose.

Mr. Hunt states, "It is not fair to judge the work of Schulze by the effectiveness of a single stop, for he was a great tonal architect and the real glory of his organs consists in the magnificent ensemble of his full Great Flue work up to mixtures, the chorus of which was treated on the same lines as he treated a single eight foot Diapason. When we speak, therefore, of the Schulze Diapason, we ought always to think of it in terms of the complete edifice of which it is an integral part." The Schulze Diapason varies in scale between 3¼ inches and 2 7/8 inches at tenor C. Such Diapasons have been copied with more or less success by modern builders. Several examples of this stop have been introduced into Ameri-

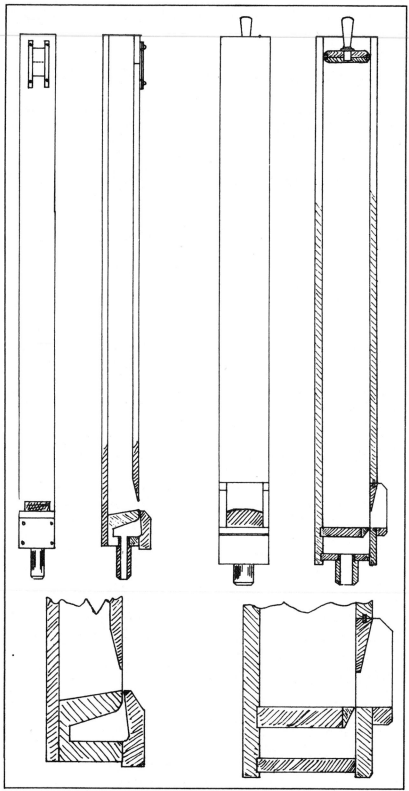

Figure 22.

On the left, front and sectional views of a Hohl Flute or Melodia. Note the inverted upper lip, a unique characteristic of these stops. On the right, front and sectional views of a Pedal Bourdon. This is provided with both "ears" and a "beard" at the bottom of the mouth to guide the wind sheet.

can organs recently, notably the Atlantic City High School organ and the organ at St. Marks Church, Philadelphia.*

It is true that the early English organ builders were very much influenced by the German builders and their work. Not until we come to "Father" Willis do we have a dominating English influence on tone. The chorus Reeds that "Father" Willis produced at St. George's Hall, Liverpool, were more revolutionary in their effect on organ tone in England (and later on in America) than any thing that has been done before or since along tonal lines.

The modern foundational type of Diapason was evolved because of the desire for abundance of unison foundational tone which Mr. Hunt believes to be characteristic of the English race, for in Germany and France even large organs possess only a small amount of flue foundation. Mr. Hunt says, "The modern English organist is not content to restrict his tonal diet to a feast upon the beauties of either the early English or the Schulze Diapason, but demands to be served with something more solid. He complains that the early English type is inadequate to cope with the heavy pressure Reeds of the modern organ, and that the Schulze type is more brilliant than foundational. What is considered to be ideal is the foundation and refinement of older examples magnified to the power of the Schulze Diapason." This has resulted in various types of Diapasons, probably the most objectionable of which was that produced by Hope-Jones, known as the Phonon type.

If we were to believe what is stated in "The Recent Revolution in Organ Building," a work attributed to George Laing Miller, we would consider that the Phonon type of Diapason was the most important invention in modern organ tone. As early as 1887, Hope-Jones introduced his discovery that, by thickening and leathering the upper lips and narrowing the mouth and increasing its height and thickness of the body of the pipe, pipes could be voiced on ten, twenty or even thirty inch wind without either hardening the tone, forcing, or producing windiness. This type of tone was considered to be vastly preferable to what Hope-Jones termed the hard and harmonically bold Diapason, into which the Schulze type had evolved.

Mr. Hunt, who has great experience and a vast fund of information, by listening to practically all the examples of Diapasons that exist in

*An anecdote is told me by Mr. Maurice Hardy, for many years associated with the Kimball Company of Chicago. He frequently would discuss organ tone with Mr. Joseph Carruthers, an Englishman in the factory. Mr. Carruther's idea of the only perfect and satisfactory organ that he had ever heard was that in St. George's Hall, Liverpool, built by "Father" Willis in 1855. Whenever he did hear a particularly effective American organ, he would tell Mr. Hardy it sounded almost as well, or at least reminded him of St. George's Hall, Liverpool. No American builder could possibly do as well as the English builders. Finally, one day Mr. Hardy suggested to Mr. Carruthers that he might be mistaken, but it was his impression that the three greatest of the earlier English builders were Father Schmidt, Snetzler and Schulze, whose names after all do not sound so English.

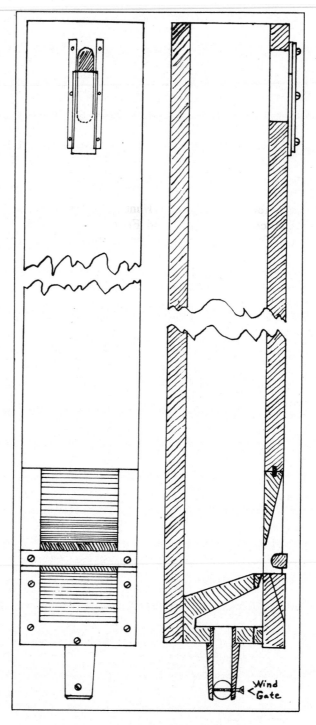

Figure 23.

Front and sectional views of a Pedal Violone. Note the harmonic bridge in front of the mouth. The scale of this stop is smaller than that of the Pedal Diapason, and the block is treated differently. Also the upper lip is made separately and is tongued and grooved onto the front of the pipe. This tongue and groove construction is employed by our best builders in joining the sides with the front and back of wood pipes also. Such a practise makes for durability of the joints.

English organs, states that in preference to the Phonon type as developed by Hope-Jones, he greatly prefers medium scaled pipes, not exceeding four inches in diameter at tenor C with ¼ width of mouth cut up 1/3 of its width, with either A, a reinforced upper lip, or B, an upper lip burnished on both edges, with a wind pressure not exceeding 4½ inches. The object of burnishing the upper lip is to eliminate the higher dissonant upper partials, without unduly curbing the first two. The difficulty with the Phonon type of Diapason is that the first two upper partials are not suf-sufficiently developed. Moreover, it is difficult if not impossible to build up a complete Flue chorus on the Phonon type of Diapason. The upper work (principal, 15th, 22nd and mixtures), must be restricted to the point of negligibility since if properly developed it will create an hiatus, by standing away from the unisonal foundation tone. As a matter of fact, Mr. Hunt's type of Diapason is a somewhat modified Schulze Diapason with slightly less harmonic development.

It is undoubtedly true that if the organ is to be supplied with a normal proportion of upper work it is essential that the unison Diapason tone have a rich harmonic development. This need not mean a hard or thin tone, but rather that the fundamental and overtones be in a reasonable balance. The expression "singing tone" best expresses what is desired, and it may be achieved by carefully studied scaling, mouth treatment, and winding.

A small scaled Diapason is frequently introduced into organs, which develops the upper partials without actually being a String stop. The principal varieties of this type of Diapason are the Viola Diapason or Geigen Principal. The scale is usually not over 2 5/8 inches at tenor C. The harmonic development is increased by the pipes being slotted, that is, by cutting out a slot near the top of the pipe for tuning purposes. French builders commonly slotted all their Diapasons.

The more foundational Diapason is tuned by having a sliding collar or sleeve affixed to the top of the pipe which may be knocked up or down to tune the pipe to the correct pitch. The sleeves should properly go entirely around the circumference of the pipe, so that no break or other irregularity occurs at the top.

The Salicional Diapason, usually termed Salicional, sometimes Viola, is a very small scaled Diapason which borders more on String tone than Diapason. Being very lightly winded, it affords a delightful contrast to the other principal types of Diapason.

The Gemshorn is a stop made with conical pipes with a diameter at the top varying between one-half and one-quarter of that at the mouth. This causes the pipes to partake of the qualities of Diapason, String, and Flute, giving a little edge to the tone. When such pipes have a moderate taper and the mouths are cut fairly high, the tone is described as Spitz Flute.

The Pedal Diapasons are generally made of wood, though when I was in England I heard a recent Willis Pedal Diapason made of hard rolled

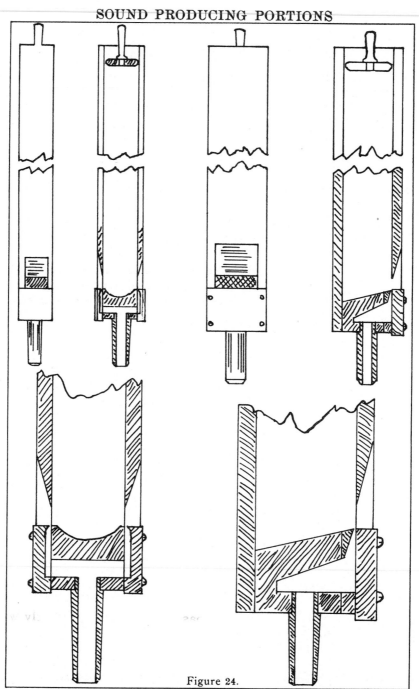

Figure 24.

On the left, front and sectional views of the Doppelflöte. This stop is generally made with stoppers in the top, but may be made with open pipes. In either case two mouths are provided on opposite sides. The pipes are normally narrow on the sides which contain the mouths. On the right, a Gedeckt. This is a modified and small scaled form of Stopped Diapason or more properly Stopped Flute.

zinc, fairly liberally scaled (about twelve inches at sixteen foot C). These pipes were quite equal and in some ways superior to pipes made of wood, the tone produced having greater definition than the more conventional wood Diapasons; a real advantage in Pedal tone, that is all too likely to be muddy and ill defined.

The sixteen foot manual Diapason is frequently of metal with much smaller scale, generally not exceeding eight inches at sixteen foot C. When the bass-portion of the manual stops is made of wood, the wood portion is generally not carried up past GG# and the break between wood and metal can be rendered quite imperceptible.

The upper work of the Diapason consists of the Octave, 15th and 22nd, and the mutation work, that is, ranks of pipes sounding a note of a different pitch from the foundation. Mutation work includes the Quint, Tierce, and Septime and their octaves. The combination of octave and mutation ranks are known by the generic name of "Mixtures," which are more fully described in our chapter on Mixtures. More particulars in regard to the scaling and formation of the pipes comprising the upper work of the Diapason will be given in subdivision under Mixtures and Mutations.

FLUTE TONE

The second general class of organ tone is that known as Flute. Under this heading are grouped all those stops in the organ whose tone is characterized by a deficiency of upper partial tones. This type of tone is obtained from stopped pipes and from open wood pipes with square blocks, from open metal pipes with very high mouths and from double length open or stopped pipes that are blown to sound their harmonics. Stopped pipes are made of either wood or metal. The principal type of stopped wood pipes that was most common to organs in both England and America is that known as the stopped "Diapason," being a large scaled pipe with a square block and hollow cap fitted a trifle below the level of the nicked edge of the block. This has been modified by Schulze into a smaller scaled pipe known as the Gedeckt. The latter pipe produces a brighter and more interesting tone of good body. The metal Stopped Flute is a thick metal pipe fitted with a wooden stopper with a high mouth and the upper lip pulled outwards, frequently by not flattening the upper lip at all, but allowing it to maintain the natural roundness of the body of the pipe. There are many kinds of stopped Flutes, including those with two mouths, one on each side of the pipe, known as the Doppel Flöte. The Quintaton is made of metal with a very low mouth which causes the pipe not only to sound its prime but its 12th, with almost equal prominence, at the same time.

Among the stopped flutes may be found the Sub Bass, Untersatz, Bourdon, Quintaton, Gedeckt, Doppelflöte, Stopped Diapason, Cor de Nuit,

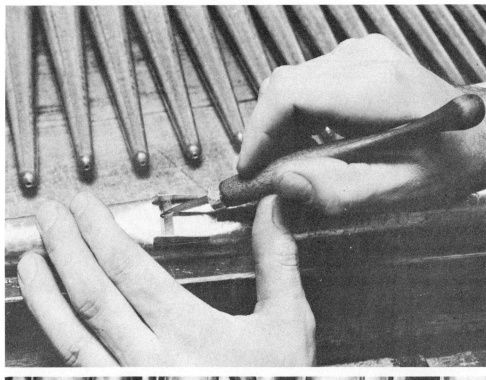

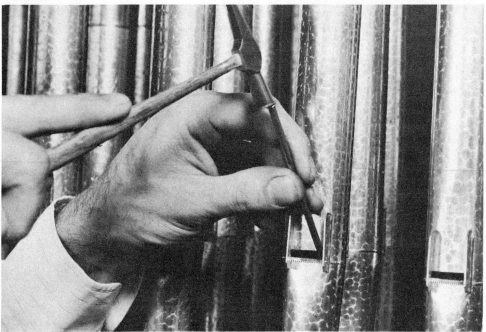

Figures 25 and 26.
Metal pipe voicing. Above, nicking the languid, as described in the text. Below, adjusting the lanquid. In this case it is being lowered.

Nason Flute and Lieblichflöte. Variations of timbre are brought about by several factors which include; choice of material, i.e., wood or metal, the type of stopper or cap, and details of mouth treatment.

The most important Stopped Flute in the Pedal organ is that called the Bourdon which has been made of inordinately large scales, as much as ten by twelve inches. A large scale is necessary to counterbalance the effect of a low mouth in order to avoid the distressing "cough" which would otherwise precede the speech of such a pipe. Usually nothing is gained by a scale larger than seven by nine inches, when heavily winded.*

The 32 foot Sub-Bourdon is rarely a success below GGGG, because of the fact that any attempt to get the wind to reach the upper lip makes the pipe speak its 12th. The pipes below this are nearly a total loss, except in the most advantageous placing where there is ample speaking room.

Many musically useful varieties of hybrid flute tone have been developed from classic and later prototypes. Among these may be cited; the capped flutes with chimneys, capped harmonic flutes, cylindrical pipes surmounted with conical caps and related forms. These registers include such voices as the: Rohrflöte, Rohrbordun, Rohrnazard, Zauberflöte, Koppelflöte and Spillflöte.

Open Flutes comprise the following principal varieties of pipes; the wood Clarbella, Hohlflöte, Waldflöte, Melodia and wood harmonic Concert Flute, orchestral Flute or Flauto Traversa. The metal Flutes include the Nachthorn and Flute Ouverte, the tapered Spitzflöte or Flute Conique, and Blockflöte as well as the double length harmonic flute and the harmonic Spitzflöte.

Metal open Flutes are made by cutting up the mouths of Diapasons until Flute tone is produced. That is until practically all the harmonic development is removed from the Diapason. This is almost exactly what is done in the Phonon type of Diapason with its exceedingly high mouth. It is more like a Flute than a Diapason. The Major Flute is simply a large scaled Clarabella and is frequently an extension of the Pedal Diapason in modern American work. The Harmonic Flute usually is made with double length pipes, overblown to speak their octave from about middle C upwards. This type of pipe produces the nearest imitation of the orchestral Flute. Harmonic Flutes were perfected and extensively used by Cavaille-Coll.

STRING TONE

String tone is obtained from pipes which are especially scaled and

---

*I recall an incident where one of our builders had completed the entire 32 foot octave of the Sub-Bourdon and the organ was being examined by several interested enthusiasts who attempted to listen for the tone produced by the low C. Finally, by rummaging through the organ, the low C pipe was discovered and my friend, being asked if he heard the note, said he felt only "an expensive draft."

voiced to give chief prominence to the upper partials at the expense of ground tone. String tone stops, therefore, present a complete contrast to the Flute tone stops, while the Diapason in its equipment of overtones should stand more or less midway between the two.

String tones are usually produced from metal pipes, though in many European examples, beautiful string tone is produced from wood pipes. William Thynne, an English voicer and builder, is usually given credit for the greatest modern development of string tone. The fundamental principles of voicing string tone pipes are briefly these: 1. Small Scales; 2. Bridges or Rollers applied to the mouths of the pipes which have been previously made to speak their octave or 12th. To produce the viol type of tone, the largest scale that can be employed is about three inches at eight foot C.

William Thynne's usual scale was 2½ inches at 8 foot C
1½ inches at Tenor C
15/16 inches at Middle C.

Scales smaller than this have frequently been introduced by others. It should be pointed out that these small scaled pipes must necessarily diminish in a very much slower progression than that of the Diapason pipes. The latter halves its diameter on the 16th or 17th pipe, while Viols halve on the 20th to 22nd pipes.

The precise fixing of the bridge or roller is a matter that has to be learned from practical experience. The pipes are voiced to overblow, or sound their octave, like harmonic Flutes. In the case of very small scaled pipes, they are usually overblown to sound their second harmonic or 12th, and then the roller is adjusted in such a way as to bring the note back to its prime or fundamental tone. In this manner the prime tone and upper harmonics are locked together and produce the required string tone.

String tone pipes are nearly always slotted, and the modern method is to spring a set of tin plated slides around the bottom of the slot that can be knocked up or down any number of times as the pipes require tuning, without danger of breaking. When the roll of metal that is cut from the slot is allowed to remain at the bottom of the slot and is used for tuning purposes by being rolled up and down, it will eventually break off.

The most commonly found members of the string family and closely related tonalities are: The Violone, Contra Gamba and Contra Viola, the Gross Gamba, Violoncello, Viola Pomposa, Viole de Gambe, Viole d'Orchestre and Salicional. This family is also represented in octave pitch with the border line Fugara and more definitely stringy Violina and and Salicet.

Echoes of the beforementioned classes of tone are these: the Echo Diapason or Principal tones as found in the Dulciana, Dolce, Dolcan and Dulcet.

SOUND PRODUCING PORTIONS

Softer Flute tones used are known as the Flauto Amabile, Flûte d'Amour and Flauto Dolce.

Miniature string tones are the Echo Viole, Echo Gamba, Aeoline, Viole Sourdine or Muted Viole and many fancifully named soft toned stops, some of which have an ethereal effect.

Nearly all types of string tone may have associated with the principal rank, an additional rank or ranks tuned sharp or flat, known as a Céleste rank.

Such stops include the Gamba Céleste, Voix Céleste, Unda Maris, Flute Céleste and Gemshorn Céleste.

THE CONSTRUCTION OF REED PIPES

Until recent years, many small American organs were built without any Reed pipes, except perhaps an Oboe. This was not the case with French or English organs. The value of Reed stops was early recognized and employed to some extent in these countries. It is true that on the whole the old style low pressure Reeds introduced into American organs were not very successful from a tonal standpoint, nor in the matter of staying in tune. The reed tongues themselves had to be made of such light weight brass to produce any tone on the very light pressure employed that the result was likely to be thin and nasal. The Trumpet stops particularly sounded like "fish horns." Such a stop was only tolerable with the full organ.

Reed tone of all varieties can be produced with the most characteristic quality anyone could desire. This is true if the pipes are properly made and voiced. Also, with the heavy tuning wires and reed tongues graded to thicknesses that are now employed, the Reeds will stay in tune nearly as well as the Flue pipes. The author is especially partial to all types of Reed tone and believes that one-third of all pipes should be Reeds, either Chorus or Solo, for a fair average. This is about the proportion employed in French organs, and is much higher than ordinarily used in America. After all, Reed tone can be made the most interesting and characteristic of any tone in the organ. Good Reeds, and as many of them as possible, are invaluable in giving character, variety, and distinction to organ tone.

The greatest enemy of Reed pipes is dirt of any kind. It may enter the pipes through the wind supply. If the blower is located poorly, coal dust may be picked up and blown into the organ. If even a small amount of foreign matter finds its way between the reed tongue and the brass tube or reed it beats against the result may either be a poor tone, or rattle, or a complete silence. If the note continues to sound, it is considerably off pitch. If the organ can be kept clean and the wind supply also, the amount of trouble that Reed stops cause will be reduced to an absolute minimum.

Obviously there was some hesitation and objection to placing Reed stops in an organ that was going to an out-of-the-way town where a tuner would seldom be available, for, when a set of Reeds does get into bad condition, it is undoubtedly the most villainous sounding stop in the organ. It then becomes quite useless until cleaned and retuned. The modern practice of enclosing the organ in chambers, particularly where the shutters are allowed to close when the wind is off keeps a great amount of floating dust and dirt from settling inside the pipes themselves. Comparatively little trouble is experienced with the Reeds under such conditions, especially when the blower is furnishing clean air to the organ.

We come now to the actual construction of Reed pipes. See Figure 24. It should first be pointed out that these pipes have no mouths like Flue pipes and that the pipes themselves play a secondary part in determining the quality of tone obtained. The real speaking part is the metal tongue, usually shaped somewhat like that in a Reed organ or mouth organ. If this tongue is properly adjusted and wind pressure directed against it, it will vibrate in or against an opening cut in a small brass tube called a reed or shallot. The length of the vibrating portion of the tongue is regulated by means of a bent wire which presses the tongue firmly against the reed. The lengthening or shortening of this vibrating part decreases or increases the number of vibrations. Accordingly, the note obtained is proportionately lower or higher in pitch. The shallot and tongue are fixed in a hole in a heavy metal block and the whole affair is enclosed in a sort of pipe foot which is termed a boot. If we now place a pipe in the hole above the reed block and test the tone, we shall find that the note obtained is very much modified in quality. So, according to the length, scale, and shape of the pipe or resonator (as the reed barrel is termed), we may obtain a variety of tones from the same reed. The tone also can be modified by manipulating the tongue.

The block of a Reed pipe into which the shallot and tongue are fitted at the bottom, and the resonator on top, is usually a circular and rather solid mass of pipe metal cast in a mold. Blocks were sometimes made of wood in old work. Especially in the case of high pressure Reeds, this block is of large proportions and considerable weight, to steady the vibrations caused in the lower part of the resonator by the powerful striking of the tongue against the shallot.

Mr. B. G. Austin of the Austin Organ Company has conducted a number of experiments in the matter of reducing the vibration of the tongue against the shallot. This vibration is excessive in large pipes. Mr. Austin came to the conclusion that a reed block of great weight and size does not accomplish the purpose as well as a heavy weight of lead affixed to the bottom of the resonator (just above where it is secured to the block).

56

This is the point of greatest vibration and needs to be steadied. He has secured some quite remarkable results with the larger pipes by treating them in this manner.

Mr. Austin contends that many builders err in considering that the top of the Reed resonator should be of great weight and density of metal, and believes that weight is more important in the bottom of the resonator where the vibrations are of greater intensity. I believe Mr. Henry Willis is in accord with Mr. Austin in this. Here is a matter that will bear more investigation and study.

The shallot, or reed itself, is a cylindrical tube of brass of varying size, becoming smaller as the pipes become smaller. It is usually slightly conical in shape, being wider at the lower end which is closed by a piece of brass affixed (in almost all Reeds) at right angles to the face of the shallot. In some special classes of Reeds, the bottom of the shallot is set at a very sharp angle to the face of the shallot. Such stops as, for example, the English Horn are so treated. In front of the shallot an opening is cut for perhaps half its length, though in old style shallots, in order to produce a sufficient volume of tone on low pressure, the entire front was allowed to be open. The former type is called the "closed" shallot, the latter the "open" shallot.

This is perhaps the most important change that has been made in organ tone in the last half century. The new style of shallot was invented by Henry Willis, the illustrious English organ builder. Prior to the advent of Willis, as has been stated, organ Reeds were rather thin, buzzy things with little or no dignity or weight and were most unmusical in quality.

It was common for students to be instructed that a Reed stop should never be used alone but that a Stopped Diapason or other rank of Flue pipes must always be associated with it to improve the tone quality. Henry Willis created an entirely new school of Reed voicing. He was the first to show that Reeds could be made really beautiful, and fit for use, without help from Flue stops. When he wanted power he obtained it by raising the pressure in order that he might still restrain the tone and retain beauty of musical quality as well. He was the first to show that every trace of roughness and rattle could be removed by imparting to a reed tongue exactly the right curve. He weighted the ends of the larger reed tongues, thereby restraining their too emphatic vibrations. He also adopted the practice of using harmonic or double length resonators for the treble notes. This practice secured from these notes a degree of power never before dreamed possible. The upper octaves of the Reeds always suffer from a tendency to become weak. It was Mr. Willis who created the magnificent Chorus Reeds which transform the Swell Organ into a rich, powerful ensemble, which had hitherto been a poor and weak department, entirely overshadowed by the Great Organ. These powerful, live, vibrant Reeds are always thoroughly musical in quality when made by Mr. Willis.

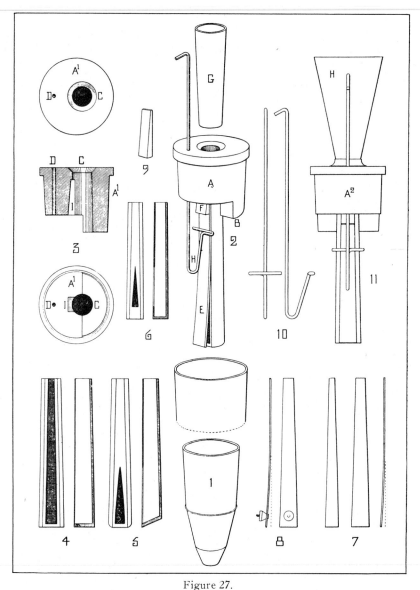

Figure 27.

Portions of Reed Pipes.
(From Audsley, "The Art of Organ Building")

Referring to the drawing on this page, Figure **27**, 1, is the reed boot, or foot that fits into the block, A, shown in 2, above. 2 also shows the reed tongue, E, wedged against the shallot by wedge, F. Also the tuning wire, H, against the tongue. 3 shows top, sectional and bottom views of the reed block. 4 shows front and side views of the "open" shallot, while 5 and 6 show two forms of the "closed" shallot. It will be noticed that the opening in the shallot shown at 6 starts above the base, forming a pocket at the bottom of the shallot. This type is used for French Horns, with a capped resonator of large scale, which has also a pocket in its top. 7 shows front and side views of a narrow and broad reed tongue. 8 shows front and side views of a reed tongue with a weight attached. 9 is the reed wedge. 10 the tuning wire. 11 a front view of the reed assembly.

58

Mr. Wedgwood, in his "Dictionary of Organ Stops," has the following to say as the secret of successful Reed voicing: "It consists in imparting to the tongue such a degree of curvature as will cause it to *roll down* rather than *strike* against the shallot, or maybe against the pneumatic buffer which is commonly supposed to intervene. Should a *flat* spot occur in the reed by reason of an imperfect curve or a speck of dust lodging between the shallot and the tongue, the tone rendered will be harsh and blatant. It is on the precise stoichiometrical curve of the tongue—the distribution of elasticity—that the nature of the tone largely depends.

"This method of voicing was essentially French in origin. It was developed by M. Cavaille-Coll, whose work reached the zenith of perfection in the voicing of orchestral Solo Reeds. It was Mr. Willis, however, who on these foundations reared the vast edifice of modern Chorus Reed voicing."

It has been pointed out that Mr. Willis was the first to systematically employ small weights screwed on to the end of the tongue, thereby rendering the tongue heavier so that it may be reduced in length. The ill effects of internal and tortional vibration, almost inevitable in the case of long tongues, can thus be avoided.

"Free Reeds" are seldom employed by American organ builders. In these Reeds the tongue passes right through the shallot as in the Harmonium or Reed Organ. Occasionally Clarinets are made with "Free Reeds." The voicer has obviously little control over the tongue, and therefore the the quality of tone is mainly determined by the shape of the tube or resonator. It also happens that all "Free Reeds" bear a strong resemblance to each other, and also to the Harmonium tone. The characteristic of "Free Reeds" is the excessive development of harmonics. They were formerly employed very largely in Germany but are seldom manufactured at present.

The open shallot reed pipes, shown at 4 in figure 27 have, during the past ten years, come to be the preferred chorus reed tone in the modern American organ by many organists and builders. The boots of these reed pipes are made as short as possible, and the tone is very prompt and intensely brilliant. There is less foundation tone than the normal English (Willis) trumpets have. Chorus reeds with open shallots are called Trompettes and are modified adaptations of the famous Trompettes developed by Cavaille-Coll. They do not cover, rather they expand, the brilliance of the flue chorus. Churches with considerable reverberation are best adapted for this type of tone, and they were developed originally for such edifices. They are effective with wind pressure of 3½" or more.

Shallots are faced with leather to secure smoothness of tone. To do so is merely a makeshift means instead of the scientific, though arduous, process of securing smoothness by properly curving the tongue. Partic-

Figure 28

Reed Pipe Making. The bodies of the reed pipes are cut from patterns, as in making Metal pipes, and shaped around a mandrel with the proper degree of taper. Reed pipes are nearly always conical in form. The reed pipe body that is being formed on the mandrel at the left has its top made of pipe metal, while the lower portion is made of zinc. The flat sheets are made to assume the proper curve by pounding with a flat board on the mandrel. The large white conical shaped parts shown near the top of the photograph will be soldered on to the tops of the pipe bodies to make them flare. This is a French Trumpet, made in the Moller factory.

ularly is this true of the base octave of Reed stops where the curve must be absolutely right to secure a smooth tone (without leathering being resorted to).

The best Reed voicers I know in this country dislike and look with disdain on this practice and never resort to it themselves. Such voicers consider it a form of cheating at the game of Reed voicing.

There is this to be said in favor of leathering shallots, particularly when padded with heavy leather: a small particle of dirt between the tongue and the shallot will not cause the unpleasant rattle that is bound to occur where the shallot is not leathered. With these leathered shallots the Gottfried Company has succeeded in producing some excellent examples of Clarinets, French Horns, and other orchestral Reeds. When leathering is employed for the Tuba or other Chorus Reed tone, the results are not satisfactory to the educated and discerning ear.

No one has condemned the practice of leathered shallots more strongly than the late Mr. Willis, as well as the present Mr. Willis. They have both conclusively demonstrated that it is not essential to smoothness of tone. The smoothest Reed tone yet produced excepting the French Horn, is the Hope-Jones Tuba Sonora, which does not have leathered shallots. Hope-Jones was too much of an idealist to make use of the subterfuge.

Without question, it is more correct, on scientific grounds, to secure the proper curve of the tongue and thus a smooth tone, than it is to merely pad the surface so that an indifferently curved tongue will suffice. I do not blame the commercial pipe makers for leathering their shallots. When pipes must be sold competitively, such practices are quite justifiable.

A device that is placed at the bottom part of the very large reed tongues (such as the 32 foot octave of the Pedal Bombarde) is a pneumatic starter and stopper. When this is not provided, the tongues are likely to be slow in starting and the note will continue to vibrate for some time after the wind has been cut off. This has been sometimes termed the "death rattle."

The Aeolian Skinner Organ Company now employs such starters on all of their 32 foot octaves of Reed pipes with excellent results.

The modern type of 32' reeds, as made by Aeolian Skinner, with French eshallots, have a very prompt speech and musical tone and require no starters as described above.

Probably the chief factors controlling successful Reed voicing are the following: 1. correct construction of the pipe, 2. correct curvature of the reed tongue, 3. correct use of wind pressures, 4. correct tuning in relation to the proportions of the reed and tube or resonator. This last is a most important point and is frequently misunderstood.

Taking up the construction of the parts of the pipe, we have learned that the tube or resonating body varies in shape in accordance with the

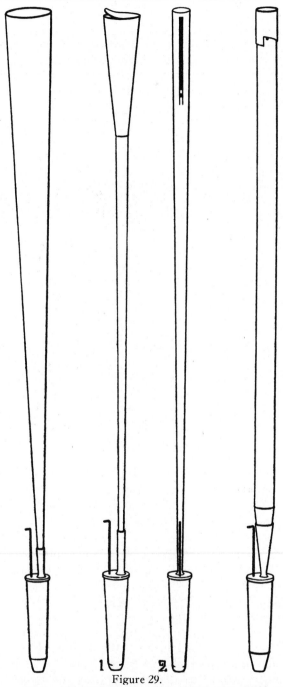

Figure 29.

At the left, the general shape of the reed barrel or resonator employed in obtaining Chorus Reed tone. 1 is the ordinary or organ Oboe while 2 is the Orchestral Oboe or more imitative stop. On the right is the Clarinet.

(From Audsley, "The Art of Organ Building")

type of Reed tone required. In the Chorus Reeds, that is Trumpets, Trombas, Cornopeans, Tubas, etc., the tube is of inverted conical shape. The diameter at the top of the pipe at 8 foot C varies from a little over four inches to as much as five and one-half inches in accordance with the type of tone required.

The Reeds that imitate the orchestral voices usually have narrower and shorter tubes than do the Chorus Reeds. An exception is the French Horn. This stop is successfully made with a pocket in the bottom of the shallot produced by cutting the opening some distance up. The barrel is capped on top, with a tuner near the top for regulating. Each imitative Reed has its own peculiar shape, a number of which are shown in Figure 29.

The tip of all reed tubes, that is the part which joins the block, should be narrow. To make the opening at this point too wide is an error made by the earlier European and American organ builders. The former practice did not permit of adequately controlling the tone at the point of juncture, between the block and tube. Mr. Hunt states, "To constrict this opening forms a striking confirmation of the *bouche fermee* method of teaching singing in which the student is instructed to practice scales on "M-Woo-ah" in order to acquire pure tone. The human voice being a reed controlled in a similar manner to that of the organ reed, it does not require much imaginative power to discern the parallelism here evident."

The length of the tube is a matter of great importance. If the tube is too long, a sort of throttled or choked note results and the tone is said to be too close. If, on the other hand, the tube is too short, the tone is coarse and said to be too "free." Exact proportion of the length of tube to the length of reed tongue permitted to vibrate is a matter of the greatest importance therefore. As a matter of practice the tubes are usually left a trifle too long and are then adjusted to a nicety so that the pipe will speak its natural "free" note without being too close nor harsh.

The tongues and shallots have already been described. The chief difficulty in the treatment of the tongue is encountered in giving it the proper curvature. This is the most difficult department of Reed voicing. The quality of a curve must be adjusted so as to enable the tongue to roll down the face of the shallot during the process of striking. This is usually tested by holding the shallot with the tongue in position in front of a light so that the light shines between the tongue and the shallot, the while slowly depressing the tongue with one's forefinger. The darkness caused by the exclusion of light is seen to travel in an even gradation along the intervening space until, with the contact of the head or base of the tongue with the end of the shallot, all light is completely excluded. The quantity of curve varies with the thickness of the tongue and the pressure of the wind employed.

If the tongue is not sufficiently curved or is too thin and pliable, the force of the wind will drive it too sharply against the shallot. Therefore, the thicker the tongue and the lower the pressure, the less the curvature required, also the less the quantity of tone obtained from the pipe. The smaller tongues are nearly always curved by hand by the Reed voicer who becomes very expert in knowing just what motions to make to create the proper curvature. An expert voicer can frequently secure a correct curve both in regard to quantity and quality after the first trial. The larger tongues are usually curved in a curving machine.

The tongues are curved by placing them flat on a block of polished steel with the top or narrow end of the tongue clamped securely down, leaving the broad end free. A burnishing tool is used, which is merely a cylindrical piece of steel. This is drawn along the surface of the tongue with a gradual increase of pressure which reaches its greatest amount at the head of the tongue. This process is repeated if necessary until the curvature is sufficiently pronounced. The curving machine performs precisely the same operation, the quality and degree of the curve being regulated by a cam. It must be again remarked that the curvature of the tongue has a great influence upon the speech and tone of a Reed pipe.

Assuming that the curve is correct, in respect to its quality, it may yet be too pronounced or insufficient. Too great a curve makes the speech slow while not sufficient curve causes the speech to be too "free" and quick. The precise amount of curvature has to be determined by the voicer when engaged in the work of final finishing. Heavy wind pressures are of enormous advantage to the Reed voicer.

Mr. Hunt states, "The length of the tongue is determined by the following factors that are dependent upon each other: 1. minimum thickness of tongue; 2. the maximum degree of weighting; 3. the length and scale of the tube; 4. the wind pressure available. A factor which is frequently misunderstood by some Reed voicers is that the length of the resonating tube must bear some definite relation to the natural pitch of the vibrating tongue, if the tone of the Reed is to be satisfactory. Sharpening the pitch of the Reed makes the tone softer and the speech slower, while flattening the pitch makes the tone louder and 'freer' and the speech quicker. If the tube is too long, the tongue has to be shortened to pitch and the tone is too 'close'. If the tube is too short, the tongue has to be lengthened to pitch and the tongue is too 'free'. Therefore, the tube must be so adjusted as to be in proper proportion to the pitch of the reed itself." In the case of most American reed resonators, the final adjustment is done on the tuning slot. In the case of most English Reeds, the tubes themselves are actually cut to the proper length.

The latter is an ideal arrangement where the temperature remains approximately uniform but where the organ has to be tuned at widely different temperatures, such as the organs in most American churches, between winter and summer heat, the regulation of the power of the Reeds would be completely upset if there were no way of tuning the Reeds except on the tongue, that is by means of the tuning wires.

We have already noted that one of the peculiarities of Chorus Reeds is their tendency to grow weaker in the upper portions of the scale. This is nearly always compensated for in the best work by making the upper 12, or frequently the upper 24 Reeds, harmonic. That is, making the resonators of double normal speaking length, and in this manner a tone of greater power and quality may be obtained from the upper notes. Even with this expedient, it is difficult to obtain as much power from the top as from the middle and lower octaves and in some instances of very powerful Tuba stops, the resonators have been made three times their normal speaking length and are therefore triple harmonic. An instance of two large Tubas so treated is the Atlantic City High School organ. These Tubas were voiced in the Midmer-Losh factory and they are fine specimens of this type of tone, with great power.

Usually with Chorus Reeds, many builders leave off the Reed pipes at the 49th note for an 8 foot stop and continue the top octave or second top octave (if a 73 note stop) with Flue pipes. Some of our builders continue the Chorus Reed tone up to the 54th pipe on an 8 foot stop. In any event, all the solo or imitative orchestral voices should be continued in Reeds to at least the 54th pipe on an 8 foot stop, in order to avoid the break in tone which is inevitable between Reed pipes and even the most closely matched Flue pipes.

This is a point that many of our builders overlook. Of course, these extremely small Reed pipes are difficult to make and voice but the additional trouble is worth while, certainly for solo stops.

The Reed stops of the organ are divided into two main categories, chorus and solo, and further into non-imitative and imitative groupings, as well as the various pitch families. Naturally these distinctions overlap and merge into each other and reflect national and period characteristics as well.

The most commonly found chorus reed stops are Bombarde, Trompette, Clairon, Trombone, Trumpet, Clarion, Fagotto, Cornopean, Ophicleide, Possaune, and Tromba.

Partaking of both chorus and solo natures are the Fagotto, Tuba, Flügelhorn, Waldhorn, Hautbois and Oboe Clarion.

More frequently found solo stops are the Clarinet, Bassoon, Orchestral Oboe, English Horn, Heckelphone, Corno di Bassetto, French Horn and Vox Humana.

Recently there has been a considerable interest in the more or less successful revival and development of certain classical and baroque prototypes such as the Krummhorn or Cromorne, Dulzian, Regal, Schalmei, Rohrschalmei and others, especially as built by The Aeolian-Skinner

65

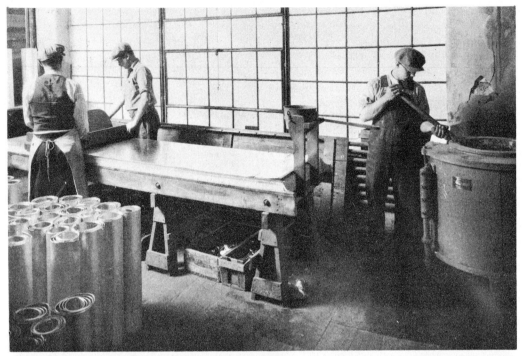

Figure 30.

Above, rolling out on the casting table a sheet of pipe metal. The men have just finished returning the trough to starting position, after moving it to the opposite end of the table. A sheet of metal has been left, which has run out through the slot in the bottom of the trough. Below, wood pipe making. Pipes have been glued up, and are drying in the clamps at the left.

Organ Company and described on page 240.

MIXTURES AND MUTATIONS

In his recent excellent book "The Modern British Organ," the Rev. Noel Bonavia-Hunt devotes many pages in his Chapter VII on "Octaves and Mutations" to arguments for the introduction of these stops in the organ. The interested reader is referred to this great authority on tonal matters for a fuller treatment of the history and theory of Mutations and Mixtures.

I feel that I can be most helpful to the earnest student of organ design by being entirely practical in my approach to this subject, and avoiding long arguments on the philosophy and history of Mixtures and Mutations. It is better to come to the point at once. I propose to give some specific information as to the composition, scaling, breaks, and other particulars of several of the more commonly introduced Mixtures in present day organs, as designed by several of our leading builders.

The past twenty-five years have witnessed a return to the production of many fine organs by a number of our leading builders, which contain either one or several Mixtures and a number of Mutation ranks. These organs have been so successful musically, and have had so much better ensembles because of the introduction of these voices, that no apology, or explanation is necessary for this type of organ. This is recognized and confirmed by all good organists and musicians who have heard them. We are getting back to the organ of tradition.

What is a Mutation Stop? It is part of the upper work of the organ which, broadly speaking, adds brilliance and vivacity to the ensemble of both the flue and reed stops. Ranks of pipes sounding other pitches than the unison or its octaves, are called Mutations.

When octaves and mutations are mixed together and are all controlled by a single drawstop, they are called Mixtures. The smallest Mixture must have at least two ranks of pipes, consisting of some octave sounding rank (usually the 15th) and a Mutation rank, (usually the 12th). Additional ranks may be added up to seven or eight. Mutation stops, when they draw separately, normally run throughout the compass, without breaking back.

It is quite impractical to make or to tune pipes any shorter in speaking length than the top C of a 15th. The speaking length of this pipe is only 3/8". As a consequence, if octave or mutation ranks are introduced in a Mixture of higher pitch than the 15th, such ranks must of necessity break back somewhere along the way up to the top of their compass, either an octave or two octaves or more. The break does not need to occur at only one point on the way up. It may occur at every octave, and only break back half an octave at a time. The exact point at which the various ranks of a Mixture break back is something which has

PLATE V

The Barnes Memorial organ in the First Presbyterian Church, Evanston, Illinois. Johnson-Holtkamp, builders. Described in the text on page 261.

been the subject of study and experiment by a number of our leading builders, as well as having been studied abroad by the best European builders for centuries. The best American builders have had the benefit of the accumulated knowledge of the European builders with which to start their own experimenting and tests.

As a matter of fact such an artistic tonal designer as Mr. G. Donald Harrison, who has probably designed more different types of Mixtures than any other American builder in the past twenty years, is still experimenting with scales and breaks. He is still trying for more perfect results. This does not mean, however, that some excellent practical results have not already been achieved, and that the subject of scaling and composition of Mixtures is not sufficiently far advanced and devel-to speak about definitely and positively.

Mr. Bonavia-Hunt says: "In all cases where music is produced by sustained tones the human ear demands pitch changes and is never satisfied with unisonal sounds only. Octave tones let in the light and lend vivacity to the whole. They raise the pitch level—the chromatic mean—of the tonal spectrum to a sane normality, so that it is neither too low nor too high. The effect of Mixture work is to infuse the tonal picture with light, just as if we were to draw the blinds and let the sun-rays play upon the objects scattered about our living-room. The objects are transformed; the light rays scintillate and sparkle happily in every crevice and on every surface where they can find their way. Mixture ranks should produce this same effect acoustically .. to suffuse the whole with *life*."

"Mutation tones enforce the high octave tones in the series. This is entirely due to the summational effect of the mutations, when combined with the lower octave ranks."

Mr. Harrison says that "If Mixtures are properly planned and voiced, they point up the unison tone in the more obscure parts of the compass and broaden the treble."

DEFINITIONS—COMPOUND MUTATIONS OR MIXTURES

(a) Those built often with no breaks.

The *RAUSCHQUINTE* or *GRAVE MIXTURE:* Usually composed of a 12th and 15th on one stop control and topboard. The pitch will accord with the 16', 8' or 4' series.

The *CORNET:* As properly formed this register consists of three to five ranks including octave and fifth sound ranks, but with a tierce on top. ie: 1-8-12-15-17. or 12-15-17. It is largely employed to create solo and synthetic effects, and voiced with large scale flutey pipes, yet it may be more along diapason lines to build up a large body of tone within a chorus.

The *SESQUIALTERA:* In its strict form this would be a fifth sounding rank with a third sounding one above, but as more commonly built the term is applied to a real mixture with breaks, but having these two above mentioned ranks within its composition. ie:

15-17-19-22

12-15-17-19

8-12-15-17

The *TERTIAN:* This stop reverses the pitch relationship on the Sesquialtera thus: 17-19-22 or 10-12-15. The latter composition has little to commend it.

(b) Those built with regular breaks.

MIXTURE—FOURNITURE—PLEIN JEU: These terms are generally applied to mixtures composed of octave and fifth sounding ranks and usually will be found to develop the best results in chorus building. Generally speaking when two mixtures are found in one division the term mixture connotes a lower pitch range than Fourniture, while Plein Jeu is sometimes employed to designate the major chorus mixture in a division. Typical layouts are:

FULL MIXTURE: 12-15-19-22

FOURNITURE: 19-22-26-29

PLEIN JEU: 15-19-22-26-29-33-36

Exceptions may be found to these usages but in general historico-musical ends will be served best if these implications be observed.

SCHARF and *ACUTA:* These names most often designate a high pitched mixture and quite often they may contain third sounding ranks as well as octave and fifth ones.

22-24-26-29   22-26-29-33-36.

CARILLON or *GLOCKENSPIEL:* This type of mixture is usually employed for special effects and is often composed thus: 12-17-22. 17-19-24-26-29.

HARMONICS: Mixtures bearing this name are often found in English work and have been copied frequently in this country. They are apt to contribute a reedy tang when employed with a diapason chorus, and on the whole their use is not considered generally conducive to clarity. This is due to the presence of tierce and septieme ranks.

HARMONICS. (manual series.)

15-17-19 21^{b}st, 22

2', 1 3/5', 1 1/3', 1 1/7', 1'.

Pedal-type. (more useful in building resultant tones.)

12-15-17-19-21^{b}st-22.

5 1/3', 4', 3 1/5', 2 2/3', 2 2/7', 2'.

CYMBALE or *CYMBEL—ZIMBEL:* This usually means a rather high pitched' mixture whose' ranks break back every octave or half-octave. It

70

may be used as a true chorus mixture, or as a special stop for brilliant, scintillating effects in combination with unison timbres. These varied uses call for specific variants in scaling and composition.

Large Chorus Cymbale.

    22-26-29-33-36
    19-22-26-29-33
    15-19-22-26-29
    12-15-19-22-26
    8-12-15-19-22
    5- 8-12-15-19
    1- 5- 8-12-15.

ZIMBEL ¼'

    36-40-43
breaking every six notes.

Before giving some specific examples of Mixtures, let us go into some elementary explanations of terminology. In all of our charts we will refer to the various notes on the organ keyboard from CC to C4 as numbers 1-61. Therefore CC will be No. 1, Tenor C will be No. 13. Middle C will be No. 25, C above Middle C No. 37 and C3 No. 49 and C4 No. 61. These numbers refer to the chromatic intervals on the keyboard, 12 semi-tones to the octave.

The other series of numbers which are used, refer to pitch of the harmonic intervals, counting only the white keys, or Major scale keys. Therefore, the octave above any given pitch is called 8^{ve} or octave. Two Octaves above, Fifteenth or 15th. Three octaves above, 22nd. Partial tones occurring between the octaves which are mutations are called 12th, 17th, 19th, flat 21st, 26th. It should be borne in mind therefore, that if middle C on the organ keyboard is depressed with an 8' stop drawn the sound will be the unison pitch, the same as middle C on the piano, a sound having 261½ vibrations per second. If a 4' stop is drawn the sound will be an octave higher, and this is called 8^{ve} on our charts. If a 2-2/3' stop is drawn, the second G above middle C will sound and this is called 12th. If a 2' stop is drawn, it will be two octaves higher and is called 15th. If a 1-3/5' stop is drawn it will sound the third E above middle C and is called 17th. And so on up the harmonic series.

Before giving the Mixture charts, some more words about mutations are in order.

Normally the Mutation stops which draw separately are used for color purposes only. Therefore, the pipes are usually of flutey intonation and Chimney or Rohr Flutes are especially suitable. A Rohr Nazard 2-2/3' is a useful color stop. For some effects, particularly for a light, piquant, scherzo type of music, the Tierce 1-3/5' is very valuable. The Larigot 1-1/3' (the octave of the Nazard 2-2/3') has also its uses. Naturally, the 4' Koppel Flöte, 2' and 1' Sifflötes, while not mutations, strictly speak-

71

Plate VI.

St. Louis Cathedral, St. Louis. The 100 rank organ is composed of four manual sanctuary division and two manual processional division. Great and solo divisions are on the upper level, swell and choir divisions on floor below, tone openings concealed by ornate grilles. Console and choir are located behind the high altar, processional division at other end of cathedral over Narthex. It was completed by the Kilgen Organ Company, St. Louis, in 1949.

72

Plate VII.

CONSOLE AT ST. LOUIS CATHEDRAL, ST. LOUIS, MO.

Byzantine in design to conform with the architecture of the Cathedral, it is moveable so that it can be placed with Choir singers for services and moved in front of the High Altar for recitals. A supplemental two-manual console is in the gallery over the Narthex, some three hundred feet away, which controls the processional organ. (The Kilgen Organ Company, St. Louis)

73

ing, being octaves of the unison tone, are necessary and essential to a series of mutation stops. They are part of the picture, used either separately or in conjunction with the true mutation ranks. When one or more mutations are used in combination with the suitable unison and octave voices, synthetic tones can be produced of surprising beauty and interest. This requires a judicious use of these mutations, in various combinations with the lower pitches. Hence any choir or positive section of a modern organ should have as nearly complete a series of mutations up to the Sifflöte, 1' as funds will permit. The color and combinational possibilities of these voices are so great as to make them worth their cost. It is presupposed that the organist who presides over these resources is sufficiently trained to make the most effective use of them. These stops have their limitations as well as uses, and a certain amount of discretion and knowledge should be present on the part of the organist, to do these stops full justice.

Coming now to some specific examples of Mixtures, the simplest and most elementary one as stated before is a 12th, & 15th, which draw as one stop. This is introduced as voice #12, or the twelfth stop suggested in our series of model specifications, as given in our chapter on Tonal Design. Even a small organ should contain this amount of Mixture work. The top 6 notes of this small Mixture may well break back an interval of a fifth or fourth.

The pipes of this Mixture, as well as all of the Mixtures now to be described are Diapason pipes. The 15th should be 4 pipes smaller than the Unison Diapason (at the same pitch). The 12th, 5 pipes smaller. The Octave 4' will be 2 pipes smaller. In all of the Mixtures given below, it is suggested that the octave sounding ranks have wide mouths (¼) and the fifth sounding ranks narrower mouths (1/5). This Mixture is designed for one unison Diapason. If there are two Unison Diapasons, the octave 4' should be bigger in scale, midway between the scales of the first and second Unison Diapasons, and the Mixtures should be about 2 scales larger than suggested above.

A III Rank Great Mixture that is most generally useful is as follows: This is in lieu of 12th & 15th Mixture.

(a) Keys #1-12	13-25	26-61
15th	12th	8^{ve}
19th	15th	12th
22nd	19th	15th

A III Rank Great Mixture which supplements and completes the upper harmonics where there is already a 12th and 15th is as follows:

SOUND PRODUCING PORTIONS

III RKS. GREAT MIXTURE—SCHARFF.

(b) Keys #1-24	25-36	37-48	49-61
19th	15th	12th	8^{ve}
22nd	19th	15th	12th
26th	22nd	19th	15th

We now come to III-IV Rank Mixtures. These are suitable for either Great or Swell. Plein Jeu III-IV Ranks. This needs no independent 12th & 15th to go with it.

IV RANK GREAT MIXTURE

(c) Keys #1-6	7-19	20-30	31-61
15th	12th	8^{ve}	1st
19th	15th	12th	8^{ve}
26th	19th	15th	12th
	22nd	19th	15th

A IV Rank Fourniture to supplement a 12th and 15th is as follows:

(d) Keys #1-24	25-36	37-48	49-61
19th	15th	12th	5th
22nd	19th	15th	8^{ve}
26th	22nd	19th	12th
29th	26th	22nd	15th

A Swell Plein Jeu of IV Ranks, which the late Mr. Richard Whitelegg of M. P. Moller designed for my organ at home, and which has proved itself to be exceedingly effective is as follows:

(e) Keys #1-19	20-31	32-43	44-55	56-61
12th	12th	8^{ve}	5th	1st
19th	15th	12th	8^{ve}	5th
22nd	19th	15th	12th	8^{ve}
26th	22nd	19th	15th	12th

Please note well that all of the above are Chorus Mixtures to supplement the Great Diapason Chorus or the Swell Reeds. None of them has any ranks except octaves and quints. There are no Tierces or 17th sounding ranks in any of them.

75

Many old Chorus Mixtures had Tierces which created an unpleasant effect when chords including minor thirds were held. The major thirds in the mixture clashed badly with the minor thirds in the chord. As a practical matter, a separate Tierce 1-3/5' which can be added or not to the Mixtures is the solution.

The majority of the Mixtures given above have been designed by late Mr. Richard Whitelegg for a number of Moller organs. Some of Mr. Donald Harrison's Mixtures are as follows:

The examples given below are the ones he frequently uses in moderate-sized organs. Mr. Harrison is very resourceful, and the following by no means exhaust all of his ideas on Mixtures, but are representative.

TYPICAL GREAT FOURNITURE IV, RANKS. (LARGE SCALE)

(f) Keys #1-18	19-30	31-42	43-61
15th	12th	8^{ve}	1st
19th	15th	12th	8^{ve}
22nd	19th	15th	12th
26th	22nd	19th	15th

CYMBAL III RANKS—(MEDIUM SCALE)

(g) Keys #1-18	19-30	31-42	43-54	55-61
22nd	19th	15th	12th	8^{ve}
26th	22nd	19th	15th	12th
29th	26th	22nd	19th	15th

TYPICAL ZIMBEL III (SMALL SCALE) (9 BREAKS)

(h) Keys #1-12	13-18	19-24	25-30	31-36	37-42	43-48	49-54	55-61
29th	26th	22nd	19th	15th	12th	8^{ve}	5th	1st
33rd	29th	26th	22nd	19th	15th	12th	8^{ve}	5th
36th	33rd	29th	26th	22nd	19th	15th	12th	8^{ve}

GREAT OR SWELL PLEIN JEU VI RANKS (VARIOUS SCALES)

(h) Keys #1-18	19-30	13-42	43-54	55-61
12th	8^{ve}	1st	1st	1st
15th	12th	8^{ve}	8^{ve}	8^{ve}
19th	15th	12th	12th	8^{ve}
22nd	19th	15th	15th	12th
26th	22nd	19th	15th	15th
29th	26th	22nd	19th	15th

Note: When there are two 15ths or two 8^{ve}, the pipes are scaled and voiced differently.

There are, of course, besides the Diapason Mixtures given above, other types of Mixtures, not so generally useful. There are Mixtures made with Dulciana pipes, and also with String toned pipes. Then there are those made usually with a series of independently drawn Flute Mutation ranks, as previously explained, under Mutations. These latter are capable of creating synthetic tones which have great interest.

One last Mixture might perhaps be given. When an organ reaches fifty or more stops, two separate Mixtures may be used on both Swell and Great, with worthwhile effect, in which case the second Swell Mixture may well be a Dolce Cornet. This is useful for color purposes, with Strings and perhaps Vox Humana, or a soft 8' and 4' Flute. It should not be loud enough to tell in the ensemble. The Plein Jeu IV Ranks is the Chorus Mixture, and it should be provided first, as being of greater usefulness, and telling effect to "take the curse off the Reeds," as someone has expressed it. A Dolce Cornet IV Ranks may be made of Dulciana pipes and consist of the following:

(i) *Keys #1-42*	*43-54*	*55-61*
12th	8^{ve}	5th
15th	12th	8^{ve}
17th	15th	10th
19th	17th	12th

This can also be made as a Dolce Cornet III Ranks, omitting the 19th, 8^{ve} and 5th.

Note that the Tierce or 17th is present until #55, then it becomes a sub Tierce 3 1/5'.

A Tierce is proper and desirable in a softly voiced Mixture such as this, as the pipes are none of them loud enough to cause unpleasant clashes, no matter in what manner the Mixture is used.

Some organists prefer to have several Mixtures, one reinforcing the 8' series, one the 4' series, and one the 2' series, rather than having a second Mixture on the Swell be the Dolce Cornet.

I hope that the foregoing will be of some practical value to serious students of the organ, who want to know what constitutes a good Mixture. Those given are none of them theoretical mixtures, whose composition may look well on paper, but when put to practical test in an organ, fail to come off properly. All the Mixtures given have proven themselves by practical use.

When there is only a III Rank on the Great, and no 12th or 15th, I recommend "A" as best. I recommend #H, the IV Rank Plein Jeu as an ideal Swell Mixture, when there are 16', 8' and 4' Chorus Reeds, and at least a Geigen 8' and 4' to support it. The numerous breaks make it particularly adapted for use with the Sw to Gt 4' Coupler or Sw to Sw 4'. The top octaves do not squeal or shriek, but tend to lower and broaden the effect of the top octave of all the Swell stops. So much for Mixtures and Mutations. They must be considered seriously. No modern organ, of more than a dozen stops, can possibly be considered as well designed, without one or more Mixtures.

Regarding Pedal Mixtures. On page 168 is a description of a Grand Cornet pedal Mixture, derived by extension from other pedal Ranks. In these days of independent pedal voices, independent Mixtures should be used in a large organ. A III Rank pedal Mixture might consist of 15th-19th-22nd running through the 32 notes without a break. A better one would be 15th-17th-19th-22nd IV Ranks, without breaks. Large organs may have two or more Pedal Mixtures, carrying the harmonics higher than the above Mixtures.

CONTRIBUTIONS TO THE TONE OF THE AMERICAN ORGAN

It would be incomplete to close the chapter on the Sound Producing Portions of the Organ, without some reference to the contributions of several American builders. Many American organ builders have made improvements and discoveries in organ tone but probably none of them has been more interested nor has done as much along these lines as Mr. Ernest M. Skinner. His interest was first aroused in Reed tone especially when he visited England many years ago. The marvelous Reeds voiced by "Father" Willis served as an inspiration. Until this time no such Reeds existed in the American organ.

The "profound impression" made upon Mr. Skinner by the Willis 16' low C Trombone has endured. The first Skinner replica was made in the Hutchings factory immediately upon his return and the many fine Reeds in which Mr. Skinner takes such pride are partly a result. There is the French Horn, the English Horn, the Orchestral Oboe. Of another family is the Erzähler with its curious name.

Among the registers that Mr. Skinner claims were especially designed by him and are peculiarly characteristic of his work are the following, as taken from the list furnished by Mr. Skinner himself. In each case the organ is mentioned in which the register was first used. All are 8' unless otherwise noted:

ERZÄHLER—Christ Church, Hartford, Conn.
ORCHESTRAL OBOE—Tompkins Avenue Congregational Church,
    Brooklyn, N. Y.
ENGLISH HORN (8' and 16')—City College, New York.
FRENCH HORN—Williams College.
KLEINE ERZÄHLER—Fourth Presbyterian, Chicago.

GROSS GEDECKT—Second Congregational, Holyoke, Mass.
CORNO DI BASSETTO—Williams College.
TUBA MIRABILIS—St. John Cathedral, New York.
FRENCH TRUMPET—St. John Cathedral, New York.
ORCHESTRAL BASSOON (16')—Skinner Studio, Boston.
GAMBA CELESTE—St. John Cathedral, New York.
BOMBARDE (32')—City College, New York.
VIOLONE (32')—St. John Cathedral, New York.
SUB BASS (32')—St. Thomas, New York.
CONTRA BASSOON (32')—Princeton University.

The author feels that he must question, especially since the first edition of this book was published, the above claims of Mr. Skinner. Several builders have written me to state that Mr. Skinner was by no means the inventor of the greater part of the list of stops noted above. It is probably a far more accurate statement of the facts to say that Mr. Skinner developed and improved some of the stops listed. It is quite certain that no improvement has been made in a Tuba Mirabilis since Father Willis' days. Also the Erzähler is practically, for all intents and purposes a Gemshorn, which is a very old organ stop. Other builders have now perfected French Horns of remarkably faithful imitative qualities, and in fact, the French Horn, which Mr. Skinner claims to have invented, embodies two very old principles in Reed voicing; the pocketed shallot and the pocketed resonator. The Sub Bass is simply a large scaled Bourdon. The other 32' registers are merely extensions downward in the 32' octave of well known pipe constructions, that may not perhaps before have been carried down below 16' pitch.

Orchestral voices of excellent imitative qualities are now made by all the leading American builders.

During the past twenty-five years, orchestras have grown up in all parts of the country. Excellent recordings of all standard orchestral works are now available on the phonograph and radio also. There is today no excuse for playing orchestral transcriptions on the organ. A quarter century or more ago there was. Such eminent organists as Dr. W. T. Best, Alexandre Guilmant and many others played many orchestral transcriptions in order to acquaint their public with the best orchestral literature, as many of their listeners had no other means of hearing this music. Today, organists should properly confine their repertoire to the great literature written for the organ, past and present. The classic organ and its literature are properly heard more and more.

As interest has increased in the classic organ ensemble, and the music written for it, it has waned with regard to the orchestral voices. In small and medium sized organs built today, ensemble voices come first, and the orchestral voices are relegated to the luxury and non-essential class.

The many fine Skinner organs, built twenty-five years or more ago, in various parts of the country, still proclaim the artistry of Ernest M. Skinner in the matter of lovely orchestral voices, Flute Celestes, Kleiner Erzählers, and similar stops. Many organists and congregations were, (and still are, for that matter) supremely happy with the sound of these voices. I have therefore taken the space to list and describe them, as being the best examples of this phase of American organ building.

Such voices may be invaluable in adapting to organ accompaniment, extended choral works, that were originally written for voices and orchestral accompaniment. Oratorios and cantatas of this kind are frequently performed in our larger churches, and when one has a Virgil Fox or a Thomas Matthews to make the organ into an orchestra, some astonishing results are possible, when the orchestral voices are available on the organ.

We have already mentioned some of the original work of the late Mr. William E. Haskell of the Estey Organ Company, with his short length pipes. In addition, he developed a family of imitative Reed voices from labial pipes which give very fair reproductions of Solo Reed tone. The Reedless Oboe, the Reedless Clarinet and the Reedless Saxophone are three of the most successful stops of this class. They are particularly valuable when a small organ is placed in a church a long distance from a tuner, as these stops will stay in tune as well as other labial pipes.

A voicer of unusual attainments was the late Mr. George Michel, tonal director of the organ department of the W. W. Kimball Co. during forty years when they were building fine organs. He developed some Orchestral Reed tone, particularly English Horns, French Horns, and Saxophones of excellent quality. The Chorus Reeds and Strings that he produced were also very superior. Another development of Mr. Michel's was a complete Diapason chorus made of pure tin, thus creating the first modern instance of such a chorus since the days of the Silbermanns. M. P. Moller have also made a Diapason Chorus of pure tin in a chapel at Chambersburg, Pa. The results are noteworthy in each instance for the clarity and cohesion of tone produced by the use of pure tin for these registers.

The late Mr. Richard Whitelegg was associated with M. P. Moller as a voicer of unusual attainments. His specialties were Diapasons and chorus reeds. He had a very definite ability, not only in scaling and voicing these stops, but he so regulated and finished them in the organ, that an ensemble of blending and cohesive quality inevitably resulted. Now that so much attention and stress is laid on this feature of the modern organ, such an ability is most important and valuable. Mr. John Schleigh succeeded Mr. Whitelegg as head finisher.

Mr. Henry V. Willis, a grandson of the famous Father Willis is now with Kilgen Organ Co. He is another unusually capable voicer with special sympathy for the classic ensemble. Kilgen was also most fortunate in having associated with them as their tonal director Dr. Charles M. Courboin. As organist of the great Kilgen organ in St. Patrick's Cathedral, Dr. Courboin has been invaluable there. He has modernized the organ tonally, and has marvellously improved the ensemble.

Mr. G. Donald Harrison, president and tonal director of the Aeolian Skinner Organ Co. has had as much to do with present day tonal ideals of American organs as any man.

The Ludwigtone, a double pipe, much like a small scaled Doppel Flöte, only with a partition down the center, so that it is in reality two pipes blown by one wind conductor, has been developed by the late Mr. H. H. Holtkamp and A. G. Sparling, of the Votteler-Holtkamp-Sparling Co. One of the pipes is tuned sharp and the other flat to the unison, producing a most charming and subtle celeste. The tone is somewhat more mysterious than that produced by two separate ranks of pipes. An original and valuable contribution to new organ voices, indeed.

When Austin Organs, Inc. made Mr. Richard Piper (formerly with Henry Willis & Sons,) their tonal director, they secured the services of an outstanding Flue voicer, and a man of great knowledge and experience in tonal design. Mr. Piper, along with Mr. William O'Brien, head Reed voicer, cause the tonal work in present day Austin organs to be of very great distinction.

Mr. Edgar Jost, and Mr. Albert Sabol of the Reuter Organ Co. make an excellent pair. Mr. Jost as head voicer, and tone expert, and Mr. Sabol for the engineering work. The Chorus Reeds, Strings, Diapasons and Mixtures which the Reuter Organ Co. are presently producing are of the highest musical standards.

The Schantz Organ Co., headed by several of the Schantz family are particularly fortunate in having Mr. John Schantz to do the final finishing and regulating on their organs. He is not only a first class organist, but has a most discriminating and well-trained ear and knows how to do a superb finishing job. Such finishing work as this is invaluable to any builder.

Plate VIII.

The casework of the Gallery organ in Emmanuel Church, Boston. Casavant Frères are the builders of the organ. This form of casework is an unusually artistic combination of display pipes and grilles.

CHAPTER 4.

PIPE SCALES

In our chapter on the Construction of Flue Pipes, we made frequent allusions to the scale of the pipes. Every organ builder, before actually starting to construct pipes, lays out a scale from which the measure of the various diameters of the cylindrical pipes for each note may be obtained. The size of the scales ordinarily varies with each stop in the organ. It is not desirable for two sets of pipes to have exactly the same scale or diameter unless in a very large organ.

The English system of measuring pipe scales is simply to state the diameter of the CC pipe in inches.

Obviously when the exact diameter of the CC pipe is known definitely in inches there can be no chance for mistake or argument and when it is known at what point the diameter is half of this, whether at the 16th, 17th or 18th pipe above, almost everything is known that can be given about the diameter of the pipes of that particular register.

A great many years ago in America a different system of designating pipe scales was devised which is almost universally used by the various builders, though the same numbers do not necessarily indicate precisely the same thing. Number 1 on this scale represents a pipe one meter in diameter, and this scale proceeded upward, halving its diamater on the 16th pipe, so that a pipe of scale 16 would be ½ meter in diameter and a pipe of scale 32 would be ¼ meter or slightly less than 10 inches in diameter. A 38 scale pipe, therefore, would be about 8" in diameter. The The 40 scale pipe about 7-3/8" in diameter. A 42 scale pipe about 6¾" in diameter. Therefore, a 58 scale String-tone pipe, which is 16 pipes above a 42 scale Diapason, would be half the diameter of the 42 scale pipe, or a 3-3/8" diameter for the CC pipe.

These dimensions are accurate within about 1/16" as there seems to be no absolute comparison. Each builder has developed his own scales, and quantities of them for the various pipes they manufacture. It is quite common to have the Diapason scale halved on the 16th pipe, but frequently it is not halved till the 17th. String-tone ranks are usually made so that they do not halve until the 19th pipe, for they grow smaller more slowly than Diapason pipes as they proceed upward in the scale.

It will appear from this that there is approximately 5/8" difference between the diameters of the CC pipe or 42 scale and 40 scale Diapasons and slightly more than this between 40 and 38 scales.

The trade pipe-makers, particularly in this country, always refer to the scale of the pipes they make by number rather than in inches and one commercial pipe maker's 38 scale Diapason is very nearly the me diameter as another's. This number-scale is for the most part an arbitrary arrangement, but so long as it is well understood and generally adopted, it serves the purpose quite efficiently.

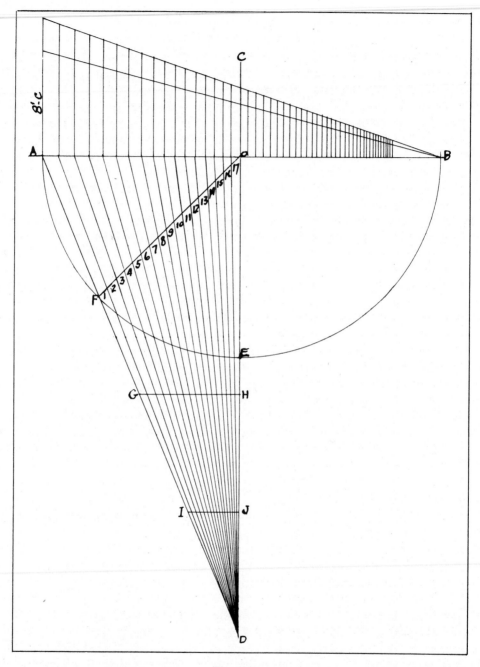

Figure 31.

A method of drawing a pipe scale devised by Joseph J. Carruthers. To lay out this scale, proceed as follows: Line AB is drawn, then at right angles line CD. From point O, a semi-circle AEB is drawn to any radius. OF bisects the angle AOE. OF is then divided into as many equal parts as it is desired to make the scale become one half. Then the line AF is drawn and extended to cut the line CD. From D lines are drawn through dividing points on line OF, until these lines cut line AB. From line AB, vertical lines are drawn upwards, at points of intersection. Then from point B a line is drawn to the desired scale at 8′ C. The scale is continued by drawing line GH midway between O and D. Again line IJ is drawn midway between H and D. The divisions on line GH and IJ are transferred to line AB, and vertical lines are drawn as before. This scale halves on the 17th note as there are seventeen equal divisions on the line OF. Other scales may be drawn halving on the 18th, 19th or any other note, as desired.

There is another matter which is important for the pipe maker to know before laying out the patterns for the construction of a set of pipes. This is the width of the mouth in proportion to the diameter, or circumference of the body of the pipe. The height of the mouth is usually determined by the voicer with a set of proportional dividers. Whatever proportion is desired may be maintained throughout the stop by setting the dividers for a given proportion, for example 1/4 or 1/3 width of mouth. The scales of reed pipes and wood pipes are referred to in both this country and England in terms of inches rather than numbers. Our chapter on voicing gives some particulars regarding the effect on tone of various proportions of widths and heights of mouths.

It is a simple matter for the pipe maker to lay out a scale designed to proceed evenly upward with a constant rate of diminution. If the dimensions of the CC pipe are given and the C above, he simply extends the scale upwards from these two points, though for greater exactness, and purposes of checking, frequently the diameters of all the Cs (or two dimensions in the case of wood pipes) are given.

Some builders have developed unusual scales that do not proceed upwards with unvarying diminution. Such scales have been evolved empirically, especially by builders who have made theater organs and other so-called "unit" work. These scales have been developed without much theory, but rather by actual experience. The Kimball Company and the Wurlitzer Company frequently employed a scale that caused the bass octave of a 16 foot stop to be of much greater size than the normal scale of the stop would indicate. This is done in order to get sufficient volume and weight of tone from the pedal extension of a manual stop. If the scale of an 8 foot manual Flute, for example, were extended down an octave lower with a regularly graduated scale, the resulting bass pipes would be too light and small in scale to make the tone properly effective as a pedal stop. The scale these builders have developed is in reality a hybrid type for a special purpose.

Another interesting scale employed is what may be termed a compromise scale for the principal unison Diapason on the great organ. The wide low-mouthed Diapason on even moderately high pressure is quite satisfactory in speech and quality from middle C up and possibly a few notes below middle C. However, the 8 foot octave of this stop and part of the 4 foot octave, when made with the same wide, low mouth on wind of seven inch pressure or more, is not very satisfactory. The pipes are inclined to be slow in speech, windy, and unsteady. Consequently, the scale which this company has devised produces Diapasons with mouths much narrower and higher in the bass and in part of the tenor octave, gradually changing to wider, lower mouths as the pipes progress upwards.

This gives a bass of greater solidity and prompter speech, and still makes available the characteristic qualities of the more harmonically developed Diapason in the portions of the compass where it is most valuable and desirable.

For most artistic results, scales should be kept within certain well defined limits. Unless for some very special purpose, it is seldom desirable to make any Diapasons larger than 40 scale. The same rule applies to Flutes, where excessive scales should be avoided if the Flutes are to blend with the other stops in the organ. In the opposite direction, the scale should not be excessively narrow, as in the case of String tone, or unmusical and unblending tone will result. All tones in an organ should be truly musical. Excessive or immoderate scales, either large or small, will not contribute to this result. For best results in a Diapason chorus, the scales of all the components should be carefully proportioned to the principal Diapason rank. These proportions are given in the Mixtures and Mutations section.

Figure 31 shows a method of drawing a pipe scale ingeniously developed by Mr. Joseph J. Carruthers, who has had more than fifty years' experience in organ building.

Within the past few years, some of our builders have adopted quite a different halving ratio for the pipes of the Diapason family. Instead of using a scale halving on the 16th or 17th pipe (formerly standard) they now use a ratio halving on the 18th or 19th pipe. This naturally creates a larger scale in the middle and top octaves of the compass. In other words, a 44 scale Diapason halving on the 19th pipe will be the equivalent of a 42 or 40 scale Diapason (based on the old halving ratio) in the top register. This makes for more clarity in the bass and tenor octaves, and more fullness in the top octaves. This scaling is used for the various stops in the Diapason chorus, including the unison, octave, twelfth, fifteenth, and mixtures. Especially the top notes of the mixtures tend to be more flutey, and less spikey with this scaling.

Some builders have developed a composite scale where the halving ratio changes in various parts of the compass, to secure power and fullness in the middle and top octaves, and clarity in the bass and tenor octaves.

Reed scales are made with much slower halving ratios than flute pipes. Normally the resonators of reeds of the Trumpet family halve on the 30th pipe, sometimes the 32nd pipe.

CHAPTER 5.

VOICING *of* ORGAN PIPES

In our chapter on "The Sound Producing Portions of the Organ," information was given as to some features of "voicing" the various types of organ pipes, particularly with regard to Reed pipes. The present chapter aims to consider the whole matter more fully and logically. Voicing is an art and it should demand the utmost attention of the artistic organ builder.

When the pipes leave the hands of the pipe maker, they are passed on to the voicer to regulate the height of the mouth and determine the manner in which they shall be "nicked," and such other operations as are necessary until the pipes produce the quality of sound that is desired. Before the pipemaker can begin construction, the scale of each set of pipes has to be determined, also the quality of metal as well as its thickness. The shape of the languid, and the width of the mouth, must all have been definitely decided. The tonal director or head voicer usually decides these matters. He also frequently voices completely the middle C and perhaps the other C's of all stops as a model for the other voicers to follow. It will be advantageous if the voicer knows the acoustical conditions under which the organ will sound.

When the pipes come to the voicer, they are merely so much metal or wood made in the form of organ pipes, usually without being capable of sounding a note. They leave the voicer as finished instruments of music, according to his skill.

The various stops of the organ in a general way may be compared to an orchestra, the number of stops or voices the organ contains, representing the instruments in the orchestra. A great difference exists between organ pipes and orchestral instruments, however. In the case of orchestral instruments, one, or at most two, are capable of covering several octaves, if not the entire range of the organ keyboard. Whereas, in the organ every separate note of every distinct stop must be represented by a pipe. If, for example, we take a French Horn, it will have sixty-one or seventy-three pipes; in the orchestra a good part of this range may be covered by a single instrument, capable of playing, however but one note at a time, whereas an organ stop may play any number of notes simultaneously.

One of the chief functions of the voicer is to cause all the pipes of a stop, both individually and collectively, to be of a certain "timbre," characteristic of that stop, and to avoid as far as possible any discrepancies between one pipe and another. This is obviously much easier for the voicer if the pipes are carefully scaled and constructed. If this is not the case, even an expert voicer will have difficulty in obtaining proper results. Voicing requires both patience and skill. Naturally, it is important to know that the precise quality, or timbre of any musical instru-

Plate IX

The case of the world famous organ in the Mormon Tabernacle, Salt Lake City. The organ was originally built by the Mormons. Later the Kimball Company rebuilt it, and still later the Austin Organ Company greatly enlarged its resources.

The unique 32′ cylindrical wood pipes, made by the Mormons, stand in the central towers of the case. The old organ, except the case, and a few souvenir pipes has been removed to a Mormon college. Aeolian-Skinner Organ Co. have installed a new organ behind the old case of nearly double the resources.

ment (organ pipes included), is determined by the nature and the degree of development which is given to the series of upper harmonics or partials. Our section on "Mixtures and Mutations" gives some details in regard to these harmonics.

When a musical note produced from a Flue pipe is characterized by an ample harmonic development so that all the upper partials or overtones sounding above the prime are prominently in evidence up to the twenty-second harmonic above the prime tone (which tends to obscure that tone), such a pipe belongs to the group known as "String" tone.

When the note from a Flue pipe is deficient in overtones and the prime tone is much more in evidence, it belongs to the class known as "Flute" tone. The mean between these two extremes of greater or lesser harmonic development will produce Diapason tone. If this were geometry, I might say that it should be self-evident from this that the timbre of a note is dependent upon the degree of harmonic development present.

The timbre may be further affected by the suppression of certain partials in order to lend prominence to others and, if all of the upper partials are suppressed in favor of one, many peculiar and subtle shades of tone may be produced.

The Clarinet is an instance where only the odd series of harmonics (the prime, twelfth, seventeenth and flat twenty-first) are permitted to develop, the even series (octave, fifteenth, nineteenth, twenty-second) being scarcely present at all.

Again the pipe may be constructed with a hole at its node (a point near the center of the pipe), that upon being overblown will not sound its prime tone at all but its octave. A stopped pipe may be overblown to sound its twelfth or seventeenth, the prime being eliminated, in this case by keeping the mouth low and boring a hole through the pipe at the nodal point. Or a stopped pipe may be caused to sound the prime tone along with its twelfth, almost equally, as in the case of the Quintaton. It is the function of the voicer to control the harmonic or non-harmonic tendencies in the speech and tone of the organ pipes which he voices.

The Rev. Noel Bonavia-Hunt* in his work, "The Church Organ," gives the following list of factors which influence the speech and tone of of Flue and Reed pipes:

"FLUE PIPES

1. The scale (i.e. diameter) of the pipe-body.
2. The area of the mouth (i.e. its width and height).

*Mr. Hunt's remarks are quoted both in our chapter on the "Sound Producing Portions of the Organ" and in the present chapter extensively, as he is not only a practical voicer but is able to describe what he knows, in clear English; a combination that is as rare as it is valuable in discussing so technical a subject as the construction and voicing of organ pipes.

3. The shape of the languid of a metal pipe, and the shape of the block of a wooden pipe.
4. The adjustment of the relative positions of the upper and lower lips and of the languid of metal pipes.
5. The shape and position of the cap of a wooden pipe.
6. The character of the nicking.
7. The pressure and the volume of the wind supplied from the windchest.
8. The size of the bore of the pipe-foot.
9. The employment of various devices and accessories.
10. The material of which the pipe is made.
11. Whether or not the pipe is slotted for tuning.

REED PIPES

1. The shape and length of the tube (or resonating body).
2. The scale (or diameter) of the tube at the top.
3. The pressure of wind from the windchest.
4. The shape and size of the shallot (or reed).
5. The shape and size of the shallot opening (or orifice).
6. The thickness, width, vibrating length and curvature of the tongue (or bass vibrator).
7. The employment of various devices and accessories.
8. The material of which the tube is made."

The power, that is, loudness or softness, of metal Flue pipes is chiefly regulated by the size of the scale, and the bore in the foot that admits the wind. Large scales and a large hole normally produce a loud note, whereas small scales and a small bore will normally produce a soft note. The power is also regulated by the wind pressure employed, as with a given size scale and hole in the foot of the pipe and, within certain limits an increase in pressure will produce corresponding increase in power.

Mr. Hunt lists the manner in which upper partials are encouraged in metal Flue pipes as follows:

"1. Small scales.
2. Low cut-up of mouth.
3. (a) Concave and (b) bevelled upper lip.
4. (a) Raised and (b) acute-bevelled languid.
5. Fine nicking.

The upper partials are normally discouraged by:
1. Large scales.
2. High cut-up of mouth.
3. (a) Convex and (b) thick, arched or leathered upper lip.
4. (a) Depressed, (b) obtuse-bevelled, (c) inverted languid.
5. Bold nicking."

VOICING OF ORGAN PIPES

A pipe is made to speak promptly, by having the upper lip pulled slightly outward, also when the languid is pressed slightly downward. If this is done to too great an extent, the pipe will "fly off its speech" and sound its octave.

If the upper lip is too far inward, and the languid too high, the speech tends to "come on" or "develop" slowly. If this is overdone, the pipe will become silent altogether.

Another important operation in the voicing of Flue pipes consists of nicking the front edge of the languid and lower lip, so that they resemble somewhat the teeth of a saw. These nicks are necessary to prevent the pipe from being windy when it speaks. The narrow windway between the edge of the languid and the lower lip (through which the wind passes when the pipe is speaking) is, by the process of nicking, broken up into a series of air columns and thus better focused on the upper lip. It converts in effect the action of the wind stream into an atomizer.

Delicate tones and many types of String tone are best produced when the nicks are close together and not very deep. Coarse and deep nicking, with the nicks farther apart, produces bolder and more flutey tone.

The voicer next considers the height of the mouth. This normally bears a fixed proportion or ratio to its width. The width of the mouth must be determined before the pipes are made as has already been indicated. Ordinarily, pipes with wide mouths tend to have greater harmonic development than those with narrow ones, when the height of the mouth remains the same. When the low mouth is made wider, the resulting tone from the pipe has more harmonic development. When a high mouth is made wider, it produces more foundation tone. The opposite effect is true when the mouth is narrowed, in which case a low mouth will produce fewer harmonics and a high mouth less foundation tone.

The width of the mouth is measured in accordance with the proportion it bears to the internal circumference of the body of the pipe. The circumference is roughly 22/7 of its diameter and, if we suppose a pipe, for example, that is 3 1/2 inches in diameter with a mouth 2 3/4 inches wide, we may state that the mouth in this instance is a quarter of the circumference. (22/7 x 7/2" = 11" = circumference ÷ 2 3/4" = 4. The circumference is four times the width of the mouth).

The height of the mouth is usually measured in accordance with the proportion it bears to the width of the mouth. It may also be measured in accordance with the proportion it bears to the internal diameter of the pipe body. The former method is usually the one employed by pipe makers and voicers. Therefore, if the mouth referred to as being 2 3/4 inches wide is cut up 7/8 of an inch in height, it is said to be cut up 1/3 of its width or 1/4 the diameter of the pipe. When the pipes are made, the upper lips are left longer than necessary to afford the voicer opportunity to cut them up to the proper height. If the upper lips are cut too high to start with, it may be necessary to have new pipes, as not much can be done with them.

Wood pipes are treated for the most part like metal pipes in the voicing, but inasmuch as the material out of which they are made is not capable of adjustment as in the case of metal pipes, a certain difference in treatment must be followed. There is not very much that a voicer need do to wood pipes after they are made. The width of the mouth of a wood pipe is necessarily determined in most instances by the width of the side of the pipe which contains the mouth, though in special forms of wood pipes the mouth is not always the entire width of one side of the pipe. Nearly all modern wood pipes are provided with metal toes, which may be reamed out or pounded in to adjust the amount of wind that is admitted to the pipes. This is a great convenience to the voicer as formerly wooden pipe feet were plugged with little slips of wood which had to be adjusted to a nicety.

One of the refinements in voicing that is sometimes overlooked is the removal of all rough or sharp edges along the pathway of the wind stream as it flows to the mouth of the pipe. Any sharp edges or corners such as may be left when the feet are reamed out should be carefully rounded off, or the pipes are apt to be windy and unsatisfactory in tone. This applies to both metal and wood pipes.

The treatment of the upper lip of both wood and metal pipes also has some effect on the tone. For example; a sharp, keen edged upper lip produces more harmonic development and a thick and rounded upper lip produces more foundation tone. Organ pipes, if properly treated should last for hundreds of years, and perishable material, such as leather, is of course undesirable for use in them.

The fitting of harmonic bridges or rollers for steadying the speech of String toned stops, though usually done by the voicer, has been described in our chapter devoted to The Construction of Flue pipes. The voicing of Reed pipes has also already been considered in our chapter on the Construction of Reed pipes, to which the reader is referred.

The art of voicing is one that can only be learned by experience and while some information is afforded by the written word the actual technique and skill required in this operation is a matter requiring years of application before proficiency is attained.

FINISHING OF ORGANS

Another department of voicing consists in the final finishing and regulating of an organ after it is installed in its permanent location in the church or other building. This matter is a most difficult one for the organ

92

builder to handle in a satisfactory manner. Competent and experienced organ finishers are scarce and from the nature of the work are apt to be temperamental. Several of the best organ finishers whom I happen to know in this country are inclined to be somewhat unreliable, and on occasion consume more alcoholic stimulants than is good for them. Whether this should be the inevitable accompaniment of an artistic temperament (which it is desirable for an organ finisher to have), is somewhat of a question. It is not too much to say that the work of finally finishing and regulating the tone of all the pipes in the organ is one of the most important, and frequently the most neglected, matter in organ building.

No matter now carefully the pipes are constructed, nor of what excellent material, and no matter how reliable and efficient the mechanism of the organ, if the final finishing is not properly carried out, the effectiveness and true musical value of the organ will be largely lost. Pipes constructed with indifferent workmanship and materials may be made to sound much more satisfactory when carefully finished and regulated than much better pipes will sound that are not properly finished and regulated. The finisher requires a good ear, judgment, discernment, and a knowledge of how to proportion the relative dynamic power of the stops to build up a beautiful and even ensemble.

It is not enough that each pipe in a given stop be of the same timbre or quality as all the other pipes in that stop. Each pipe must also be regulated to a nicety in regard to volume so that there are no loud or soft notes standing out as the series of pipes are sounded, one after the other. These matters are, of course, important. When the pipes come from the voicer, these qualities should have been taken care of. The skill of the finisher lies in adjusting the relative strengths of the various stops so that the organ will build up evenly, and gradually, without serious breaks or jumps in the strength of tone as one by one the stops are added. The various voices must be capable of not only gradually being built up, but must be so adjusted in strength of tone, one to the other, that the greatest number of combinations possible of the various voices will be pleasingly balanced and proportioned. Such a balance will insure good blending qualities.

The octave, sub-unison, and Mixture work of the Diapason section must be accurately proportioned in strength of tone to the foundation Diapasons. There must be sufficient difference between the various unison Diapasons in both strength and quality. The same is true of all the other classes of organ tone.*

*A story is told of a very particular, not to say fussy, organist, who took a large part in the final finishing of a very large organ. The organ finisher was up in the organ which was located at considerable distance from the console. The organist was regulating a soft register by running over the keys, and picking out loud and soft pipes to be adjusted by the organ finisher. Finally, he yells to the finisher, "Is that F sharp sounding," The finisher yells back, "Yes." The organist replies, "Well, make it softer." This story should take the prize as the ultimate in organ finishing.

A very indifferently constructed organ properly finished and regulated may be made to sound more truly musical, and far more pleasing to the cultivated ear than the most carefully constructed instrument possible of finest materials, that has not been so fortunate in final finishing. Organ builders know this, and do their best to secure such finishing of their organs. Unfortunately it is extremely difficult to supervise men a long distance from the factory especially when the builder is making several hundred organs a year. The organ builder has in many cases to rely solely upon the judgment and competence of the finisher for the final result. This is inevitable, in a country as large as the United States where distances are so great. In England it is possible for the principal tonal director of the builder, personally to supervise the finishing of at least all that builder's important organs. There would be better organs in this country if this were the case here. I have come to the conclusion that a finisher who is thoroughly competent and conscientious is one of the biggest assets that any organ builder can have. It is really vital. Nowhere in the construction of so complicated an instrument as the organ, is it desirable or advisable to cut corners on either material or workmanship. But if it must be done, I would rather it were done anywhere else than in the final finishing. Even if the organ is not so reliable mechanically as it might be, when it does work, a beautifully finished organ will be worth listening to and a joy; whereas, the most reliable organ mechanically will be disappointing and unsatisfactory to the listeners if the pipes are not regulated to blend and build up properly. After all, efficient and reliable mechanism and convenient gadgets on the console for the organist are all valuable, and much of this book is devoted to their description, but all that the listener of the organ cares about or knows, is what he hears. What he hears, must be *right* first of all. Mechanical matters come second. Some builders have unfortunately placed the emphasis the other way around.

CHAPTER 6.

TUNING *of* ORGAN PIPES

Having given some particulars concerning the construction and voicing of the various classes of organ pipes, we shall now consider how they are tuned.

It is a curious circumstance that, though J. S. Bach clearly demonstrated the superiority of the system of equal temperament tuning, over two hundred years ago, equal temperament was not introduced into English organs until 1852. Bach demonstrated its advantages in a series of studies called "The Well-Tempered Clavichord."

It should be noted that the modern keyboard is imperfect. One black key is made to serve for example for D sharp as well as for E flat, whereas the two tones are in reality not identical. To secure correct tuning in the intervals throughout, at least forty-eight keys would be required to an octave instead of the twelve that are now made to suffice. In what is called the equal temperament system the attempt is made to divide the octave into twelve equal parts or semitones, thus rendering all keys alike. To do this, it is necessary to slightly flatten or narrow all the fifths and slightly widen or sharpen all the fourths, resulting in considerable sharpening of the major thirds and sixths. The difference in just intonation is about a fiftieth of a semitone.

There are no doubt ears so sensitive that the sharp thirds and fourths and the flattened fifths and other discordant intervals of our modern keyed instruments are a considerable source of pain, but the average organist and pianist has become so accustomed to the defect that he fails to notice it.

To tune in equal temperament, is in reality to divide up the twelve semitones in such a manner as to compromise between the out-of-tuneness of the intervals, rendering no intervals perfect except the octaves and unisons, and no intervals too badly out of tone to make their use highly unpleasant.

There is no mystery about tuning an organ or piano and it does not require a musical ear, as that term is usually understood. It does require, however, an ear keen enough to be able to detect the wave beats that occur when two pipes or two strings are sounded that are not tuned to perfect intervals. These wave beats are caused by interference in the sound waves of two or more sounding notes. The beats are never present when the ratio of the frequency of vibrations produced by the two pipes, or other musical tones, may be expressed in some simple ratio such as 1 to 2, or 2 to 3. Therefore, when a note is sounded with its octave above and no wave beats are audible, it is in tune with its octave and if the octave is absolutely true to pitch then the lower note must also be true to pitch. In other words, both are in tune.

Plate X.

An American Organ Case of 1774, with Colonial designs, in white and gold. It was built by David Tanneberger of Lititz, Pa., for Trinity Lutheran Church of Lancaster, Pa. The organ was rebuilt in 1923, at which time the wings of eight pipes were added to each side of the case. The main portions of the case work have been preserved intact.

It is customary to tune the 4 foot Diapason in the organ or one of the keener toned 8 foot strings first throughout as nearly perfectly as possible. Every other stop of the organ can then be tuned to it.

If, for example, we wish to tune the Trumpet 8', we can draw the Octave 4' with it and tune each note by eliminating the beats caused by the Trumpet being out of tune with the Octave. Every other stop in the organ can be subjected to the same treatment, until all are in tune with the octave and therefore with each other. This is a comparatively simple process and one which some organists know how to accomplish.

The only difficult matter is that known as "laying the bearings" or "setting the temperament" on the tuning stop, from which the rest of this stop may be tuned, and after that the balance of the organ. To lay these bearings, the tuner has to narrow all the fifths, and widen all the fourths and at the same time keep the octaves perfect, as stated above. As a practical matter, the fifths are generally first tuned perfectly, that is, with no beats and then slightly narrowed, so that a slow beat is produced. In the middle section of the keyboard from F below middle C to F above on an 8 foot stop, the beats that occur when fifths are held should be about three beats to five seconds. The fourths are first tuned perfectly and then slightly widened. The widening of the fourths is slightly greater in extent than the narrowing of the adjacent fifths, or about four beats in five seconds.

Taking middle C as a starting point, we may hold the G above, which is a fifth. The G is tuned to sound a perfect non-beating interval with the C below, then the G is slightly flattened until a slow wave beat is perceptible. Still holding middle C, we take the F above, or the fourth. This interval is tuned perfectly and then the F is slightly sharpened so that it beats with the C below. The beat of the C-F interval, or fourth, is a little quicker than the beat of the C-G interval, or fifth. The pitch of the F and G will be correct and of equal temperament.

The reason why the out-of-tuneness of the fourth should be greater than that of the adjacent fifth is because the rate of the beats of C and F above is equal to the rate of beats of F and the C above middle C, that is, the higher in scale the interval occurs the quicker the beats.

The organ tuner proceeds throughout the scale of the twelve semitones by fourths and fifths, tuning them in succession. When the scale has been completed, the test is to find if the last interval tuned will come out correctly with the starting point, or middle C.

The method outlined above is theoretically correct. In practice a good tuner sets several temperaments, one on the Octave, and at least one other on a String toned stop, or Geigen, especially if the organ is divided in more than one chamber. He then tunes some stops with the tuning stop, but checks by holding 4ths and 5ths on the stops being tuned, especially if they are softer than the tuning stops. Flutes particularly

97

have a bad tendency to "draw" into tune with a louder stop so that checking is necessary.

Test intervals of major thirds and sixths can be, and usually are, employed during the process of tuning the various fourths and fifths.

In the part of the scale we have suggested the major thirds and sixths have four beats per second, which may be heard plainly when carefully listened for. The rate of these beats is very sensitive to slight changes in the pitch of either element of the interval. Therefore, by making use of the major thirds and sixths, a test of the work may be had as the tuner proceeds, without waiting until all the fourths and fifths have been tuned and the original starting point has been reached.

An expert tuner can set the temperament the first time around, whereas a less experienced tuner may have to go over these intervals a good many times to make the proper adjustments so that each interval will be equally out of tune and no interval will be too perfect at the expense of some other interval that will be too violently out of tune to sound even passably well.

The whole matter of tuning by equal temperament is a compromise, and expert piano tuners have told me that it "gets on their nerves" after many years of it, because they can never tune perfectly. The principles underlying piano tuning and organ tuning, particularly in regard to "setting the temperament," are precisely alike. As both instruments have twelve semitones to the octave, there must necessarily be a compromise.

The pitch of the Flue pipes is altered by lengthening or shortening the pipes themselves, thereby flattening or sharpening them respectively. Formerly all the metal Flue pipes except the large sizes were tuned by having the tops of the pipes coned in for flattening and coned out for sharpening by means of brass tuning cones or horns. This was an objectionable practice, as the constant beating on the tops of the pipes, especially by a careless tuner would tend to pound the body of the pipe down on to the languid or otherwise injure the pipe, to say nothing of endangering the soldered joint at the top of the pipe.

A somewhat better means of tuning, generally employed for many years, was to slot the pipe near the top and the metal cut out of this slot was rolled down to a point which would bring the pipe in tune. When this style of tuner is adopted, the pipe must necessarily be made somewhat longer.

A much better method of tuning metal Flue pipes is the one which is now nearly universally adopted. It consists of applying cylindrical slides usually made of tin plate, that fit the tops of the pipes with a certain amount of spring, so that they will stay firmly where they are placed and yet are capable of being knocked up to flatten the pipes and knocked down to sharpen them. These tin plate tuners on the larger pipes are usually held in place by a clamp or friction tape, so that there is no danger of their sliding out of position.

The larger open wood Flue pipes are tuned, preferably by a wooden slide that is capable of being adjusted up or down in a slot near the top of the pipe. The smaller wood Flue pipes have pipe metal flaps fixed on to their tops which can be opened up and closed down like a trap door. This method of tuning open wood pipes is not as desirable as to leave the pipes long enough so that a roll tuner may be applied at one edge of the top of the pipe, covering an area too small to affect the tone quality. This latter form of tuner is not in danger of falling down from its own weight, as sometimes happens in the case of flat metal tuners.

All stopped wood pipes are tuned by means of the stoppers at the top of the pipes, the stoppers being knocked down to sharpen, and drawn up to flatten the pitch.

Reed pipes are tuned by means of a small spring wire which passes through the Reed block. The tuning wire shortens the vibrating portion of the tongue when it is knocked down (thereby sharpening the note) and lengthens the vibrating portion when raised up (thereby flattening the note). The slots cut near the top end of the tubes or resonators with the pieces of metal so cut out and rolled down, are intended for regulating the power of the pipes, and are not generally used for tuning purposes. Similarly the slides or collars sprung on to the tops of the Clarinet are for regulating.

There are exceptions to this rule, however, as for instance when a sudden change of temperature will interfere with the scientific relationship that exists between the tube length and the length of the vibrating tongue. In such cases, if the tongues be readjusted to the altered tube length, the pitch of the pipe will be rectified at the expense of its tone and perhaps the general regulation of the stop as a whole. In this instance, if the pitch is adjusted by regulating the tube at the slot, the tone and pitch can both be maintained at their original standard.

Ordinarily, it is not desirable to tune either the Flue pipes or Reed pipes of an organ except at a normal or standard temperature. The pitch of all pipes in the organ is affected in greater or lesser degree by changes of temperature. The pitch of wood pipes is affected also by changes in atmospheric conditions, such as extreme dryness or dampness, even though the temperature remains constant, because the actual dimensions of the pipes are changed by shrinking and swelling of the wood. The wood pipes will nearly always have to be tuned after a prolonged dry spell, or after a prolonged season of dampness.

Mr. Skinner in his work on the "Modern Organ" gives perhaps the best explanation as to why the pitch of organ pipes varies with changes in temperature. He states, "It is well known that the more forcibly a pipe is blown, the sharper its pitch becomes. A change in temperature does not affect the wind pressure which remains constant. Consequently, a sheet of wind issuing from the mouth of a pipe always has the same degree of intensity. As the temperature rises, the pipe contains less air than before, as some has left it through expansion. The remainder is lighter than formerly, and it is therefore more forcibly excited by the wind sheet, as the latter has not changed. The pipe is, in effect, blown harder. As the air becomes cooler, the process is reversed and the pitch flattened."

It might be assumed that the pipes of an organ should grow flatter in pitch as the temperature rises because the additional heat would cause the metal in the pipes to expand. Such is not the case. It appears that this factor is practically negligible, but that the heat causes the *air* in the pipes to expand, and therefore permits the rarified air to be more forcibly excited by the wind sheet. This explanation seems logical and certainly agrees with the facts — a desirable quality for an explanation to have.

So sensitive are the smaller pipes, particularly, to slight changes of temperature that the warmth of the tuner's hand, if he should apply his hand to the top of the pipe for the purpose of changing the position of the tuner, even momentarily, will materially affect the pitch of the pipe. Upon the pipe so treated again reaching its normal temperature, it will be found to have perceptibly flattened. It appears, then, that the first rule for any tuner to follow, when actually tuning an organ, is to stay as far away from the pipes as possible with his hands or body. Ordinarily a chisel, or equally flat piece of steel is used (in tuning both the Reeds and Flue pipes), of such length as to allow the tuner to stay a respectable distance from the pipes themselves.

Mr. Skinner has also a very ingenious and I believe correct explanation of why Reed pipes have a tendency to fly off their speech in a cold church. He states that, "if a Reed is tuned too sharp, that is too short a length of tongue in proportion to the length of the resonator, it has a tendency to break into an interval above, as the resonator is then too flat in pitch for the tongue. This is a case identical in principle with that in regard to Reeds in cold buildings. The temperature has not greatly affected the tongues but it has increased the density and consequently the amount of air within the pipes, made them proportionately flatter, giving them the same tendency to fly off that is noticed when they are tuned too sharp on the tongues." In other words, the natural vibration period of the tongue and resonator must be maintained at a fairly definite proportion.

Modern organ Reeds, as was noted in our chapter on Reed Pipes, stay in tune vastly better than formerly. Somewhat thicker tongues, and thicker tuning wires both contribute to greater stability of tuning. The tuning wires should preferably fit quite tightly where they pass through the Reed block. When the Reed pipes have full length resonators, as in the case of Trumpets and Chorus Reeds of most descriptions, they are

100

affected by changes in temperature very similar to those of the Flue pipes themselves, and are consequently apt to be quite well in tune with the Flue pipes, even though there has been a material change of temperature since the organ was tuned. The pitch of such Reeds is very strongly influenced by the size of the resonator and the air becoming more rarefied or compressed in the resonator tube produces a similar effect on the pitch of the Reeds as its does in the case of the Flue pipes.

In the case of Reed stops with short resonators, such as Vox Humanas, Orchestral Oboes, Clarinets, etc., the resonator does not have so strong an influence on pitch. The reed tongue itself is very little affected by changes of temperature. These pipes tend to remain at a more constant pitch than the other pipes in the organ. Instead of the Vox Humana being out of tune, it has remained at the pitch at which it was tuned and the rest of the organ has either sharpened or flattened from this pitch, if there has been a considerable change in temperature (colder or warmer from that at which the organ was originally tuned). As a practical matter, it is much easier to tune the Vox Humana or Orchestral Oboe than to tune the rest of the organ to these stops.

The standard pitch of the organ has varied from time to time from C = 545, down to C = 517.3 or A = 435. This latter pitch is generally adopted today as being more suitable for accompaniment of the voice, and for use in conjunction with the modern orchestra. This pitch is equivalent to the standard American pitch of C = 523.3 or A = 440 at 70 degrees. The pitch as stated of C = 517.3 for 60°, at which temperature most English organs are tuned (the churches in that country are seldom above this point) will almost exactly correspond with the present American standard that C = 523 at 70°, which is the standard temperature for tuning American organs.

Plate Xa.

The large Aeolian-Skinner organ in The First Church of Christ, Scientist (Mother Church)

102

One of the great consoles of the world, controlling one of the greatest organs built up slowly through the decades by Frederick C. Mayer for Cadet Chapel at no cost to the tax-payers. The new console by M. P. Moller Inc. is now in process of being coupled to its enormous organ.

103

CHAPTER 7.

SPECIAL TONAL EFFECTS

THE TREMULANT, VIBRATO TONE AND PERCUSSION TONE

It appears that many of us have gone a long way in our estimate of the value of the Tremulant from the day when Sir John Stainer in his treatise on the organ described that device as "a mechanical contrivance for causing a regularly recurring disturbance in the wind supply." Opinions on this matter are still varied and there seems to be a permanent disagreement between the Purists and the Sentimentalists in regard to the use of the Tremulant. Fifty years ago, Mr. James Wedgwood, in his "Dictionary of Organ Stops", stated that "contrary to the accepted precedent," he was not "reiterating the staple stock-in-trade arguments against Celestes, Tremulants, and Vox Humana." The reason he gives is that he is "honest enough to confess that when used with due moderation he finds nothing objectionable in such effects." This statement might be regarded as somewhat negative, but still more friendly toward the Tremulant than Sir John Stainer's.

The modern view of the Tremulant as held by some of the finest American organists, (for example Dr. Charles M. Courboin, Mr. Virgil Fox and Mr. George Markey) is that the Tremulant is a most useful device, and one which they frequently employ.

True, the more classic-minded organists consider that a Tremulant should only be used when a deacon dies. But even Bach had a Tremulant. Judicious and sparing use is the secret of its effectiveness. Certainly a moderate use is not only not objectionable, as Mr. Wedgwood states, but is of the very greatest value in imparting a sympathetic quality to the tone of such stops as Flutes, Solo Reeds, and Strings. The most common use of the Tremulant, of course, is with the Vox Humana stop which most closely parallels the human voice. It is a fact that of all the instruments of music, none produces a more pleasingly vibrant tone than a fine human voice. This vibrant quality is the chief attraction also in all stringed instruments. Also, the vibrato effect of a singer's voice is one that can scarcely be trained into the voice by direct methods, though in many cases an excessive tremolo must be trained out by any methods that are available. The vibrato proper occurs in some singers naturally, and in others as a consequence of vibrant emotion. Caruso's voice had a marvelous natural vibrato. Many voices have a permissible vibrato range of slightly less than a half-tone, and every voice is affected by the beating of the heart against the breath column. An organ without a vibrato is like a singer without a heart-beat.

Hence, a voice without any vibrato, if there is such a voice, is impossibly crude and expressionless no matter how good the actual tone may be. Yet, that is the vocal counterpart to the organ tone without the

the use of the Tremulant. Wind instrument players in the orchestra, outside of Jazz orchestras, do not cultivate an intentional vibrato. It comes as a natural result of proper playing, and sometimes from emotional tension.

The overdone tremolo formerly heard in the usual theater organ, especially in connection with the Vox Humana and big Solo Flutes, has obviously no connection with serious music. The tone of the violin is particularly hard and unsympathetic when played without any suspicion of vibrato, though this too can be overdone. The great violin teacher, Leopold Auer, used frequently to tell his overly sentimental pupils, "don't viber." When the vibrato is wisely used, it causes string tone to be perhaps the most eloquent produced by any instrument other than the human voice. When entirely without the vibrato, string tone is extremely tiresome.

The one real difficulty in giving to the tone of the organ a tremolo that will correspond to the effect of the vibrato in vocal or wind instrument tones and those of the strings is, that the organ tremolo must operate at a constant rate of speed and with a never varying amplitude of oscillation, whereas the other instruments respond instantly to the slightest shading and emotional intensity, so necessary to artistic effect. This difficulty may be overcome to some extent by adjusting the tremolos, in organs where there are two or more, to different speeds and intensities. A contrast is thereby afforded.

VIBRATOS CAUSED BY PITCH BEATS

Another type of vibrato effect has been liberally introduced into the modern organ. Ranks of pipes of various qualities and strengths of tone are employed, which are tuned slightly sharp or flat with another rank which is tuned perfectly in unison. The sharp or flat rank usually is made of the same scale and quality as the unison rank with which it is associated, but not necessarily.

The originator of this method of adding "warmth" to organ String tone appears to have been Cavaillé-Coll, the eminent French organ builder, who some hundred years ago, introduced the Voix Celeste for the first time, and later in nearly all of his organs. The large present day organ has frequently as many as six ranks of the Celeste type. The Celeste effect has been extended to light toned metal Flutes, such as the Spitz Flute or small scaled Concert Flute, also to Dulciana pipes and all strengths and qualities of String tone. Another Celeste is a hybrid tone of the Gemshorn type, termed by Mr. Skinner "Kleine Erzähler," which gives a particularly lovely subtle effect when two ranks are provided, one tuned slightly sharp. The purpose of all of these Celestes is to make the tone of the organ more "warm" and vibrant. The softer Ce-

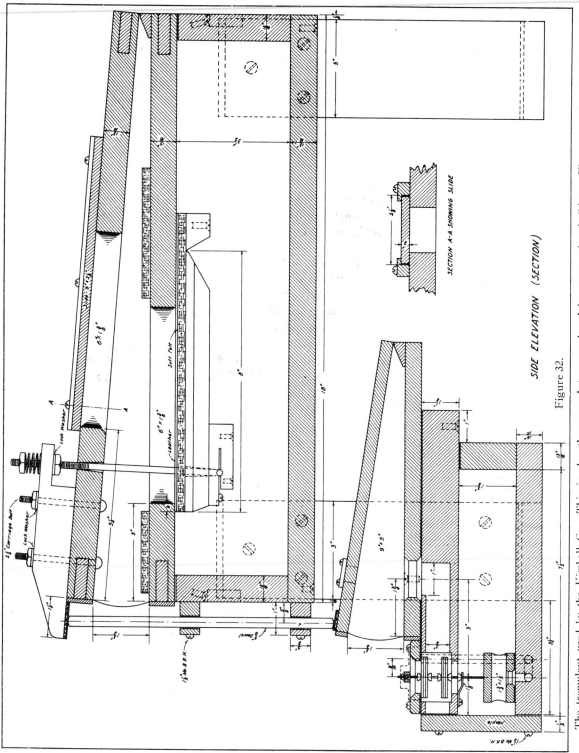

SIDE ELEVATION (SECTION)

Figure 32.

The tremulant used by the Kimball Co. This is also the general type employed by many other builders. The stop action that starts the device into operation exhausts the pneumatic shown at the lower left, which allows the dowel to drop and the tremulant bellows to fall, admitting wind through the pallet. This starts the tremulant bellows to vibrating as explained in the text.

106

lestes may, without detriment, be used with the full organ, but the more pungent String tone Celestes should never be used for ensemble purposes. In fact, keen Strings of any sort are extremely injurious to a proper organ ensemble and have an uncanny way of asserting themselves even though the tone with which they are associated may have many times the power of the Strings themselves.

So far from dismissing the matter of the Tremulant and the more individual means of producing a vibrato on certain stops by tuning certain ranks sharp or flat, with the cursory statement of Sir John Stainer, quoted above, I believe the modern view of these means of obtaining warmth of tone and relieving monotony is that they are greatly appreciated. They are very valuable to the artistic organist and a liberal supply of both Tremulants and Celestes should be available on an organ with any pretensions to completeness.

It is not common to place a Tremulant on the Great Organ as this department primarily contains the Diapasons which are least in need of its aid. However, in most three manual organs of smaller size, the Great Organ nearly always contains the principal large scaled Flute with which a proper tremolo is most useful and certainly a Tremulant is justified on the Great Organ if used for no other purpose than that. Please note it should *not* be adjusted for a violent vibrato to imitate the sobbing theater Flute.

CONSTRUCTION AND OPERATION OF TREMULANTS

There are two common types of Tremulant in use in organs of the present day. In either case they are best placed at a considerable distance from the organ chamber, preferably in another room, which may usually be done conveniently. All that is required is a galvanized iron or zinc conductor from the windchest or regulator, ordinarily of three inch diameter, and two wires run to the magnet that opens the valve that permits the compressed air to escape into the Tremulant itself.

Figure 33 shows the "beater" type of Tremulant, which consists simply of a pivoted rod with a weight at one end and a round disc of wood at the opposite end, padded with felt and leather. This disc is so placed as to close the hole which permits the wind to escape out of the box when in the "closed" position.

There is a small coil spring which causes the beater to remain in the open position, normally. When the wind is allowed to enter the beater chamber, it immediately starts to rush out the opening and causes the beater to close against the opening, thereby momentarily shutting off the escape of wind and allowing the spring to return the beater to its normal position. By carefully adjusting the balance between the counter-weight, the spring and the length of travel that the beater is permitted, the beater

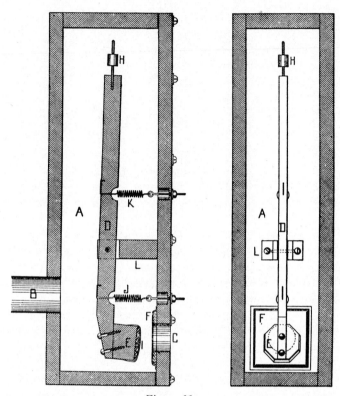

Figure 33.

Cross sectional, and front views of the valve or beater tremulant. (From G. A. Audsley, "The Art of Organ Building.")

may be caused to vibrate at one of the most desirable periods (either fast or slow, with large or small amplitude) that is required for the best effect to be produced on the pipes.

The form of Tremulant shown in Figure 32 is very similar in principle to the beater type, except that the air is permitted to enter a small bellows which in turn is raised by the compressed air entering, thereby shutting off its escape by closing the valve at the top of the bellows momentarily. This may also be regulated to any speed or amplitude of beat.

There are several factors that assist in securing a successful Tremulant. The size of the Tremulant and the amount of air that is permitted to escape periodically must be governed by the size of the windchest, (a very large chest obviously requiring a larger Tremulant to produce the proper effect than a smaller one). A compromise also must be reached between obtaining perfectly steady wind (which is most successfully done by the use of springs alone on the reservoirs without any weights) and a certain elasticity that the reservoir must have in order to be properly affected by the Tremulant. Therefore, it is found necessary in most cases to have a certain amount of weight on the reservoir as well as springs in order to make the Tremulant effective. The reason for this is made clear in our chapter on The Wind Supply of the Organ.

Some builders have installed fast and slow Tremulants on the same manual. This is a step in the direction of varying the speed of the vibrato to suit the needs of various classes of stops. String tones frequently sound better with a faster vibrato than Flutes or Solo Reeds, so that two Tremulants to a division permit of this. With one Tremulant the speed is adjusted to a rate that is most generally useful.

Another special form of Tremulant is described in our chapter on The Universal Air Chest.

PERCUSSION TONE

Another tonal effect, that was not found in the classic organ, is that of the chimes. This tone came into the modern organ somewhat later than the Celeste or vibrato caused by pitchbeats. This bell-like tone has become very popular with congregations during the past forty years. It is easily recognizable, and arouses many a nostalgic memory of church bells echoing from distant hills. Certainly a chime note introduced here and there, and especially as an after beat, adds a distinct color and contrast to the normal organ voices.

J. C. Deagan, Inc., Chicago; Maas-Rowe Organ Company, Los Angeles; Beach Organ Company, and R. H. Mayland and Son, New York City, and Schulmaerich, Sellarsville, Pa. are today producing both chimes and actions for operating them, electro-magnetically. In addition, nearly all are producing amplifying equipment to make organ chimes capable of being broadcast for miles around, from the tower of the church. These manufacturers also make extraordinarily successful harmonically tuned steel rods, that, when amplified, sound more like real church bells than do the tubular chimes. The sound of these steel rods is so pure and with so few dissonant harmonics, that it is possible to play several notes at a time, without anything but a pleasant musical effect; something impossible to do with tubular chimes, because of too many dissonant harmonics. These harmonically tuned rods may be played either as organ or tower chimes, when proper amplifiers and speakers are provided, thus gaining two uses of the same chimes. One difficulty has been overcome by Maas-Rowe. The strong major or minor third (the chimes can be tuned to either kind of third sounding harmonic) makes it necessary to make the thirds of accompanying harmony conform to the kind of thirds in the chimes. Complete concord and smoothness is secured by providing a small dual keyboard,

Plate XI.   Organ in the Cleveland Art Museum. The main organ behind the curtains was built originally by the Skinner Organ Co. The exposed pipe work by Walter Holtkamp, and he also did considerable modification to the original Skinner. Specification on page 255.

Plate XII.
Liverpool Cathedral. Henry Willis and Sons have here built the largest organ in England.

111

and employing two sets of harmonically tuned bars, one with prominent major thirds, and the other with prominent minor thirds; the set with the major thirds being used when employing harmony with major triads, and vice-versa. Thus unpleasant clashes and harsh dissonances are completely avoided. The sound of these harmonically tuned bars or rods, when arranged in this manner is so smooth and truly musical, as to be almost unnatural, and quite uncanny.

The so-called organ Harp, with the sound produced by metal bars, unamplified, is a thing of the past. It is no longer being made. Both Deagan and Maas are making an electronic version of the Harp, with several qualities of tone and vibraharp effects. Occasionally a church will want to add such a percussion. Their use is not so great as for Chimes, and they are distinctly in the luxury class for a church organ, even though many in the congregation will lie back in the pews and purr when they are played.

Regarding the action which strikes these percussions: it consists of a suitably covered hammer or plunger that is forced against the chime tube or bar by a solenoid. The voltage on the solenoid may be adjusted for loud, soft, or medium effects.

All organ percussion actions, whether for Harp, Chimes, Xylophone, or any other must follow the same principle that applies to the piano action. That is, the hammer must not remain touching the string, tube or bar, even if the key is sustained. Should it remain the tone so created by the impact of the hammer would be damped. The characteristic of all percussion instruments is a tone sustained at first, then gradually fading away. Dampers are desirable which gradually cause the tone to die, after the key is released, rather than abruptly. These are provided in the direct electric actions made by the builders today.

Compass of Chimes: Either A below middle C to second F above, 21 notes, or G-g, 25 notes.

Compass of Harps: Tenor C to top C, 49 notes.

Other organ percussions, formerly used in theater organs, such as Glockenspiel, where the steel bars are struck with hard hammers, the wooden Marimba, Xylophone and so forth are all built along lines similar to the regular organ Harp or Celesta. They may have a reiterating mechanism, for more accurate orchestral effect.

The "Traps" formerly used in the theater organ, including Bass Drum, Snare Drum, Tambourine, Triangle and all manner of imitative effects, are produced by the instruments themselves, struck by some form of pneumatic hammer, instead of by hand. They proved themselves most useful for the purpose intended, and are now among the curiosities of organ building.

Electronics have practically finished the organ percussions as formerly built. Amplified steel bars and rods produce better tone, take up less room, and are mechanically sounder than those which relied on normal acoustical procedure for their effect, rather than radio tubes. Don't misunderstand me, please. This applies *only* to organ percussions and not to organ pipes.

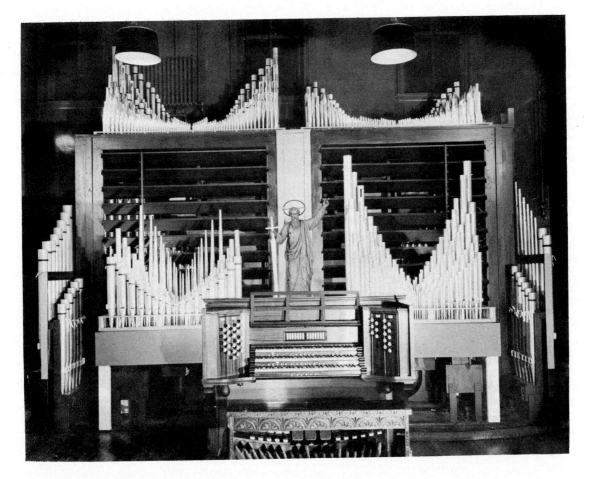

Plate XIII.

Organ in the Studio of Ernest White, in the parish house of St. Mary the Virgin, New York City. Aeolian-Skinner Organ Company, builders. Described in detail on page 255.

CHAPTER 8.

MEANS *of* OBTAINING EXPRESSION

THE SWELL BOX

Mr. Ernest M. Skinner in his book entitled "The Modern Organ" very properly starts his chapter on the Swell Box with the statement that in order to have an effective swell in an organ it is necessary that there be something of real tonal proportions inside the box to sound when the shutters are open. It is perhaps an unfortunate circumstance in connection with organ tone that it has never been possible to increase or diminish the strength of tone from a given set of pipes directly, as is possible with practically any other instrument. The shading of tone in an organ must always be done indirectly, that is, by enclosing the sounding pipes in a box or chamber with shutters (at least in the front and perhaps on top of the chamber) that open and close like the shades of a Venetian blind.

The invention of the first Swell Box is attributed to an Englishman by the name of Abraham Jordan, who, in London in the year 1712, invented a means of enclosing the pipes of one division of the organ in a box with a lid at the top that could be opened or closed by a pedal. This was termed the "Nags-head Swell." It was superseded by a series of shutters placed in the front of the box. Even though this invention was made nearly two hundred and fifty years ago, it is strange that it was never extended to any other division than the Swell organ for the longer portion of this period. The Swell shutters of almost all organs were made to fall shut by their own weight or by means of a spring. The organist might leave the Swell Box shut or, by means of a catch on the pedal, hitch it full open. Sometimes intermediate catches were provided, but it was at best an awkward means of controlling the shutters. Yet, some English organists still persist in wanting this type of swell pedal on the organs they play.

The introduction of the balanced swell pedal, which is due to Walcker in 1863, has greatly increased the tonal flexibility and expressiveness of the organ. This is the type used exclusively in America at present. The shutters themselves are either actuated by mechanical means directly from the pedal, as was always the case in the tracker organ, or by some kind of pneumatic motor, several forms of which will be described later. With the balanced swell pedal the shutters will remain in any position in which the pedal is placed.

Dr. Audsley, in his "Art of Organ Building," was perhaps the first to urge the greater extension and use of the swell in the organ in a systematic and logical way. He argued, that the organ when left unenclosed was the only musical instrument whose tones could not be controlled in the matter of shading. He consistently advocated the enclosure of all divisions of the organ in separate chambers, including the Pedal Organ, though perhaps allowing the Principal Diapason on the Great Organ to remain unenclosed.

These ideas seemed quite revolutionary at the time they were advanced, though Hilborne L. Roosevelt, in the large organ in the Auditorium at Chicago, as early as 1889 had placed every division of this important organ under expression except a few ranks of Diapasons on the Great Organ and the Pedal Organ. This was sixty years ago. In this matter Roosevelt was more advanced than any of his contemporaries.

At present, after a good many years experience with organs totally enclosed, the concensus seems to indicate a return to unenclosed Great organs, and also the presence of an unenclosed positiv division, in lieu of or in addition to an enclosed Choir organ. Separate enclosure of Great and Swell divisions is advantageous in the case of a small organ of under fifteen sets of pipes, where all of the tonal resources should be available for maximum variety and flexibility of use.

In fact, any organ of over ten sets of pipes should have at least two expression chambers. Certainly a three manual organ should have a separately enclosed Choir division, before it has an unenclosed Positiv section. If the organist insists on having the latter, and there are insufficient funds for an enclosed Choir organ as well, the Swell division may advantageously be enclosed in two Swell chambers. The organ described on page 255 exemplifies this treatment. In this case the Swell Reeds are separately enclosed, and couple independently to the other manuals. The Swell flue work is enclosed in a second expression chamber, and couples independently to the other manuals.

The modern practice of placing the pipes in well-constructed chambers with hard reflecting wall surfaces is of the greatest advantage to the tone of the pipes when the shutters are open as compared with the small, cramped, boxes that were formerly employed. These latter were often so cramped and filled with pipe work that it is astonishing any residue of tone found its way into the church.

We come now to the construction of the shutters, which are practically all that need to be considered in the majority of present-day organ installations. Adequate and suitable chambers are usually provided at the time the church is built for the enclosure of the pipe work. There seems to be considerable difference of opinion among the various builders as to the proper thickness of these shutters.

One of our leading and most successful builders has for many years built organs with shutters of a thickness of only one and one-quarter inches. From this limit of minimum thickness, shutters have been built of various thicknesses up to three inches. It has been my experience that little is gained in using shutters more than two and one-quarter inches in thickness. This size is employed by several of our leading builders. It is more important to have the shutters themselves fit tightly at the joints than to have them extraordinarily heavy.

There are some difficulties in having the shutters fit too tightly, as a prolonged damp season will cause them to swell and probably bind. A prolonged dry period will cause them to shrink, and the distance between them become too great to render them properly effective. Austin Organs, Inc. has very ingeniously overcome these difficulties by making their shutters of sheet metal, mounted on wooden frames. The Kimball Company used instead of the customary white pine a hard wood such as chestnut, that seems to be less affected by atmospheric changes than white pine and enables them to fit their shutters more closely. To overcome warping and twisting of the shutters, they are usually made of a series of strips of wood glued together with the grain running in reverse directions. This laminated construction overcomes a tendency to warp.

There are two major types of mechanism in present day use for the control of the swell shutters. The one employed by the Skinner Organ Company and the Austin Organs, Inc. operates all the shutters of one chamber as a group by means of a trace, as shown in Figure 36, and provides one large motor for moving the whole set.

Both of these builders make use of a very ingenious type of pneumatic motor for this purpose, called the "whiffle-tree" motor. By an examination of Figure 36, it will be seen that very gradual operation of the driving rod is accomplished by the operation of any one of the pneumatics, because of the series of levers that are interposed. This is very important. The very gradual opening of the shutters, particularly in the initial stages, is the chief quality that any efficient swell motor should have. The first few stages of opening the shutters must necessarily be very smooth and gradual. After the shutters are open a short distance, they can be moved a greater amount without a corresponding increase and decrease in tone.

The other type of shutter mechanism was that employed by the Kimball, the Wurlitzer and Moller companies, as well as several others. It employs individual small pneumatics for each shutter. In the case of a very large front, two or more shutters may be hooked together to operate on the final stages when all the other shutters are open. Figures 35 and 38 show the individual shutter motor.

With this latter type of swell movement, it is necessary to have two or three of the shutters considerably narrower than the average width, as these individual motors either open the shutters wide or permit them to close. Therefore, the first shutter is permitted to open only a small distance and is very narrow. The next one is permitted to open a greater distance and the shutter is a little wider. After the first two or three stages, the standard width shutters opening the full distance are employed. By this means a very gradual opening of the shutters is possible, rendering an extremely even crescendo and diminuendo with the utmost nicety.

116

There are arguments in favor of both types of mechanism. Some organists have contended that with the individual shutter control, the tone is more or less localized by issuing from a restricted opening at one end or other of the shutter front, rather than from a series of openings across the entire front as is the case when all the shutters are hooked together and moved at the same time to a greater or less extent. I have never been able to observe this disadvantage of individual shutters. It appears to me that when they are properly regulated and designed to do the work with the greatest efficiency, that even greater speed of operation is possible with the individual shutter action than with any form of single large motor operating on an entire shutter front. It is true, however, that the new single motor type that the Austin Organs, Inc. are currently using particularly with the new style of shutter construction, permits an extremely rapid operation of the shades, quite rapid enough for any legitimate requirements.

The matter of the efficient and rapid opening and closing of swell shutters is of great importance, and all of our American builders have spent considerable time and effort in perfecting these mechanisms. One of the most serious obstacles to obtaining a fast action is the difficulty of preventing the shutters from slamming when closed too rapidly, even though they are padded with felt.

Austin Organs, Inc. has recently overcome the difficulty of shutters slamming, when rapidly closed, with a new form of construction, illustrated in Figure 37, which is as ingenious and clever as are so many other of the Austin inventions. Instead of allowing the shutters actually to close upon each other, thereby creating the possibility of slamming, they have designed the shutters to rotate on their centers in a complete circle. The shutters may be adjusted to open either in or out, whichever is most desirable. A very small clearance is provided so that they may actually pass between one another. Figure 37 illustrates this.

The construction of shutters as shown also compensates for any swelling or shrinking of the wooden portions. The narrow strip at each edge of the shutter is subject to a small amount of swelling and shrinking, according to atmospheric conditions. With the small clearance between the shutters, they might swell sufficiently to cause them to bind. This possibility is compensated by the large six-sided white pine strip into which the center pins are driven and which forms the backbone (so to speak) of the shutter. The sheet metal that is attached to the end strip and this center strip naturally will not be affected by atmospheric changes. In case of swelling of the wooden parts, the swelling of the center member will tend to draw the narrow wooden strip at the edge closer to the center and thus compensate for its swelling. It will act in the opposite way when the wood shrinks.

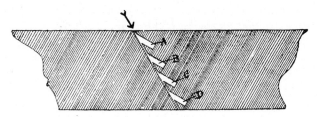

Figure 34.

The "Sound Trap" joint, used by Hope-Jones. The
arrow points to the joint through which the sound passes.
The theory was that the sound woulld not pass through
the joint but become dissipated in the sound trap pockets,
A, B, C, D.

This has been tested by soaking the shutters in a tank of water for
some time, after which it was found that they functioned perfectly. This
seems to be a real improvement in shutter construction. The advantage, of
course, lies in being able to adjust the motor to close the shutters with
extreme rapidity without the possibility of slamming.

As it is most important for an effective swell to have a tight fitting
shutter front, which is obviously difficult to maintain at all times, it appears that some rather inert hard wood might better be employed. Chestnut, for example, is not so much affected by atmospheric changes. Such
wood enables the shutters to be fitted rather more closely. This matter is
distinctly worth more consideration than some of our builders have given it.

Nothing has been said previously about the construction of Swell
Boxes, should these be necessary. They often are, when the organ is
placed in the open, instead of in its own chambers. The latter automatically provide the best type of Swell Box, especially when the walls are
lined with hard material capable of reflecting sound to advantage. In open
location, the Swell Box can be made more effective if shutters are also
placed in the top of the box, and if feasible, on two sides of the box.
With such construction, when the shutters are open, the pipes will sound
about as freely as if they were totally unenclosed.

Some builders make use of two thicknesses of half-inch yellow pine
with a space between stuffed with sawdust and two thicknesses of building paper, making the entire thickness of the walls close to three inches.
The yellow pine outer surfaces, when well varnished, make a hard and excellent reflecting surface for the tone, and the sawdust makes a very
good sound insulator.

Swell Boxes are now frequently built with various forms of wall
board that are on the market, panelled in thick wooden frames. This makes
a reasonably good type of Swell Box and when interlined with deadening
material is very satisfactory. Masonite is excellent for Swell Boxes.

MEANS OF OBTAINING EXPRESSION

The matter of Swell Boxes is becoming of less importance in American organ building, as the majority of installations are in chambers. Some builders now even make an extra charge when they have to provide Swell Boxes, considering that normally all they need to provide is the shutter front.

When there are several expression pedals controlling a number of separate Swell Boxes, their order from left to right becomes of some importance. Two expression pedals may be operated conveniently with one foot. It is difficult with more than two. A switch or series of switches is frequently furnished by builders in such cases, that makes one of the pedals a "master" pedal, which operates all the shutters of the entire organ from one pedal. This is a convenience, but like the crescendo pedal it is liable to abuse and inartistic use by incompetent players. I have known a much heralded foreign recitalist to play an entire program on a large organ with five independent Swell Boxes, with all the expression pedals attached to the one Master pedal, so that all the subtle effects possible in the organ by means of the gradual opening of one box, and closing of another, were completely ignored and wasted. Once more this case proves my contention that many more means of expression are available than some organists are willing (or able) to use.

The order from left to right of the expression pedals, which is standard for any three expression pedals is: Choir, Swell, Solo. If there is a separately enclosed Great, that pedal should be to the right of the Swell pedal.

The Swell expression shoe is invariable centered above E and F of the pedal board. In a two manual organ, with separate expression on each manual, the Great expression shoe takes the place of the Choir expression shoe, and is placed to the left of the Swell shoe. On a four manual organ, if there be four separate swell boxes, (quite unlikely and unnecessary)

Figure 35.

A series of individual pneumatics for operating the swell shutters of a Moller organ. The pneumatics are operated similarly to that explained for the Kimball pneumatic shown in Figure 38.

119

the Great shoe is placed to the left of the Choir shoe, and Solo to the right of the Swell shoe. These are standard locations, now almost universally adopted by our leading builders. Any organist whose whim or fancy would change this order should think twice before doing so, and have regard for visiting or successor organists. The register crescendo shoe is invariably placed to the extreme right, and preferably a little raised above the level of the expression pedals, so that it won't be unintentionally operated.

Figure 36.

The Whiffle-tree motor for operating the swell shutters employed by the Skinner Organ Co. A similar motor is now used by the Austin Organ Co. The outer cover of the box has been removed to show the series of square pneumatics. Each pneumatic draws one end of a lever as it collapses. The lever so drawn is connected in turn to a series of other levers, so that the net result of such motion is a very small, but powerful movement of the square shown at the bottom of the photograph, which is mechanically connected to a trace that draws the shutters simultaneously. The mechanism is in effect geared down to produce a gradual opening or closing of the shutters, with absolute control over the motion at all points. The great advantage of this motor is that all the pneumatics will collapse nearly as quickly as a single one will, thus the shutters may be fully opened or closed nearly as quickly as they can be moved a small distance. Sforzando and accent effects are thus easily possible. Of course one cannot open and close a door all the way as quickly as one can open and close it a few inches. But with the Whiffle-tree engine, when the shutters are to be moved a large distance, the power is proportionately increased. Inertia and momentum are forces which must be overcome, however.

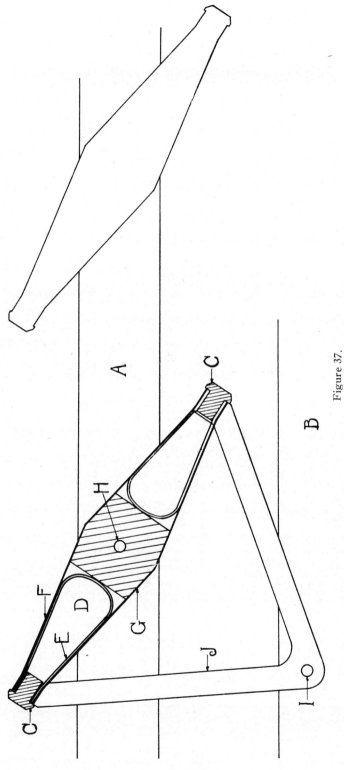

Figure 37.

Sectional view of the new Austin Swell Shutter. A is the frame work of the shutter front, in which the centre pin of the shutter H fits. The six-sided piece of pine, G, forms the backbone of the shutter. The narrow end strips CC are made of hard wood, and are joined to the centre strip by means of steel plates, F. Heavy tar paper lines the interior of the shutters at E. The series of shutters for the entire front is moved simultaneously by means of a trace that is attached at I, to the bracket, J.

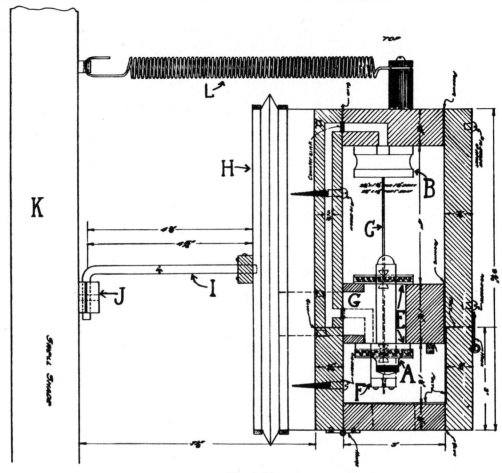

Figure 38.

The Kimball swell shutter pneumatic. K represents a swell shutter, which is drawn closed by the coiled spring L. The shutters therefore close when the wind is out of the organ, the contrary of the usual practise. The organ is kept much cleaner by this arrangement. H is the square pneumatic, which will produce twice as much power from a given size and pressure as the hinged pneumatic, a distinct advantage. It connects with the shutter by the rod I which is pivoted at J. When the magnet A is energized, the auxiliary pneumatic B is deflated, drawing with it the double valve E, allowing the compressed air from upper chamber to pass through the port G into the pneumatic H. This inflates the pneumatic which pushes open the shutter against the action of the spring L. It should be noted that spring and pneumatic act on opposite edges of the shutter. When the magnet is not energized, the pneumatic is allowed to exhaust into the atmosphere, as the double acting valve is in the position shown in the drawing. The spring L can then act and close the shutter and pneumatic at the same time. The exact size of the pneumatic, spring, air ports, etc. are all of great importance to the successful operation of this shutter mechanism. Such matters have been determined only after careful tests, and the results have proved adequate.

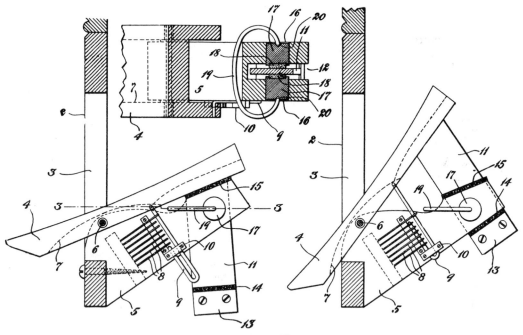

Figure 39.

The Austin expression pedal. 8 represents the series of contacts which are progressively made as the pedal is closed by the large round wire 9 being drawn underneath the contacts. The pedal shown on the left is wide open with no contacts being made, while at the right, the pedal is entirely closed with all contacts made. The tension on the pedal is regulated by the peculiar shaped spring 19, shown more clearly in upper drawing. As in the case of key or stop action contacts, the expression pedal contacts close circuits leading to the magnets on the motor that operates the shutters.

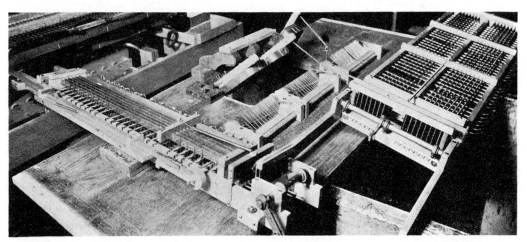

Figure 40.

The Moller expression pedals and crescendo pedal, are shown in the center of the photograph. In this case the pedal rotates a roller or cylinder with a contact strip running diagonally across the face that will progressively make or break contacts as the cylinder is rotated by the pedal.

123

CHAPTER 9.

A HISTORY *of the* ORGAN ACTION

Before proceeding with our account of the history of the development of organ actions and at the risk of being elementary to many, it may be wise to give a brief explanation of some of the technical terms that we shall use in this account.

As everybody knows, the tone of the organ comes from the pipes. It was the custom to place the pipes of the lower notes of the Diapasons in the front of the organ for many years. These pipes many people believed to be all that there were in the organ. The present day custom of placing the organ behind a screen or grills without any "show" pipes whatever does not give the interested observer an idea of what even the bass pipes look like unless he actually goes into the organ chambers.

Pipes are of various shapes and sizes and vary in length from 32 feet long, in large organs, up to pipes no greater in speaking length than 3/8 of an inch. They are usually arranged in double ranks or rows upon a box of wind with valves directly beneath the top of the air box or *windchest*, that permits air to enter the pipes when the keys are depressed, with certain modifications as will be explained hereafter. Each of these ranks consists of a complete series of pipes of similar tone quality and called a *stop* or *register*.

The word "Stop" in this connection refers actually to the rows of pipes and not to the stop knob at the console which operates the mechanism bringing the row of pipes into play. Considerable confusion arises in the minds of the uninformed on this point as they are inclined to look upon the number of stop knobs or stop keys at the console as indicating the number of actual rows of pipes the organ contains. All of the reliable and competent builders in the United States at the present time make it very clear in the specifications which they submit to the intending purchaser of an organ exactly the number of sets of pipes that the organ will contain and do not permit such confusion to arise between stops and stop knobs.

The average church organ built during the Nineteenth Century contained three or four windchests each with its quota of pipes and designated as follows: 1. the Great Organ, consisting of the bolder and loud speaking stops, such as Diapasons, whose bass pipes frequently were placed in the front of the organ as part of the case work. Back of this, and usually elevated above the level of the Great Organ, was 2. the Swell Organ, all of whose pipes were contained in a wooden box with Venetian shutters in front, the opening and closing of which modified the tone. Below the Swell Box was placed 3. the Choir Organ containing the soft speaking stops useful for accompaniment purposes and back of these divisions, or on either side, was 4. the Pedal Organ, containing the large pipes of the deeper pitches played by the pedal keyboard.

It was seldom that a church organ exceeded three manuals for reasons that will appear evident as we describe the action.

These various divisions of the organ make it possible for a much greater variety of effects where solo melodies may be played on one keyboard, accompanied on another, or an entire change of tone quality may be obtained by alternating from one keyboard to the other without a change of stops. Perhaps the origin of so dividing a church organ was the impossibility of supplying a large number of stops with wind from a single windchest. It will be seen from this that the average church organ is in reality made up of three or four small organs combined, under the control of one player.

The windchest is an oblong box supplied with air under pressure from the bellows. The box contains the valves called "pallets" which control the admission of wind to the pipes. We are now describing the typical windchest that was invariably used with the tracker action. Between the pallet and the foot of the pipe another valve is interposed called the "slider," which controls the access of the wind to the whole row of pipes or stops. The pallet is operated from the keyboard by the key action. Every key on the keyboard has a corresponding pallet in the windchest and every stop knob operates a slider which controls a set of pipes, so that both the stop knob must be drawn, and a pallet must be depressed, before any sound can be obtained from the pipes.

THE TRACKER ACTION WINDCHEST

Figure 42 is a front view, and Figure 41 a side view of the windchest. Wind is admitted by means of the wind trunk B into the interior of the windchest A. The pallets C, C, C, are held against the openings or channels leading from the windchest to the feet of the pipes, by springs underneath them. The spring S in our figure holds the pallet C against the opening into D. The pallet is drawn down by means of a wire, known as a pull-down, which passes through small holes in a brass plate affixed to the bottom of the windchest. This wire is connected with the keyboard by means of a series of mechanisms which we shall presently describe. The pallet is hinged at the back and guided in its downward motion by means of a guide pin. The top of each pallet is covered with felt and on top of this, soft leather to make it fit airtight against the grooves and to work quietly. When the pull-down wire is pulled down, the pallet C is opened and air from the windchest A rushes through the channel D into the pipe above. However, the slider F which is a narrow strip of wood that is placed between the wood work G and H in such a manner that it may be moved backward and forward transversely across the chest may interfere with this. At the time the windchest is made, holes are bored through the top board or the board on which the pipes are placed, and the slider and

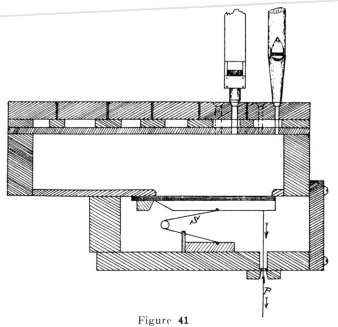

Figure **41**
Sectional view of the pallet and slider windchest.

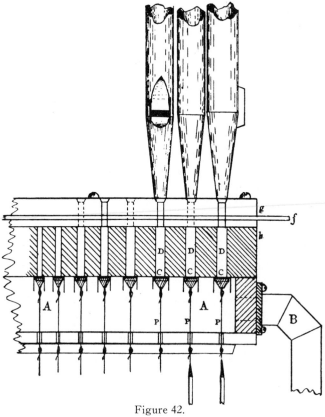

Figure 42.
Sectional front view of the same windchest.

the table part of the windchest, so that the holes in both the top board, slider, and table exactly correspond when the slider is in the open position. If, however, the slider has been moved a short distance, usually 3/4 or 7/8 of an inch to one side, the holes in the slider no longer correspond with the holes in the top board and table and no air may be admitted to the pipes, even though the pallet is open. When the holes in the slider exactly correspond with those below the pipes, the stop, the handle of which controls the position of the slider is said to be out, or drawn; when the holes do not correspond the stop is said to be in. Thus it is evident that when no stops are drawn no sound is produced, even though the windchest is full of air and the keys are depressed.

The mechanism which connects the back end of the key with the pull-down wire of the pallet is shown in Figure 43. In its simplest form, it consisted merely of a small dowel of wood called a "sticker," into which a small pin was driven at either end, that was fastened in a hole at the back end of the key, the top of which actuated the square, which in turn actuated the thin strip of wood called "tracker" from which the name tracker action is derived. The tracker had secured on one end of it a tapped wire (that is, threaded so a leather button could be screwed on), which connected with another square which in turn was the pull-down wire. Our illustration makes this clear. It was quite the principle of the old-fashioned bell pull that was mechanically operated, by means of wires and bell cranks. See Figure 43.

Occasionally in place of the two squares and trackers for each note, a lever was introduced between the back end of the key and the pull-down wire which transferred the motion with even greater simplicity. The difference in the scale at the back end of the keyboard and the wider chest scale from which the pull-down wires proceed, required either the trackers or levers to be arranged in a fan shape. Actions were still further complicated by reason of transferring a number of the bass pipes to the opposite end of the windchest, instead of arranging all the pipes in chromatic order from large to small. As this does not correspond with the way the keys progress regularly upward, the motion of the keys had to be transferred across the windchest by means of rollers, a series of which were called a roller board. All of these connections and joints (usually there were as many as six), were causes of friction between the key and the pallet. To overcome this resistance and friction a strong spring was required to return the pallet to its closed position. The pallets had to be larger in the bass end of the chest to supply the additional wind the larger pipes require, and as the area of the pallet was increased its resistance to opening was increased, by reason of the pressure of the wind against it. When the organ was a large one with many stops and the keyboards were coupled together, it required considerable exertion to bring out the full power of the instrument, as the resistance of the

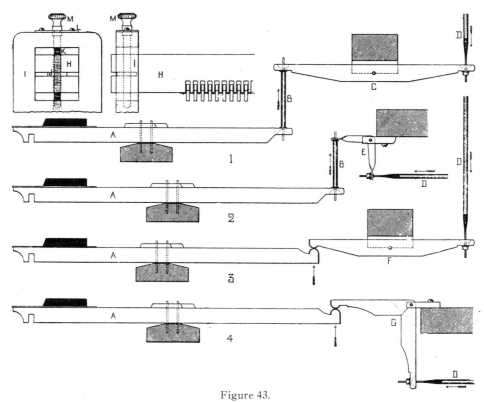

Figure 43.

Four ways of making the mechanical connection between the keys and the pallet valves in the tracker action. In drawing 1, the motion is transferred by the sticker, B, to the lever, C and thence to the tracker, D, which connects with the pallet in the windchest Drawings 2, 3 and 4 show variations. (From G. A. Audsley, "The Art of Organ Building.")

air against the pallets increased with more stops drawn. Sometimes the organist had to stand on the pedals, and throw the weight of his body on the keys to secure a big chord. All kinds of schemes were tried to overcome the resistance of the "touch," as the required pressure on the keys is called. The most successful of which was dividing the pallet into two parts which admitted a small quantity of wind to the groove or channel and thereby released the pressure before the pallet was fully opened. Naturally, with the tracker action, the weight of the touch was proportionately increased with each manual coupled to the one which was being played, and manual couplers were, therefore, introduced very sparingly. Most Tracker organs usually had nothing but unison couplers between the Swell and Great and Choir and Great, though occasionally on two manual organs there were two couplers, coupling the Swell keyboard to the Great at both unison pitch and an octave higher.

Some of the work of our best American organ builders during this period, as exemplified by Hook and Hastings, and Johnson and Son, was quite remarkable for its extraordinarily careful workmanship, and the surprising thing is that large organs of this type could ever be made to work at all. Unless the workmanship and material had been of the best, it would have been quite impossible to play upon a large tracker organ.

In addition to perhaps the most serious disadvantage of the tracker organ, namely, the heaviness of the touch, especially with couplers added, the windchest also was never adequate to supply an even pressure of wind to the various rows of pipes. While there might be ample wind admitted through the channels for two or three stops, when all the stops were drawn there was a certain amount of "robbing" of the wind that caused the pipes to more or less flatten in pitch as not sufficient air could be admitted through the channel to properly blow all the pipes of a windchest. Leakage would also occur between the slider and top boards. To prevent adjacent pipes from sounding because of this leakage when only one pipe was intended to sound, grooves or channels were cut diagonally between the various pipe holes of the bottom of the top board and the top of the table of the chest. In damp weather the slider would swell and in dry weather there would be too much leakage.

With all of its difficulties, the tracker organ was a miracle of mechanical skill for its time and I even now get a thrill out of being in the interior of a large tracker organ such as may still be found in France, when it is being played, and seeing all the squares, trackers and levers moving. I probably feel about this as one of my friends said he did about a merry-go-round, that he knew of "no other instrument ever invented that had so much machinery devoted purely to pleasure." Tracker organs have practically not been built in this country for the past twenty years. They are nearly extinct, though occasionally a small one is still manufactured. An organ building friend of mine, while visiting a certain builder's factory recently, saw a small new tracker organ standing on the floor of the erecting room and remarked that "here was a tracker organ that hadn't been used yet." They are indeed a rarity now, though used tracker organs of all degrees of age are the chief source of income of some organ repair men, even today. The trackers have a way of breaking and many other derangements are possible. With the reliability that the electric organs have developed in recent years, it seems odd that it was ever thought that a tracker organ was more reliable than the modern electro-pneumatic organ.

In England, the windchest I have just described is still clung to by some of the builders, strangely enough, though all of their leading builders have adopted the electro-pneumatic action as standard for some time past.

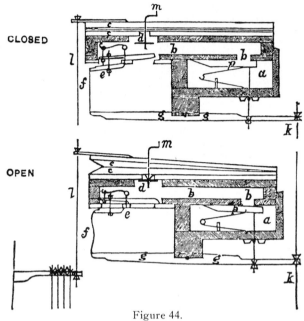

Figure 44.

One of the original forms of the Barker lever. Its operation is described in the text.

THE BARKER LEVER

The next stage in the development of the organ action occurred when an organ builder, in the city of Bath, England, named Charles S. Barker, in the year 1832, invented a contrivance known as the pneumatic lever. This device used the force of the organ wind itself to overcome the resistance of the pallets in the windchest to the key action. It consisted of the introduction of a small bellows about nine inches long and varying in width between one and one-half and three inches, that was inserted in the middle of the key action. The exertion of depressing the key was then reduced to the small amount of force required to operate the very small valve which in turn admitted wind into the little bellows. The bellows, upon being expanded by the wind pressure, pulled down the pallets in the windchest, thereby doing all the hard work.

Our Figure 44 shows the introduction of this device as improved by the eminent English organ builder, Mr. Henry Willis. "When either the finger or foot is pressed upon a key connected with K the outer end of the lever GG is pulled down which opens the pallet P. Compressed air in the box A then rushes through the groove BB into the bellows CC which rises and lifts with it all the action attached to L. As the top of the bellows CC rises, it lifts open the throttle lever D regulated by the

130

wire M which prevents the ingress of any more compressed air through BB with the action of the key on the lever GG. When the bellows CC opens, the double acting waste valve E closes, and the tape F hangs loose. The compressed air, therefore, cannot escape. On the other hand, when the key raises the outer end of G the tape F becomes tightened and opens the waste valve permitting CC to drop into its closed position, and no more compressed air flows through the pallet P."

This device enabled the organ touch to be as light as that of the piano and eventually proved revolutionary in its influence by rendering possible extraordinary developments. When it was first invented and for many years thereafter, it was very much ignored and opposed by the English organ builders. Barker had to go to France and demonstrate the value of his device to Cavaillé-Coll who, together with Willis, joined in its development and eventually all difficulties were overcome and the pneumatic action was brought into general favor. It was not used, however, except for large organs for a good many years. Modifications of this Barker lever were quite generally employed in large tracker organs built in this country up to within thirty years ago.

THE TUBULAR PNEUMATIC ACTION

Even when the Barker lever came to be adopted for use in large tracker organs, it was always a matter of great difficulty to run trackers for large distances, particularly where a keyboard was placed in a reverse position or at some distance from the organ itself. If the trackers had to be run down and under the floor and up to the other side, in the case of a divided organ on either side of a chancel, it necessitated the transfer of the motion of the keys by direct mechanical means for a large distance, with many attendant difficulties.

Dr. Gabriel Bedart of the University of Lille, France, apparently has brought to light the fact that the first tubular pneumatic action was constructed under Moitessier in France in 1835 and was designed upon the exhaust principle. Henry Willis built an organ for St. Pauls Cathedral, London, in 1872, which was divided in two sections, one on each side of the junction of the Choir with the dome, at an elevation of about thirty feet from the floor. The keyboards were placed inside one portion of the instrument into which he introduced the first tubular-pneumatic action in England.

In the tubular-pneumatic action an impulse of wind is made to travel through a series of lead tubes of moderate diameter between the end of the key and the Barker lever. The tubular-pneumatic action was reasonably satisfactory where the distances were not excessive between the keyboard and the organ, fifty feet being about the limit of usefulness of this type of action.

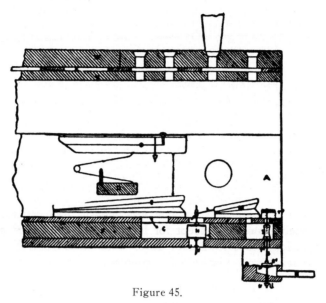

Figure 45.

Early form of the tubular pneumatic action.

Sir John Stainer was the organist at St. Paul's at the time this action was introduced and describes it as a "triumph of mechanical skill," whereas the eminent English organist, Mr. W. T. Best, said that when this type of action was used for concert organs it was a "complete failure," "You cannot play a triplet on the Trumpet" and considered it "the most damnable invention ever placed inside an organ."

These actions were quite freely introduced into many important English organs especially by Henry Willis and Sons, and this firm brought them to a high degree of perfection. Some of the tubular-pneumatic actions I played, on very old organs of this famous make in London, when I was there a few years ago, were quite remarkable for their speed and efficiency. Figure 45 illustrates this type of action.

Tubular-pneumatic actions were never so much used in this country for some of our American builders jumped at one step from the tracker action, or tracker action with Barker lever, to some form of electro-pneumatic action. Most of the tubular-pneumatic organs which have come to my notice in this country were not models of reliability and had many drawbacks. The Kimball Company made a reasonably successful tubular-pneumatic organ, some examples of which are still extant. It is obvious that since pneumatic impulses travel rather slowly, a speed which does

132

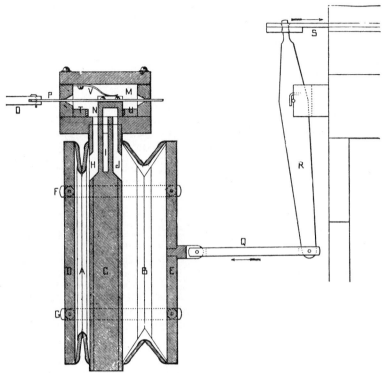

Figure 46.

The pneumatic stop action applied to the operation of a slider windchest. Compressed air is contained in chamber VM at all times. The stop rod, O, actuates the valve, N. In the position shown air will pass through the channel, H, into the pneumatic, A. At the same time the compressed air in pneumatic, B, will be exhausted through the channel, J, through the opening, I, in to the atmosphere. By this means the slider, S, can be moved to right or left, in accordance with the position of the valves. (Audsley, "The Art of Organ Building)

not exceed 1100 feet a second, that no tubular action could be entirely satisfactory when the distance between the keys and the organ is large, even though the action may be very perfect in design and workmanship. In the case of large organs where necessarily some of the tubes are short and some have to be very long, it is impossible to procure simultaneous speech from all the divisions of the instrument.

The tubular-pneumatic action has been abandoned by American builders the past forty years in favor of the electro-pneumatic action.

Today we find a few builders, who are to my mind mentally unbalanced, who urge a return to the tracker action.

CHAPTER 10

GENERAL DESCRIPTION *of the* ELECTRO PNEUMATIC ACTION

Early attempts at the electric action seem to have been to place an electro-magnet inside the windchest under each pallet, which would obviously have required an enormous amount of electric current. Such a scheme was shown at the Vienna Exhibition in 1873. It was carried out by Karl G. Weigle of Stuttgart, Germany. The credit for the invention of the electro-pneumatic action is usually ascribed to Dr. Gauntlett and Dr. Albert Peschard, though the former in 1852 took out a patent covering an electric connection between the keys and the pallets of an organ which was never successfully carried out. Bryceson Brothers were the first to introduce electric action into English organs. In 1868 under the Barker patent they built an organ for Her Majesty's Opera House in London. Dr. Peschard worked in connection with Charles Spachman Barker in the improvement of the pneumatic lever.

One of the early difficulties that surrounded the experiments with the electro-pneumatic action, was the inability to obtain a good contact. The best one available in the early days was obtained by dipping a platinum point in a cell containing mercury. Other forms of contacts rapidly oxidized and became useless. Henry Willis & Sons, even as late as 1890, refused absolutely to build electric organs as they did not wish to sacrifice the artistic reputation they had built up.

In the United States, Hilborne L. Roosevelt was no doubt the pioneer in developing the electric action. Casavant Freres of Canada also did pioneer work of great importance. The partly electro-pneumatic organ which Roosevelt installed in 1884 in the Garden City Cathedral on Long Island, and which has been rebuilt by Casavant Freres, was a very interesting example of Roosevelt's experimenting with the electric action. The other leading American builders of Roosevelt's time, such as Hook and Hastings, Johnson & Sons, George S. Hutchings and Jardine, took small stock in electric action in those early days and throughout this period built simple tracker organs or tracker organs with a modified form of Barker lever. Jardine and Kimball did some tubular-pneumatic work quite early.

It appears that none of the early electric actions performed with quickness or reliability and all were costly to install and maintain. One who made most important improvements in the electric action was Robert Hope-Jones, who, being a skilled electrician, entered the field about 1886. In a way, he was at an advantage in knowing little concerning organs and the previous attempts that had been made to utilize electricity for this service. He made with his own hands and some unskilled assistance furnished by members of his volunteer choir, the first movable console, also stop keys, double touch and suitable bass, etc., with electric action that were a great advance on anything hitherto done, particularly in regard to speed and reliability.

Roosevelt, Farrand & Votey, and Casavant in their early electric actions employed contacts made of flat spring brass, with short pieces of platinum wire soldered on. Hope-Jones introduced round wire contacts. These were first made of gold and platinum and later silver was substituted. He replaced previous methods by scientific calculations, recognizing the value of low voltage, good insulation and the avoidance of self-induction in the magnets, and was for many years probably the most important man at work on this problem.

We shall now consider specifically the elements of a successful electro-pneumatic action. This action operates, in its simplest form and in the earlier models, a magnet which opens a valve admitting wind to operate the small bellows, or Barker lever, electrically. Formerly this valve was moved by a tracker leading from the key. The electro-magnet is energized by a contact that is made when a key is depressed. The closed contact completes an electric circuit which exists between the key and magnet, by means of a wire of any desired length. We illustrate this simplest form of electric action, called the electro-pneumatic lever in Figure 47.

It is necessary to give at this point some consideration to the elementary principles involved in the electro-magnet used in organ action. Every one is familiar with the horse-shoe magnet, which is permanently magnetized. This is made of hardened steel so that the magnetism that is originally placed in the magnet is retained. If the magnet is made of soft iron, preferably Norway iron, it will not retain its magnetism, though it is capable of being strongly magnetized. Consequently, this is the type of iron used for the core of a magnet employed in organ actions. The disc or armature which the magnet attracts must only be attracted when the contact is made, and the magnet must lose its magnetism, or the greater part of it, instantly upon release of the key.

Without going into the theoretical reasons why it occurs (if anyone really knows), it is a perfectly demonstrable fact that, when a coil of wire is wound around a piece of iron and a current of electricity put through this coil, the iron which the coil surrounds becomes magnetic and assumes for the moment the qualities of the ordinary horse-shoe or permanent magnet. By increasing the number of coils to a very large extent and winding these coils with wires of fine diameter a high resistance is set up to the passage of a current, so that a small amount of current is needed or consumed when it is passed through this long coil of fine wire and yet the magnetic effect produced on the iron core by this small current flowing through these many coils is quite pronounced.

The organ magnet is formed in the shape of a letter U, or approximating that of a horse-shoe magnet. In fact, some old types of organ magnet were horse-shoe in shape. Efficiency is increased by this con-

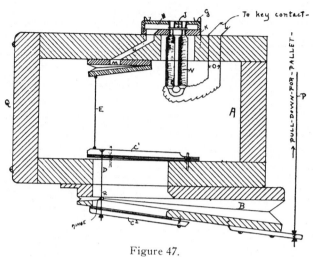

Figure 47.

Early application of the electro-pneumatic action to the slider and pallet windchest.

struction as both poles of the magnet are available for attracting the armature. The disc or armature that is attracted when the current passes through the coils is purposely made as light as possible. It acts as a valve to either admit air to the exhaust hole, or to close it, depending on whether or not the armature is attracted by the magnet. Several forms of the magnet used by various American organ builders will be illustrated in later chapters.

One of the earliest forms of magnet that quite approaches what is being used at the present time, both in design and efficiency, is that invented by Hope-Jones. We show a large scale drawing of this magnet, taken from George L. Miller's work, "The Recent Revolution in Organ Building" in Figure 48. The facts are, that it was extraordinarily efficient for its day, and in some respects has not been improved upon. To explain the action, referring to our figure 47, we shall quote from Mr. Hope-Jones' description of its working as follows: "The box A is connected with the organ bellows and so (immediately the wind is put into the organ) is filled with air under pressure, which passes upwards between the poles of the magnet N. Lifting the small iron disc J, it finds its way through the passage L into the small motor M, thus allowing the movable portion of the motor M to remain in its lower position, the pallet C^1 being closed and the pallet C^2 being open. Under these conditions, the larger motor B collapses and the pull-down P (which is connected with the organ pallet) rises.

136

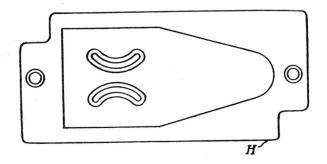

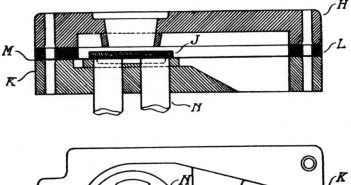

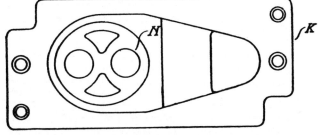

Figure 48.

Full sized views of the Hope-Jones Magnet. Top view is the removable bottom plate of the assembly. The center view is a section through the bottom portion of the magnet. The bottom view is the plate K, into which the poles of the magnet are fitted at N. J is the disc or armature.

"When a weak current of electricity is caused to circulate round the coils of the electro-magnet N, the small armature disc J is drawn off the valve-seat H onto the zinc plate K.

"The compressed air from within the small motor M escapes by way of the passage L, through the openings in the valve seat H into the atmosphere. The compressed air in the box A then acts upon the movable portion of the small motor M in such a manner that it is forced upwards and caused (through the medium of the pull-wire E) to lift the supply pallet C^1 and close the exhaust pallet C^2, thus allowing compressed air to rush from the box A into the motor B and so cause this latter motor to open and (through the medium of the pull down P) to pull the windchest pallet from its seat and allow wind to pass into the pipes.

"The valve-seat H has formed on its lower surface two crescent-shaped long and narrow slits. A very slight movement of the armature disc J, therefore, suffices to open to the full extent two long exhaust passages. The movement of this disc is reduced to something less than the 1/100 part of an inch. It is, therefore, always very close to the poles of the magnet, consequently a very faint impulse of electricity will suffice (aided by gravity) to draw the disc off the valve-seat H. The zinc plate K being in intimate contact with the iron poles of the magnet N, protects the latter from rust by well-known electrical laws. All the parts are made of metal, so that no change in the weather can affect their relative positions. R is the point at which the large motor B is hinged. G is a spring retaining cap in position; O the wires leading from the keys and conveying the current to the magnet N: Q the removable side of the box A."

This is an excellent description of one form of electric action which was applied simply to the old tracker organ windchest and Barker lever. This form has been very much improved and modified in many respects by all of our American builders, particularly with regard to the old tracker type of windchest. This has been almost wholly superseded in American organs by some form of windchest with individual pneumatics for each pipe.

Without making any direct statements or comparisons as to the specific builder or builders who make the most efficient and reliable modern action, which would be obviously unfair and unwise in a work of this kind, it is perhaps advisable to state what is most desirable in an electro-pneumatic action. Then details will be furnished as to just how the various builders accomplish these ends and let the reader judge for himself which style of action he considers the best. The two qualities that are most desirable in a modern organ action are 1. Reliability, and 2. Speed; that is, quickness in attack and repetition.

There is, of course, a considerable similarity between most of the action work of our best builders. As a matter of fact, there is not a great deal of choice. Nevertheless, certain of our builders have gone into some

THE ELECTRO-PNEUMATIC ACTION

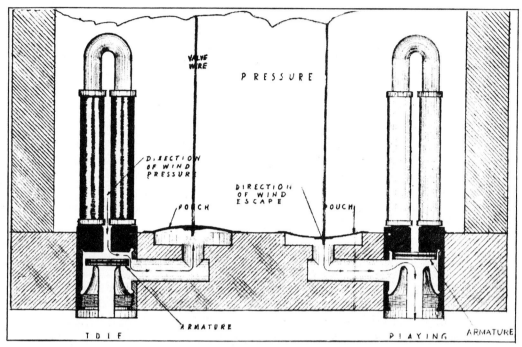

Figure 49.

Sectional view of two magnets, one, on the left shows the armature closing the exhaust port. The arrows show the direction of the wind pressure, which travels through the magnet to the underside of the pouch, thereby equalizing the pressure on both sides. The pouch will stay up, keeping the pipe valve closed, in this case, as the spring holds the pipe valve closed. The magnet on the right is attracting the armature, which in this position does two things. First, it closes the ports permitting the passage of wind pressure through the magnet, and opens the bottom of the magnet to the atmosphere, permitting the air to escape from the bottom part of the pouch, and the pressure of air above the pouch to collapse it, drawing with it the pipe valve. The drawing is of a portion of a Kilgen windchest, kindly furnished by Geo. Kilgen & Sons. This drawing is one of the clearest expositions of the exact function of the magnet, with its armature acting as a two way air valve, that has ever come to my notice. It will repay the study of the uninitiated. From it may be obtained a very clear idea of the function of any magnet and pouch, as made by any builder, as the principles are the same in all cases.

The Kilgen Organ Co., successors to Geo. Kilgen & Sons, are using to-day this same magnet.

matters more carefully than others and have reached a higher degree of perfection. Nearly all modern organ actions are electric, or more properly electro-pneumatic. It should already be clear that compressed air which is available in every organ is used for power. Wind pressure and electricity are employed to transmit the playing and other impulses. It can readily be seen that electric transmission aids the responsiveness of the action, as the impulses are transmitted with the velocity of light. Such transmission also aids in reliability because the coupling, switching, and transmission is done on prepared circuits, some permanent and some temporary. A permanent electric circuit with soldered joints is absolutely reliable and durable. A temporary one is also provided that the contacts or points of closing and opening the circuit are reliable and durable.

The electric organ action is operated on low voltage, and direct current is necessary. Organ magnets will not operate on alternating current. The voltage varies between eight and fifteen with different builders. In years past it was quite a problem to secure a reliable source of this kind of current. It was usual to employ storage or other batteries in early actions. There are now on the market a number of very reliable generators capable of producing the low voltage current necessary in organ action that are generally attached directly on the same shaft with the large motor that turns the fans for supplying wind to the organ. This method of directly connecting the generator on the same shaft eliminates breaking of belts and slipping and other generator troubles that can occur when the generator is placed separate from the blower. Owing to the very uneven and sudden demands that are made on generators used for supplying current to organs, it has been a matter of considerable difficulty to design a generator which would meet these requirements. When an organ is 'not being played with the generator going at its normal speed, there is little, if any, demand upon the generator for output of current. When a heavy chord is struck upon the organ there is a sudden demand for the entire output of the generator and it must be instantly available, or the voltage will drop to such an extent that the magnets will not work properly.

In 1946, Mr. Austin La Marche made available for organ use, a silenium rectifier, which was developed to meet the varying load demands, and all other requirements of a perfect current supply for organs. It is called the Orgelectra, and it has none of the unsatisfactory features that characterized earlier forms of rectifiers. In fact, it is the best and most reliable source of low voltage direct current that can be had today.

An unreliable source of low-voltage current has finally been discovered to have been the reason for the unsatisfactory performance of older electric actions. Failure to discover this fault for years delayed the cause of the electric organ in England. Some of these old organs have been rehabilitated and new generators of an improved type installed, whereupon the old electric action has been found to function perfectly. It

Figure 50.

Winding the magnets used in the Kilgen organ. The soft iron cores are placed in a lathe. After paper insulation has been applied to the core, it is wound with a proper number of turns of enameled magnet wire. The iron cores are then bent into a U shape in a press, and are ready to be assembled in the magnet base.

Figure 51.

Parts of the Moller magnet. From left to right, the parts are: front and bottom views of the base, blotting paper packing where base is attached to the windchest, front and bottom views of armature base, with armature or metal disc in foreground. This part may be readily unscrewed to get at the armature for cleaning or adjusting. Next, two paper straws on which the coils of magnet wire are wound in a lathe as above, and then slipped on to each side of soft iron core, that has previously been bent to shape in this case. The last item is the completed magnet.

will, therefore, be seen that a reliable source of current is perhaps the most important essential of a successful electric organ action. Happily, such a source may now be taken as a matter of course and need not be considered further.

It is interesting to note, however, that much of the trouble that earlier electric actions encountered, giving them the name of being unreliable, was not so much due to faulty design or construction of the action itself as to the unreliable and faulty current supply.

We shall now trace the operations of the action following the electrical impulse created when a key is depressed through the various steps in the action until the pipe sounds. An analysis of all these operations will give a more general idea of what the electric action consists of. We shall also, at the same time, consider in some detail some of the features that go to make this source of operation reliable and efficient or the contrary.

When a key is depressed, it makes either a single or a multiple contact. That is, it closes or completes one or more series of electric circuits. On account of the coupling system in modern organs whereby all of the separate divisions of the organ can be collected together on the Great keyboard, or different combinations of divisions can be made on any of the other keyboards, it is necessary for the key to close simultaneously a rather large number of circuits. This is accomplished in one of two ways, either by mounting a number of contacts directly on the key itself, or having the key mechanically operate in one of a number of ways (described later) a series of contacts which are not directly attached to the key. Or the key itself need only close one circuit which leads to a relay mechanism in the organ. This mechanism when operated will close the desired number of contacts.

The first method described is always preferable whenever it can be used because it dispenses with the relay mechanism and permits of a closed electric circuit from the key to the pipe chest with no relay operations in between which must inevitably slow down the train of operation to a certain extent. In organs which have a large number of stops of the unit variety where a large number of separate contacts must be made, one for each magnet, it is frequently imperative to introduce a relay mechanism, if a sufficient number of contacts cannot be directly operated by the keys themselves. With most church organs, quite enough contacts can be readily placed on the keys for operating the various couplers, each of which requires a separate contact for every key. The distance from center to center of the keys is approximately 5/8 inches, so, in addition to possessing reliability and durability, these contacts must be quite small to fit in such a small space. They also have to be of very sensitive and gentle action in order that the organist's sense of touch may not be disturbed, when a greater or lesser number of contacts are "made" by depressing the keys.

The number of circuits completed and broken by an organ key during a year's playing is almost incredible in cases where the organ is used for several hours a day (as was always the case with theater organs and sometimes with church organs). The ideal contacts, therefore, must not only be reliable but they must "make" every time and the first time, even after long periods of disuse. The chief problem in this matter is to build them in such a way and of such material that they will stay clean constantly. Dirt and dust settling from the air may cause the contact not to "make." Fouling of the metal, caused by electrolysis due to arcing at the contact when the circuit is opened, may cause unreliable contacts. The first difficulty is overcome by making the two elements of the contacts from suitable material and placing them so that the axis of one is at right angles to the axis of the other, thus securing always a point of contact, and eliminating a dust-collecting flat plate.

The motion of the key in all properly designed electric organs is such that the two contact elements form a rubbing touch which makes the points self-cleaning. There are two ways of eliminating the difficulty caused by arcing of the contact point, first, by finding material that is as impervious to corrosion as possible; and second, by designing a magnet that will operate with the smallest possible consumption of current in order that the electrical load may be reduced to a minimum. Again, magnets of which there are many different types (some of these are illustrated later) have a varying degree of resistance to the passage of current. The resistance varies in different makes of magnets, averaging around 100 ohms, though some builders make a great point of the fact that the resistance of their magnet is much greater than this, up to 400 ohms. The higher the resistance the less current consumption for each magnet and the less arcing or burning of the contacts is likely to occur, provided the same voltage is employed in each case. Other things being equal, therefore, a magnet of high resistance is preferable to one of low resistance though, if the resistance be too high, the magnet will not have as great pulling power on the small disc which it is designed to attract.

There are arguments on both sides of this question, and the undoubted advantage of a small current consumption is sometimes offset by the failure to accomplish what is intended quite as well as if a larger current consumption is permitted.

We now come to a highly disputed point in present day organ building, the question of the most suitable material for contact purposes. A good many of our leading builders use nothing but silver wire for this purpose. This is what was generally employed by Mr. Hope-Jones in the organs which he built.

Only three metals; platinum, tungsten and silver, have stood up under the following laboratory test: A reciprocating device designed to reproduce the motion of the keys had mounted on it contacts of different design and many different metals including three alloys of silver, two alloys of phosphor-bronze, tungsten, platinum, German silver, "meteor" metal and others. This test was run constantly for a period of six months at a rate of two hundred and forty contacts per minute, forty-eight hours a week, with each contact loaded with coils consuming one-fifth of an ampere. As has been noted, the only three metals to stand up under this test were platinum, tungsten and silver. Silver may be obtained in a suitable alloy so that it has a certain amount of spring when made into wire, an essential quality for any contact to have. Phosphor-bronze is also employed for contact purposes by several of our leading builders, whose chief argument is that phosphor-bronze wire has splendid spring quality and that any alloy of silver which produces the same elasticity nullifies the excellent conductivity of the silver itself. Phosphor-bronze contacts, when carefully designed and all the workmanship perfectly carried out, seem to answer the purpose about as well as silver wire contacts, though in very damp weather phosphor-bronze contacts will not "make" the first time, whereas silver will make a contact at all times and under all conditions. The silver oxide formed by exposure of silver to the air is itself a good conductor.

It is indisputable that silver is a better conductor of electricity than other metals available in commercial quantities, but the qualities of additional springiness which, for instance, phosphor-bronze contacts possess, may in large measure compensate for its smaller degree of conductivity. I prefer silver wire contacts myself and do so because of the engineering reasons given above for using them in preference to any other metal at present known or available.

To proceed with our description of the operation of the electric organ action: From the key contact, the current impulse flows through prepared electric circuits. The circuits are made up into cables. These are usually partly exposed and partly in iron conduits. They should be durable and damp proof. For insulating, the different wires are usually double cotton-covered impregnated with paraffin. The cables run to the organ proper and the various wires are soldered to a union or junction board. From this point, additional cables are provided also soldered to the union board that connects directly with the magnet action box and the current flows into a magnet coil. The reason it is of such importance to solder all the joints that occur between the key contacts and the magnet in the electric action, is that only low voltage current is employed. A small amount of corrosion on the copper wire where a joint or splice is made in it may render the joint a non-conductor of electricity, as this corrosive material is in reality a dialectric. There is not sufficient voltage to jump across this corrosion and a silent note may result.

If the joints of the various wires are merely wound onto a junction board corrosion may not occur until the organ has been in use for six months or a year. Then silent notes will develop in various parts of the action if any of the joints have not been properly soldered, which process at once makes the joint permanent and not subject to corrosion. It is, therefore, of the utmost importance that all joints or splices of the cables be soldered at all points, or otherwise permanently joined. It would be an enormous job to determine where the circuit was dead if all joints had to be examined after the organ was installed. When the joints are systematically soldered all such difficulties are removed once for all.

A magnet is placed wherever an action or operation is desired. The magnet merely transforms the electric impulse into a pneumatic one by raising a small iron disc, thereby exposing an exhaust hole starting the train of the pneumatic action, as previously explained. Very little energy is required to lift this armature and the electric impulse around the magnet coils does this with extreme rapidity. Builders are not agreed as to whether the motion of this armature should be permanently fixed at a definite distance. Some builders insist that this is the only way a magnet should be built, while others consider it to be an advantage to be able to adjust the motion of the armature for different conditions and wind pressure. These are the chief features of the electrical side of the organ action.

To sum up, the reliability of the electric system is primarily dependent upon four distinct factors:—1. A reliable source of low voltage electric current, 2. a reliable contact point, 3. a reliable magnet and 4. reliable transmission system.

Trouble is most frequently caused in a magnet by dirt blown under the armature and thereby preventing its proper seating or closing. When this occurs, the same effect is produced as if the magnet were permanent in action and the note is caused to sound constantly or "cipher" until this dirt is removed. The possibility of this is minimized by some builders who construct the magnet with a thin gauze glued over the air ports which will catch stray pieces of dirt before they become imbedded under the armature seat. Whether this practice is of any great value is something of a question.

When the electric impulse arrives at the magnet, the action then changes to pneumatic. The armature, which up to this point has been viewed from the electrical side, should now be considered in regard to its function, which is in reality that of a pneumatic valve, which exhausts a small bellows or pouch. The latter has a large valve attached to it which this pouch opens. By the opening of this large valve the pipe valves themselves are operated through fixed air channels. These primary valves when complete weigh from one-fourth to one-half an ounce.

The pipe valves are in many standard actions mounted upon diaphragms or pouches and are operated by the motion of these diaphragms, the average weight of each pouch is one-tenth of an ounce. Most of the builders do not attempt to operate over six to ten sets of pipes from one primary valve, though with the pitman chest this is not important for obtaining speedy action. The total weight that has to be displaced when a key circuit is closed is the weight of one armature, between .023 and .050 of an ounce, one primary valve assembly weighing about one-fourth of an ounce, which operates six to ten pipe valve assemblies, weighing one-tenth of an ounce each, or a total combined weight of all this mechanism of about an ounce. The greatest movement of any valve is about three-eighths of an inch. This is the largest amount of material moved individually because each division of the organ has its separate action. These figures apply to manual chests where the greatest speed of action is important. Other types of electro-pneumatic organs contain pneumatics which are partly made of wood, some having the valve mounted directly on the bellows, others having the bellows operate pivoted levers of all kinds on which the valves are mounted. All these various types are illustrated hereafter in this work.

It should be observed that with the small amount of wind pressure utilized in organ building, the additional weight and friction involved in using pneumatics with wood and levers in their construction affects somewhat adversely the responsiveness of the action. The leather on these bellows pneumatics, by its very construction, has to be folded in creases which causes these then to wear out more rapidly on the lines of the creases. The pivots in the levers will also work loose in time, and have to be replaced. This is all eliminated by the use of the round pouch, or diaphragm which moves the pipe valves. There is absolutely no creasing of leather whatever and no additional material of any kind to move except the valve itself, in this type of pipe valve. The pouch or diaphragm pneumatic with the valve attached to the pouch was developed by Casavant Freres of St. Hyacinthe, Canada.

It may appear from this description of what an electric organ action is designed to accomplish that the two primary requirements it must have to be satisfactory, namely, 1. reliability and 2. speed, are best obtained in the manner we have outlined though as will be seen later the diaphragm or pouch chest is by no means the only type of action that will accomplish these results. It is the type of action, however, that is used by a majority of our leading builders and seems to be steadily becoming standard.

By this the writer does not for a moment wish to have it appear that the widely varying types of action made by other builders which may be entirely different in every respect from that of the action just described are not satisfactory for action purposes. These other types of action have many points in their favor, though I believe it has been established with considerable certainty that no action except Wurlitzer's is as speedy as the pouch or diaphragm pneumatic, combined with some form of the pitman stop action. This type of action has a speed greatly in excess of that with which the lower pipes of the manuals can be made to speak. There is no great advantage in having an action faster in its operation than the pipes can be made to speak. The craze for excessive speed has been engendered quite largely by the demands of theater organists. Legitimate demands for speed are met by nearly all the types of action to be described presently.

CHAPTER 11

TYPES *of* MODERN WINDCHESTS

THE "UNIVERSAL AIR CHEST"

A form of windchest and action that is in use at the present time which presents many unique features is the one known as the Universal Air Chest, invented by Mr. John T. Austin.

The first organ in New England that was built along these lines was installed in the Fourth Congregational Church of Hartford, Conn., in 1898. The installation of this organ created such widespread interest that it resulted in the formation of the Austin Organ Co. of that city. Mr. Robert P. Elliot was largely instrumental in the formation of this company, though he has had no connection with it for many years. Prior even to 1898 the Clough & Warren Co. of Detroit had made an airchest of somewhat similar design while Mr. Austin was associated with them.

The Universal Air Chest is the first to be described in this work because it is one of the simplest and easiest forms of electro-pneumatic action to explain. It combines some features of the tracker organ along with the most modern application of electro-pneumatic motions.

It is possible that a general work should not devote so much space to the description of a highly specialized form of action used by only one builder, but this firm has nearly two thousand organs to its credit, among them some of the largest and most important in America, which fact alone seems sufficient reason for a detailed description of the system that has been consistently employed during these years on all organs which the Austin Organ Company have built, and their successor, Austin Organs, Inc.*

*Note: It is not the author's intention to praise one builder at the expense of another, but in all fairness, it seems just to give credit where credit is due, particularly with regard to original inventions in organ-building.

I realize that general statements are sometimes dangerous to make, but I believe it is generally agreed among the organ builders of this country that the late Mr. John T. Austin was one of the most ingenious and clever men that have given their attention to mechanical matters relating to the organ during the past fifty or sixty years. One of the distinguishing features of the Austin organ both in regard to air chest mechanism and console mechanism is its entire originality. Nearly every detail has been invented by Mr. Austin or by his brother, Basil G. Austin. At no point along the line have they been content to use the ideas of other builders, but have originated a vast number of organ mechanisms of all types.

Some American builders have copied as closely as possible many of the details of the Austin console, though no other builder has apparently cared to copy the chest mechanism. The Austin Organ Company has doubtless more patents covering organ mechanism than any other builder in the country. Experience has proved that these patents are not particularly successful in avoiding copying of ideas by other builders. Mr. Austin himself, when told that other builders had appropriated certain of his ideas, was very "easy-going" about the matter and usually replied, "Oh, well, by the time they get to using that, I will have something better."

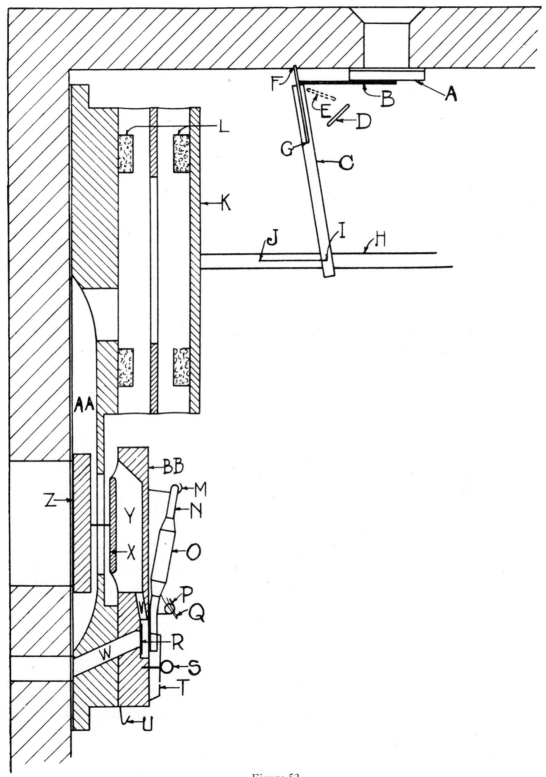

Figure 52.
Section through a portion of the Austin Air Chest.

149

At the time the Universal Air Chest was invented, electro-pneumatic and tubular pneumatic organ actions, as made in this country, were largely unreliable and caused a great amount of trouble. Windchests were frequently built so that ready access could not be had to the valves and magnets or other mechanism liable to derangement. It frequently necessitated the removal of the pipes from the top board and unscrewing a vast number of screws to get at the mechanism. This was a long, laborious process. Mr. Austin has told me of working on such windchests, and of his exasperation and annoyance at being unable to tell whether the trouble had been rectified until the top board was screwed into position again and the pipes replaced, only then perhaps to find that the trouble had not been remedied, and all his work had to be done over.

To overcome these difficulties entirely, Mr. Austin conceived the idea of a large box which could be entered with the wind inside the box. This box is like an air-tight room, ordinarily about six feet high, with one side a movable reservoir, and in the ceiling, rows of holes covered with valves, with the pipes directly above these valves. It is impossible to have the slightest variation in pressure in this chamber. There is an imaginary conductor to every pipe, as large as the whole head of the reservoir itself. The chief features of the Austin Air Chest are its easy accessibility and absolutely steady wind at unvarying pressure supplied to each pipe.

At the time the Austin windchest was invented, the reasons for its superiority were more manifest than at present. Then the unreliability of the usual pneumatic windchest and the difficulty of making adjustments therein, coupled with the unsteadiness of pressure, were much greater than they are now.

Practically all of our American builders have improved the other forms of electro-pneumatic windchests to a point where they are extremely reliable, and at the same time are more accessible in case adjustments are required. With the modern system of constructing deep air boxes and ample conductors from a large number of reservoirs or regulators, a perfectly satisfactory and steady pressure is obtained from any good windchest built along conventional lines. The Austin Air Chest is the only one of its kind being built at present. For that matter, it is the only one that has ever been built successfully. The Austin mechanism, when compared with other modern windchests is extraordinarily simple.

By an examination of Figure 52 it will be observed that the pipe valve "A" consists merely of a small metal disc of the proper size for the hole to be covered (varying from a disc covering a large hole admitting wind to a bass pipe to much smaller discs for the treble pipes). The metal discs are covered with felt and leather so that a soft air-tight covering is provided when the discs are in the closed position. A wire B, is riveted through this disc in the shape shown in our drawing to which is attached a little strip of wood C which is pivoted a short way below its top. The bent wire B is pivoted at F. The bottom of the wood strip C is attached by means of another wire at I and J to a long strip of wood or tracker H. The tracker runs across the entire width of the air chest, having connected to it as many pipe valves as there are stops or sets of pipes planted on the chest. One end of this tracker has a coiled spring attached to return it to its normal position. The other end of the tracker is attached to the power-pneumatic K which draws the tracker "H" to the left when it is collapsed, by exhausting the air from the pneumatic bellows through the ports AA and Z to atmospheric pressure. When a key is depressed, the valve Z is opened by means of the magnet M, whose action will be later described. When the tracker is drawn to the left by the collapsing of the pneumatic K, all the wooden strips "C" are rotated on their pivots at G, without opening the pipe valves if no stops are drawn.

The stop action consists of a metal bar 1/16 of an inch thick by ½ inch wide, which runs the entire length of the chest at right angles to the trackers. This is pivoted, and is shown in our illustration in both of its positions, "off" position at D and the "on" position, in dotted lines at E. It is caused to assume its "off" and "on" positions by means of a power pneumatic mounted at one end of the chest. When the stop is in the "on" position, the pneumatic causes this long metal bar to assume the position shown at E. When the stop action bar is in position E, and the strips C are moved by the tracker, the stop-action bar acts as a fulcrum, and the strips C can no longer rotate freely on pivots G but must cause the pipe valves to be drawn open whenever the tracker H is moved to the left. All of this mechanism can be seen in actual operation with the pressure on, by entering the air chest, and any small adjustments can be made, such as proper seating of the pipe valves, with great ease.

It will be observed that there is only one set of pneumatics for each note on the windchest instead of one pneumatic for each pipe valve. This simplifies the mechanism. Should releathering of the pneumatics become necessary, only one set need be redone as compared to five to ten times that number in the regularly constructed windchest. Furthermore, the leather on the rectangular motor pneumatic is not tightly creased or folded, for it is prevented from shutting tightly by thick felt pads placed on the inside of the pneumatic. It has been found from long experience that the leather on this pneumatic has outworn the leather on the round pouches which were formerly used in conjunction with it and Austin have a number of organs over 30 years old that have been in constant use which show no signs whatever of the leather on this pneumatic wearing at the folds. Without such provision, the leather on a rectangular pneumatic would tend to wear faster than the pouch pneumatic.

The construction of the Austin Air Box is such that changes of at-

Figure 53.

Complete electro-pneumatic power unit employed by the Austin Organ Co. A portion of the "tracker" or strip of wood is shown. This is attached to the power pneumatic and runs across the entire width of the air chest, to which all the pipe valves belonging to one note are fastened. Figure 60 shows a sectional view of this same power unit. There is one of these units for each note on the manual keys. They vary in size, becoming larger, and consequently more powerful for the lower notes, which require more power to operate. If there are ten stops on the air chest, controlled by one manual, there will be ten pipe valves attached to the tracker, that will be opened by one power pneumatic.

mospheric conditions do not affect the air-tightness of the box. To with-
stand the considerable pressure of the air, it is strongly braced at all
points. The wood sidewalls have wide joints left between the various
strips which are made tight by leather and rubber cloth. This construction
allows for expansion or shrinkage in the wood without opening up any
joints. The top of the air chest is made of a series of wooden bars about
three inches wide and two inches thick through which the holes for the
pipes are bored. The pipe valves are attached before the bars are placed
in position. If the pipes are small in scale they will be placed in a single
row on one of these bars. If of wider scale, two bars will be used, placing
the pipes alternately. If a very wide scaled stop such as a large Flute or
Diapason, three bars are used. The system of using a standard sized bar
is more economical to manufacture and yet has great flexibility in accommodating any size pipes that may be required. The pipe bars are then secured to the frame of the air box at appropriate distances apart to give
ample speaking room for the pipes, and the spaces between them are
filled in with rubber cloth to make the entire top of the chest air-tight.

The reservoir mounted vertically instead of horizontally forms one
side of the air box and is termed an "Expansion Board". Such a reservoir
must necessarily rely on springs for regulating the pressure as weights
can not be used. The Austins were the first to use springs exclusively
for reservoirs although the idea of this use probably originated with Mr.
Hope-Jones, as stated in our chapter on the Wind Supply for the Organ.

Formerly the wind pressure in the Austin Air Chest was invariably
so steady that it was impossible to shake it with any form of valve tremulant or any other means. Later Austin Organs have been enabled to produce a fine tremolo effect by an ingenious remodeling of the air box. The
upper portion is panelled, thereby separating it from the main air chamber
and it is supplied with air by means of a very large opening that can be
shut off with a damper. When the tremulant is not in action, this damper
remains wide open and all of the advantages of the Universal Air
Chest are still available. When the tremulant is drawn, the damper
closes automatically and wind is admitted to the panelled sections by
means of a long pipe which causes the air in this section to become sufficiently elastic to be effectively shaken by the tremulant. In this manner
a tremolo may be obtained quite equal to that possible with the ordinary
type of windchest construction and a real weakness in the Universal Air
Chest is effectively overcome.

Before this construction was adopted a tremolo of a certain kind
was obtained by placing a large board three feet long and two feet wide,
pivoted in the center immediately above the pipes themselves. This board
was rotated by an electric motor at a speed that caused a pleasant undulation to the tone of the pipes, much on the same principle of the fan
tremolo in a reed organ.

Some organists consider this latter tremolo superior to the usual pneumatic tremolo; others like myself, greatly prefer the valve tremulant and fortunately it is now possible to suit either taste.

The complete operation of the power pneumatic that draws the tracker operating the valve mechanism may be described as follows: There are two parts: 1, the power pneumatic that actually draws the tracker; 2, the electro-pneumatic valve mechanism that exhausts the air from the larger power pneumatic. The latter mechanism now employed was patented May 24, 1926, and is an improvement on earlier actions. It is shown in detail in Figure 53, a front view. Our references, however, are to Figure 66, which shows a cross section through a complete power pneumatic unit. These units may be readily mounted or demounted from the air chests by the means of two screws, in case releathering or replacement is necessary.

For further clearness and understanding, Figure 53 is also shown, which is an actual photograph of the complete power pneumatic and of the magnet portion. If the operation of this unit is once clearly understood, the principle of many modern organ actions is explained. All the action parts used in the Austin Organ including stop action pneumatics, pedal note pneumatics, which are individual (one to each large pipe) are all built on the same principle. Other moving parts of the Austin action are all mechanical and for this reason the Universal air chest action may be termed a combination of the tracker or mechanical action with the most modern electro-pneumatic developments.

Examining Figure 52, it will be seen that when the magnet O is energized, it draws the armature R toward the poles of the magnet thereby uncovering the exhaust port W. The small pneumatic BB is thereby exhausted through the channel V, drawing the exhaust valve Z of the large motor pneumatic off its seat and simultaneously cutting off the supply of air into AA. This permits the air contained in the large pneumatic K to be rapidly exhausted through the air channel AA, because the exhaust port uncovered by Z is of generous size. The power pneumatic K is prevented from closing too far by the felt strips L.

Remembering that we are looking at the interior portion of the air box, it is evident that the exhaust ports uncovered by the magnet and the larger valves open directly to the atmosphere. When the armature is allowed to return to the position shown in Figure 66 wind again flows through AA into the motor pneumatic K, which opens, bringing all the action back to its normal condition. The success of this action lies in the fact that no channeling and only one pneumatic is required for each note on the keyboard (not each pipe on the windchest), and the sureness and rapidity with which this motor pneumatic can be made to operate by the system just described.

TYPES OF MODERN WINDCHESTS

WINDCHESTS WITH VENTIL STOP ACTION AND INDIVIDUAL PIPE VALVE PNEUMATICS

We have described in our chapter on the History of the Organ Action, the manner in which the Barker Lever was applied to the old type of slider and pallet windchest. In this form of action the valves that admitted air to the Barker Lever might be opened by mechanical means, as in the tracker action, or pneumatically by means of the tubular action, or electrically. But whatever action was employed for operating the Barker Lever, the stop action was controlled by sliders in the same manner as it had been for hundreds of years before.

In large tracker organs built in France (and for the most part they are still in use), the wind is shut off from certain divisions by means of ventils or large air valves that are operated by either stop actions or foot levers. In this manner several stop knobs (usually the Reeds) may be drawn at any convenient time and not be brought into action until the ventil is open that permits air to enter the windchest, on which the pipes are planted. Also, it was customary in nearly all tracker organs, so to build pedal windchests that their stop action could be controlled by means of a ventil.

Thus it is apparent that the ventil was used for stop action purposes long before the modern windchest was invented. Hilborne L. Roosevelt was the first in America to introduce individual pipe valve pneumatics in a windchest that operated in connection with a ventil stop action. A drawing of the original and authentic type of windchest known as the Roosevelt Chest is shown in Figure 54. Many builders have made modifications and changes in this windchest, though retaining its general principles.

Air is admitted individually to each set of pipes by means of a ventil, or stop action valve at one end of the windchest. This is shown clearly in Figure 56 and its operation is also described there. From this form of stop action is derived the general name for all windchests using ventils by means of which air may enter or be cut off from the pipe valve chambers. It is not necessary that individual pipe valve pneumatics be employed with a ventil windchest. For example the one built by Hillgreen, Lane and Company later described, is in reality an adaptation and improvement of an earlier form of windchest used in Germany, where one pneumatic is caused to operate a series of pipe valves.

The individual pipe valve pneumatic used by Roosevelt is shown in Figure 55. The operation of this windchest, referring to Figure 54 is as follows:

When the pneumatic attached to the tube leading to the key action is exhausted, the double valve, connected to a channel in the bottom board of the windchest, is drawn to the left, opening the channel to the

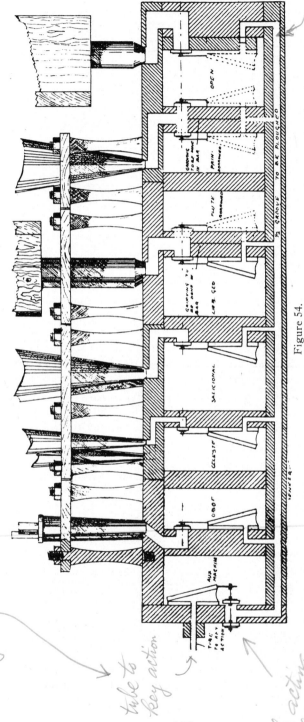

Figure 54.

A sectional view through an original and authentic Roosevelt windchest, with tubular pneumatic action. This was one of the first windchests to be built with individual pipe pneumatics. Its operation is described in the text. (From W. & T. Lewis, "Modern Organ Building.")

156

Key is up in this fig.

good

When key is depressed air escapes from tube to key.

tube to key action

double acting valve

ventil

One note

supply of air introduced any here

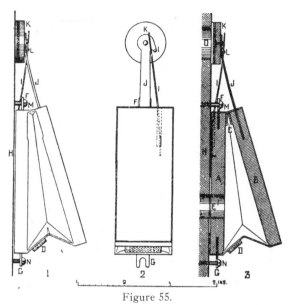

Figure 55.

Side, top, and sectional views of a Roosevelt pneumatic.

atmosphere and shutting off further wind from the primary box. When the wind is exhausted from the channel in this manner, all the pipe pneumatics that connect with this channel are exhausted simultaneously. If the ventil allowing wind into the partition under a set of pipes is open, the pressure of this wind on the pipe valve pneumatics will cause them to collapse and allow air to flow into the pipes. If, however, no ventils are open to allow air to pass into any of the air compartments under the pipes, the pipe valve pneumatics will all remain stationary as there is no pressure of air against them to cause them to collapse and the spring holds them closed.

When the double acting valve on the primary is returned to the right (or the position shown in Figure 54), air from the primary box flows through the channel back into each pipe valve pneumatic, so that there is equal pressure on both sides, if the stops are on. The pipe valves are then held closed by their springs. If the stops are not on, wind pressure is only being exerted on the inside of the pneumatics, as the pipe chambers are open to the atmosphere. If the pneumatics become damp, there is danger that the leather will blow off of them, and that leakage will ensue. I have found by actual experience with this type of chest that this is more than a possibility in damp locations and is a serious disadvantage. In none of the other forms of windchests we shall describe, is there a tendency for the leather to blow off the pneumatics when the stops are not drawn.

157

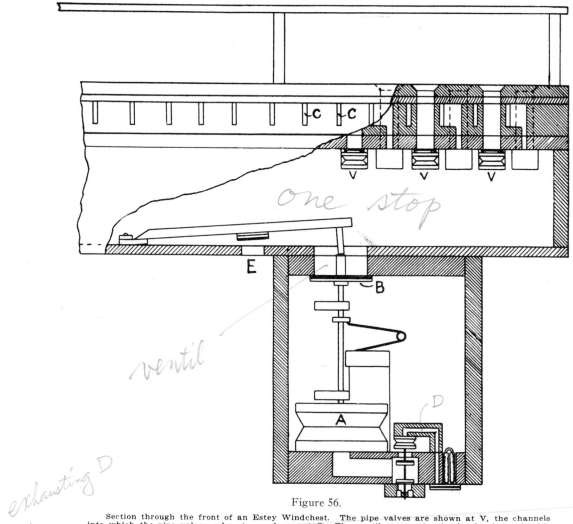

Figure 56.

Section through the front of an Estey Windchest. The pipe valves are shown at V, the channels into which the pipe valves exhaust are shown at C. The ventil stop action is clearly shown in this drawing. All builders using the ventil stop action use somewhat similar method of admitting air to the various sections of the windchest. Compressed air is present at all times, when the blower is running in the box under the windchest. Upon the magnet operating the primary valve being energized by the stop action, the power pneumatic, A, is exhausted drawing with it the large disc valve or ventil, B, which permits a large quantity of air to enter the pipe valve chamber. The stop is then in playing condition. It is shown in the above drawing in the closed or off position. It should also be noted, that when the ventil is in the off position it raises an exhaust valve, E, which allows all the air in the pipe chamber to escape instantly and thus silence the stop as soon as the stop action is shut off. This valve also permits any small leakage of the pipe pneumatics to find its way to the atmosphere, without gradually filling the pipe chamber with compressed air that might cause the pipes to sound, even though the ventil was not open.

An interesting point to observe in connection with the operation of the Roosevelt and many other modern windchests is that it is only necessary to displace the amount of air contained in the pipe valve pneumatics through the channel in the bottom board to cause them to collapse. Conversely, only sufficient air need be replaced in the channels to refill the pneumatics. Therefore, the action in reality takes place more rapidly than would be possible if the pneumatics did not collapse until all the air was exhausted from both the pneumatics and the channel; or on the return motion, both the channels and pneumatics had to be refilled, before the pneumatics would close. This same principle holds true fortunately, for all pipe valve pneumatics and the speed of the action is thereby greatly increased. The channels referred to here and in our discussion of the various forms of pitman windchests are in reality a series of air channels or grooves either in the bottom board or top board of the windchest that connect directly with all the pipe valve pneumatics that are playable from a single note on the keyboard. If there are twelve stops playable from one manual key, there will be twelve pipe valve pneumatics that are controlled by this channel through the primary valves. The key action merely operates the primary valves either pneumatically or electrically, which in turn permits the wind to exhaust from or reenter the channels.

Figure 58 shows the bottom boards with the veneer removed. The grooves, together with the holes bored into them corresponding with the pipe valve pneumatic holes are clearly depicted.

In the Estey windchest already shown in Figure 59 it will be seen that the action is a modified form of the Roosevelt windchest with the channels in the top board. The individual pipe valve pneumatics are made with the pipe valves attached to the pneumatics instead of being attached to a lever actuated by the pneumatics as in the original Roosevelt example. Such differences are not important in describing general principles, though the Estey form is undoubtedly an improvement on the original, and gives a greater speed to the action.

The Kilgen Company employ a ventil windchest with a pouch or diaphragm, instead of a pipe valve pneumatic partly made of wood, with folding leather sides like a small bellows. The same form of action is used also by the Wangerin Organ Company of Milwaukee. Figure 60 shows the Kilgen adaptation of the ventil windchest. The stop action is the same as in other examples already described.

The pouch form of pneumatic is quite old and was probably first used by Walcker in Germany, at least the oldest examples of the diaphragm or pouch pneumatic may be found there.

It has since come to be very largely used by American builders, Casavant being the first, so far as I can determine, to employ the pouch pneumatic in America. In the Kilgen action the pouches are mounted directly onto the bottom boards, and thus may be exhausted directly into

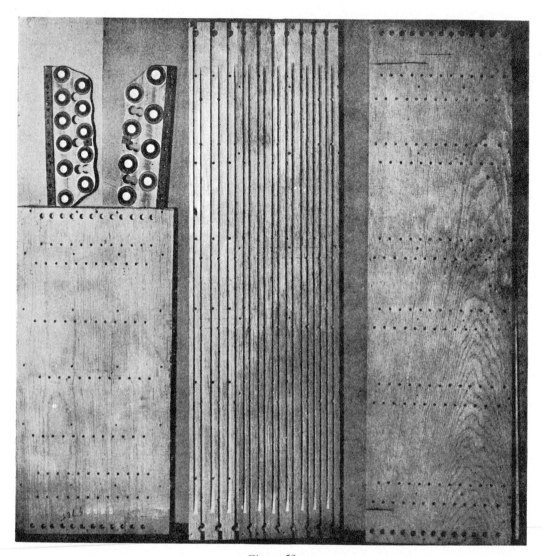

Figure 58.

A photograph showing details of the bottom boards of a Moller windchest. The bottom boards have their channels cut on a special saw, and then a thin piece is glued on enclosing the channels in the central portion of the bottom board. At the right, the top side of the bottom board is shown, with the holes bored corresponding to the holes in the stop action bars shown in Figure 80. The bottom boards are packed with leather where they are joined with the main portion of the windchest, and securely screwed thereto, so that they fit air-tight. In the upper left is shown the pouch boards, which are made in short sections, permitting of easy removal, by taking down only one bottom board. The pouches are more clearly shown in our sectional drawings.

TYPES OF MODERN WINDCHESTS

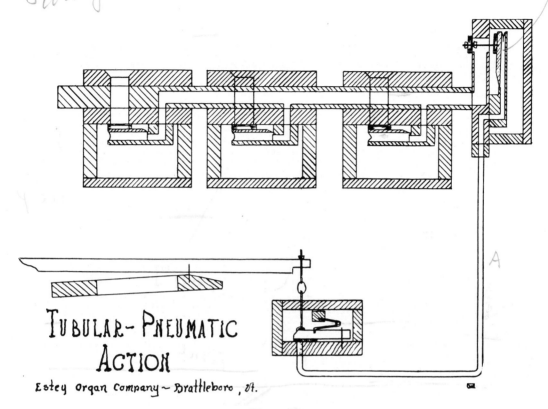

TUBULAR-PNEUMATIC ACTION

Estey Organ Company — Brattleboro, Vt.

Figure 59.

Sectional view of the individual pneumatic windchest with the pipe pneumatic exhausted by tubes, which in turn are exhausted by valves operated mechanically by the keys themselves. This is a later form of the tubular pneumatic action than that shown in Figure 50, and still employed by the Estey Organ Company in small organs.

the channels. A large amount of boring of holes necessary in other forms of windchests, where the pipe valve pneumatics are placed directly under the pipe holes, is thereby eliminated. A tapped wire connects the pipe valves with the pouches. The wire is secured in the pouch leather by means of a leather nut. These valve wires run through guides, that also serve to support the coil springs that hold the pipe valves closed when the pouches are not being exhausted of air.

When it is necessary to make repairs or adjustments in the Kilgen windchest, a bottom board is removed, which has attached to it all the pouches and pipe valves for that section of the windchest. Such an action has a good deal to commend it, and when carefully made should give very little trouble. There is sufficient "play" allowed in the valve stems to compensate for swelling or shrinking in the wood of the windchest, and the mechanism will not become deranged from this cause.

161

All windchest mechanisms, to be really successful, must necessarily make allowances and have means of compensation for atmospheric changes. Hair trigger and fine adjustments beyond a certain point must prove impractical, as they are too sensitive to swelling and shrinking. A certain margin of safety should be allowed in the design of any successful organ action, to permit the wood portions of the windchest to come and go, without readjustment of the mechanism being required.

The reliability and freedom from trouble of the majority of modern actions has been accomplished for the most part by having the above features in mind when the actions were designed.

WINDCHESTS WITH SOME FORM OF THE PITMAN STOP ACTION

See p. 168

We come now to the description of the windchest that is more generally employed than any other by present day American builders. Mr. Ernest M. Skinner says that he is the inventor of the pitman windchest. The term pitman I find by reference to the International Dictionary means merely a connecting rod. It was applied to sewing machine pedal connecting rods. The pitman valves in an organ windchest take the place of ventils in controlling the stop action. It must be clearly understood at the outset, in examining any of the drawings of the various forms of pitman windchests, here presented, that the wind pressure is beneath the pipe valve pneumatics at all times when the blower is running. With all ventil windchests such pressure is in the pipe valve chambers only when a ventil is open. The pitman windchest is sometimes called a universal windchest for this reason. The pipe valve pneumatics are permitted to exhaust or remain closed in accordance with the action of the pitman valves which will be later described.

In a letter I have received from Mr. Skinner, he makes the following statements:

"I see the frequent mention of the pitman, which is sometimes spelled with a capital 'P'. In Senator Richards' Atlantic City specification, he speaks of the pitman windchest and follows with a mention of Austin's 'Universal windchest', but he does not give me the same credit that he gives Austin. The pitman windchest is the invention of your humble servant and was published for the first time in Audsley's 'Art of Organ Building', page 347, volume 2. I made this drawing for Audsley but he did not give me credit for it. This chest bids fair to become universally used, but the unfortunate inventor is lost sight of. I think I will have to write up the pitman windchest and take the credit that belongs to me before I lose it for good.

"This drawing that I made for Audsley also shows the use of a high pressure arrangement which can be located anywhere in the chest. It also shows for the first time, an arrangement for playing a stop from

TYPES OF MODERN WINDCHESTS

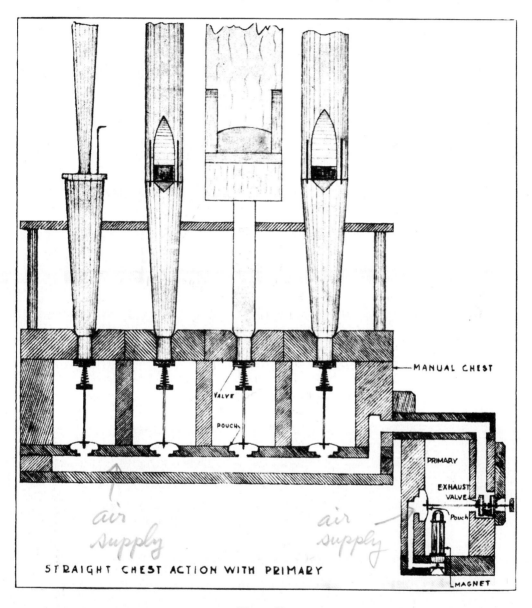

Figure 60.

The pipe valve assembly used by Geo. Kilgen & Sons of St. Louis consists of fibre discs on which are glued felt and leather. A tapped wire controls the motion of the disc valve by connecting it to the pouch located in the bottom board of the windchest. The pouches are exhausted directly into the channels in the bottom board. This style of windchest requires much less boring of holes than any form of the pitman windchest.

But It is a ventil windchest.

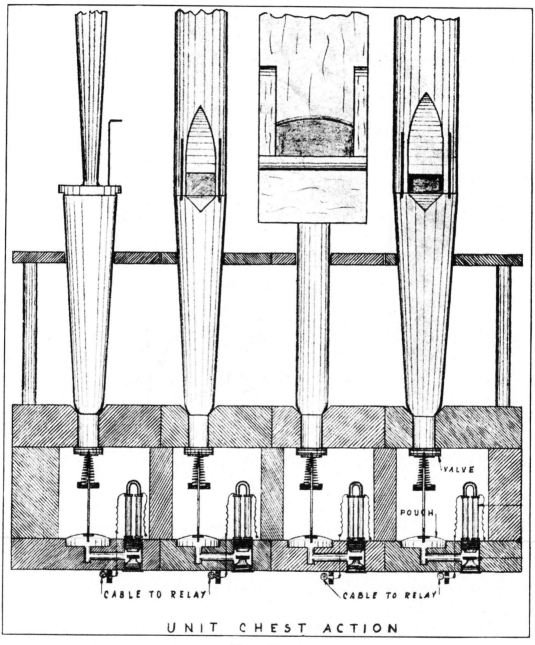

Figure 61.

A section through a unit windchest, where each pipe has its own magnet, permitting it to be played in any manner it is desired, by means of a series of switches, which allow the magnet circuit to be closed. Kilgen Organ Co., Builders.

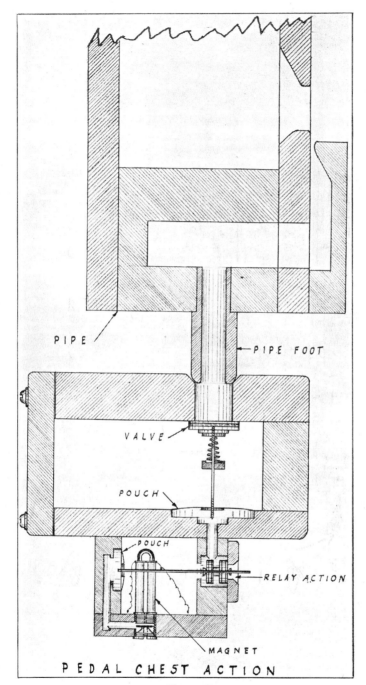

PIPE

PIPE FOOT

VALVE

POUCH

POUCH

RELAY ACTION

MAGNET

PEDAL CHEST ACTION

Figure 62.

Kilgen Organ Co., Builders. A section through a pedal wind-chest. In this case the magnet does not exhaust the pipe valve pouch, directly, as the pouch is too large for drawing down the pipe valves for the larger pedal pipes to be exhausted quickly through the small hole in the magnet. An additional valve mechanism is interposed, similar to that used in the primary valves of the straight windchest action. The magnet in this case has merely to exhaust the air from the smaller pouch which in turn exhausts the air from the larger pipe pouch by opening the double acting valve, labeled "Relay action" in the above drawing.

Probably ventil

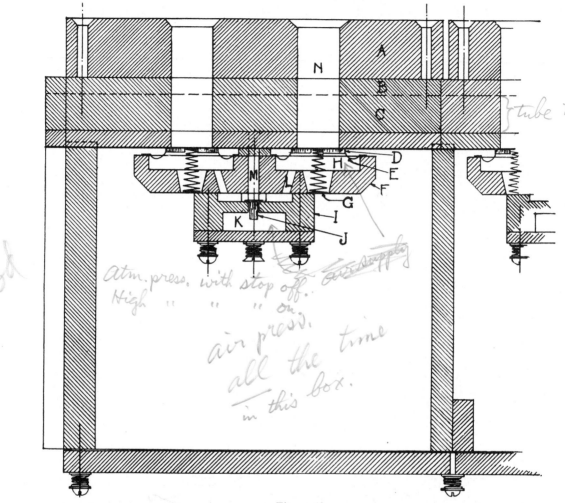

Figure 63.

A section through the Straight manual windchest manufactured by the Skinner Organ Company. This is known as the pitman windchest, and is described in the text. The primary valve mechanism that exhausts the channel, C, is not shown in the drawing, but this mechanism is similar to that shown in other drawings of the pitman action, except that the Skinner Company employ two valves to exhaust the channels, a primary and secondary valve. It is considered that the two valves increase the speed of the action. Other builders secure satisfactory results with one primary valve.

The Aeolian-Skinner Organ Company have occasionally built this action with a 4" thick laminated board introduced between the top of the windchest and the top board on which the pipes stand, with as large holes drilled in this 4" board as possible. This provides the equivalent of expansion chambers between the pipe valves and the toes of the pipes. This is only needed for pipes over 2' long. The speech of the larger pipes is somewhat improved by this means. Probably the same results can be produced by longer pipe feet on the larger pipes. Other builders have also adopted some similar means to improve the speech of the larger pipes. For the bottom octave of a 32' Bourdon, for example, Austin Organs, Inc. run about 3' of conductor between the pipe valve and the toe of the pipe.

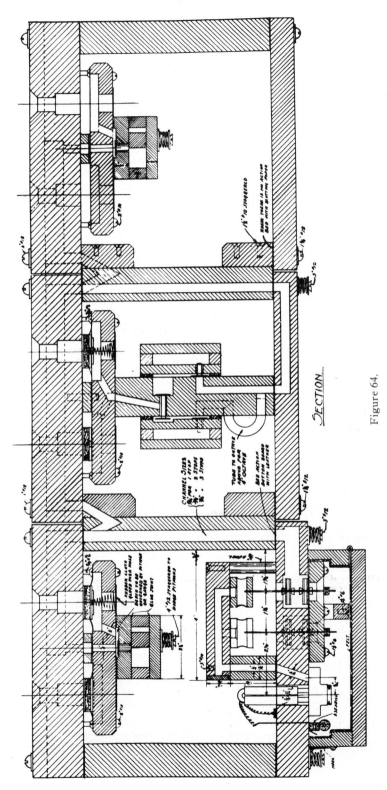

SECTION

Figure 64.

A section through a three stop Kimball windchest. This shows the manner in which the channels are run in the top board of the windchest, by cutting V shaped grooves in the sections of the windchest to which the top and bottom boards are screwed. This permits of channeling the top boards without making them all in one piece as is done in the windchests made by the Skinner Company and the Aeolian Company. The center section of the drawing shows the "Duplex" action, whose operation by means of a shifter is similar to that which has been described in detail for the Moller "Duplex" action. The same duplex action in all essentials is employed by the other builders of the pitman windchest.

167

two manuals which was discarded many years ago, in view of the single pipe valve and an arrangement for operating it from two sources. This pitman device arrangement is now about 50 years old, or as old as the pitman windchest itself.

"Mr. Richards stipulates that only eight stops shall be placed on any one chest showing that he, along with the balance of those interested in this chest, does not know that the pipe pneumatic is not exhausted through the key channel, but on the contrary, exhausts into the stop action channel when rush of air in the key channel sucks the pitman over to the key port leaving the channel open for the pipe pneumatic to exhaust directly underneath said pipe pneumatic and out the stop action. This exhaust of the key channel not only reaches atmosphere in rushing out the key primary, but develops a very positive suction owing to the inertia of the air, which still further serves to suck the pitman over towards the key exhaust.

"I suppose musically, as far as the mechanism goes, that the instantaneous stop action incident to the pitman chest should be regarded as extremely valuable on account of the orchestral precision that it makes possible in registration."

Mr. Skinner also states that he is the inventor of the closed circuit stop action and states the following:

"The closed circuit stop action eliminated one contact on each register and one magnet at the stop. There used to be an on and off contact and an on and off magnet. I believe I was the first to use a high resistance closed circuit stop action, and made the modern Crescendo and Sforzando possible. At all events nobody else ever used it until I did, and now they are all using it. I don't believe there is one out of the lot who knows who started it."

We shall first describe the pitman windchest in the form used by the Aeolian-Skinner Organ Company. Figure 63 is a cross section through a portion of such a windchest. The pitman valve is shown as J. It consists of a small piece of hard wood with square sides about 1/2" long and 1/8" on each side, on one end of which is securely tacked and glued a disc about 1/2" in diameter of suitable leather. The pitmans are well black leaded and all edges are smoothed to avoid the possibility of sticking in the hole in which they work back and forth.

Each pipe valve pneumatic shown at H has a corresponding pitman valve. The pitman valves are placed in a box K which runs longitudinally throughout the length of the windchest. The box K may have wind

Note: I have avoided, as far as possible, making direct statements concerning some original inventions in organ building. So many builders have worked on the same problems at about the same time that it is frequently difficult to be absolutely sure which one was first in many matters. To avoid controversy that might otherwise arise, I have quoted the builders themselves or other authority when I have good reason to believe their statements are correct.

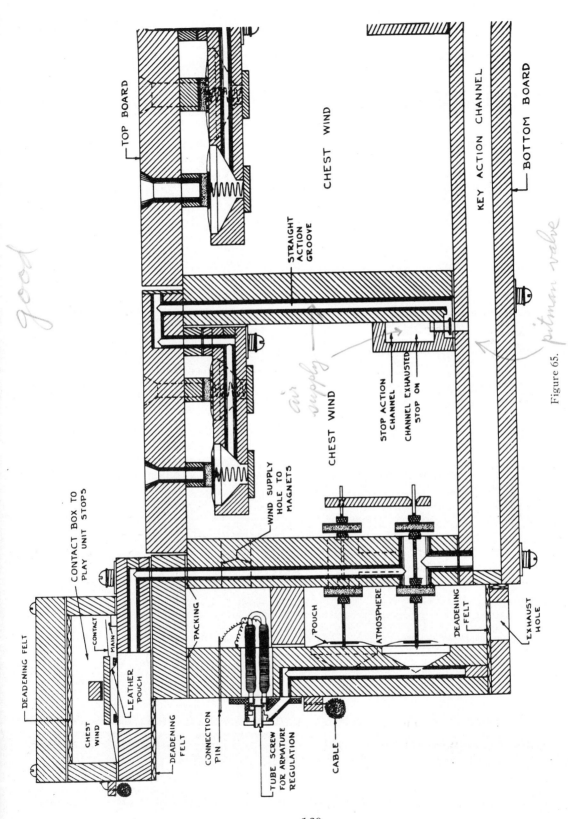

good

pitman

air supply

pitman valve

TOP BOARD

CHEST WIND

STRAIGHT ACTION GROOVE

CHEST WIND

STOP ACTION CHANNEL

CHANNEL EXHAUSTED STOP ON

KEY ACTION CHANNEL

BOTTOM BOARD

WIND SUPPLY HOLE TO MAGNETS

CONTACT BOX TO PLAY UNIT STOPS

DEADENING FELT

CONTACT

MAIN

LEATHER POUCH

CHEST WIND

DEADENING FELT

PACKING

CONNECTION PIN

TUBE SCREW FOR ARMATURE REGULATION

CABLE

POUCH

ATMOSPHERE

DEADENING FELT

EXHAUST HOLE

Figure 65.

A section through a Moller windchest showing the manner in which the contacts for a relay are attached directly to the windchest and are operated pneumatically by the primary action.

169

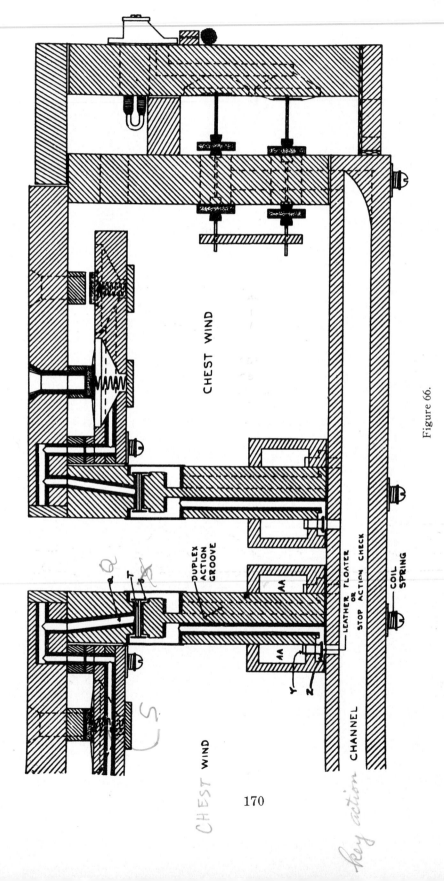

CHEST WIND

CHEST WIND

DUPLEX ACTION GROOVE

LEATHER FLOATER
STOP ACTION CHECK

COIL SPRING

CHANNEL

AA

AA

Figure 66.

A section through a "Duplexed" Moller windchest. The primary is compactly placed inside the windchest itself. All of the pipe valve boards are still readily accessible.

170

Key action

admitted to it or it may remain open to the atmosphere. The stop action valve controls the entrance of wind to the pitman box or opens the box to the atmosphere.

When wind is present in the box K, the pitman valve J remains in position shown in Figure 63, providing no key is depressed and air is present in the channel C. This is true, because there is equal pressure on each side of the pitman valve and gravity holds it down. Upon the channel C being exhausted by the key action primary, the air cannot escape from the pouch H as the pitman immediately blows upwards covering the port M leading into the channel C. In reality the pitman valves remain stationary when the stops are on and also when the stops are off, except when a key is depressed in which case the pitman valve affected by the key action will blow upward as explained above and cut off the egress of wind from the pouch, thereby preventing the pouch acting and the note sounding.

When the box K is exhausted of air, the pitman valves remain as shown in the drawing and prevent the escape of air from the pouches that flows to them through the port M and the channel C from the key action primary box. When the channel C is now exhausted the pouch H will collapse as the pressure of the air on the outside of the pouch is no longer balanced by similar pressure on the interior. The pouch exhausts through M and L and C into the atmosphere. This is the majority opinion of the manner of operation of the pitman windchest. The inventor holds a different view which we have already quoted above. Here is a case where authorities disagree, and perhaps it is not of so much importance, how it works, as the fact that it does work and with the greatest possible speed.

It should be noted that in this windchest the channeling is all done in the top board. The channels obviously must run on either one side or other of the pipe holes N as they cannot run into the pipe holes. The top of the windchest is in reality double—the top board A on which the pipes stand and the channel board BCD. This latter board is made in a single wide piece glued up, and is subject to a large degree of swelling and shrinking, particularly if the windchest is a wide one. The lumber used for the ends of the windchest has the grain running in the same direction as the top board so that the whole windchest may swell and shrink without causing any undue strain on its parts. To facilitate the "come" and "go" of the lumber, rollers are placed under the chest but scarcely seem necessary for when the top board starts to swell, many tons pressure cannot prevent its movement. Forces set up in lumber by moisture that cause expansion are of enormous power, and expansion or contraction cannot be prevented by any known means. In this windchest no effort has been made to prevent swelling and shrinking. Careful designing allows this to take place without injury to the windchest itself or to the satisfactory performance of the action.

Casavant Freres and Reuter Organ Co. also build pitman windchests, very similar in principle to the Aeolian-Skinner windchest, with channeling in the topboards. Figure 67 illustrates the Reuter windchest with a sectional drawing.

The Moller pitman windchest differs from the ones used by the three builders just mentioned principally because the channeling is done through the bottom boards. Also the form of pitman valve has been simplified. Instead of using the wooden tail piece with the leather disc valve tacked and glued onto it, the former is discarded, and a leather disc is all that is used. This disc seats against an eyelet and rests against a paper punching.

Referring to Figure 66, Z is the pitman; Y is the eyelet against which it blows, when AA, or the pitman box is open to the atmosphere, and the channel or groove is exhausted of wind. The action otherwise is similar to the Skinner windchest action already described.

The Duplex Action between two manuals is also shown in Figure 66. This consists of two complete sets of pitman stop action valves applied to one stop. By this means the stop may be drawn or shut off from either manual at will. The grooves in the bottom board must then be double for each note. One groove is exhausted by the Great organ primary; while the groove immediately adjacent is exhausted by the Swell organ primary valve, if the chest is duplexed (that is, has stops made interchangeable) between Great and Swell.

There are in this case, not only two complete stop actions for a single stop, but two grooves leading from the point where a "shifter" is located. T is the shifter. It is simply a pitman valve with leather discs tacked and glued on each end of a hardwood strip. The strip is sufficiently long to permit the shifter to move easily to the right or left. Now if the right hand pitman box AA be exhausted of air, pitman Z will blow up against Y until the groove is exhausted which connects with this pitman. The pipe valve pouch S will be exhausted at the same time through Q and the right duplex groove, as the shifter T blows to the right. If wind is in the left pitman box or the stop is off, wind will blow up through the left duplex groove and hold the shifter to the right. When both pitman boxes are exhausted to the atmosphere, the stop will play on either keyboard and the shifter T remains midway between.

This same principle is applied when a stop is duplexed an octave higher or lower on the same manual. In this case double grooves are not required in the bottom board. A series of tubes is merely run from the shifter box to the octave above or below. Two stop action pitman boxes are required with this duplexing as with ordinary duplexing, one for the unison pitch and one for the octave borrow. This is a very economical method of borrowing an 8' stop an octave higher or lower, as the mechan-

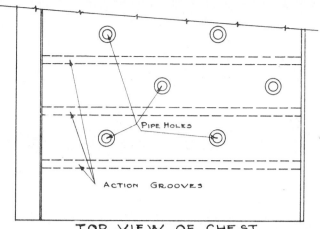

TOP VIEW OF CHEST

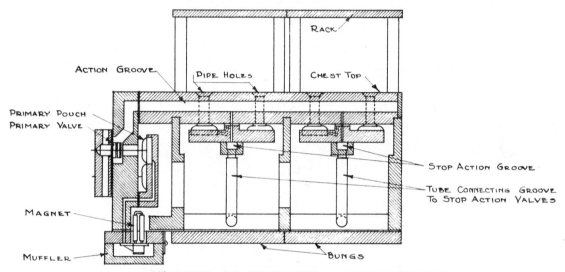

SECTION OF CHEST THRU ACTION GROOVE

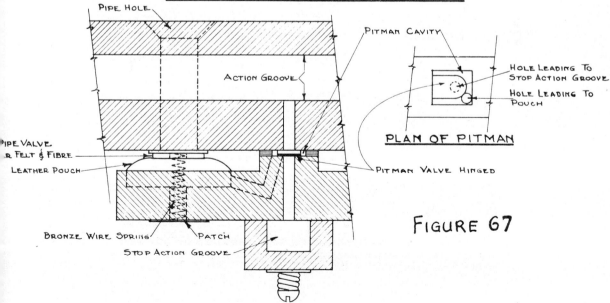

PLAN OF PITMAN

FIGURE 67

FULL SCALE SECTION SHOWING VALVE & PITMAN ASSEMBLY

THE REUTER UNIVERSAL WIND CHEST

THE REUTER ORGAN CO.   LAWRENCE KANSAS

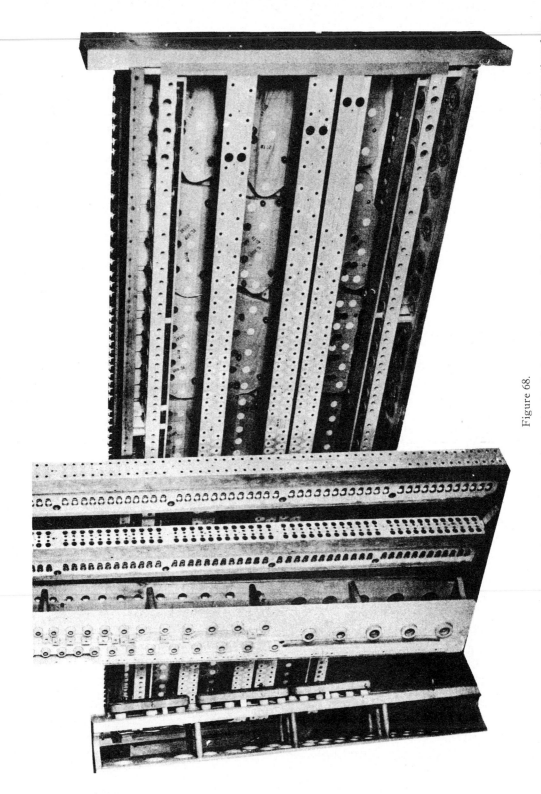

Figure 68.

A photograph of a Moller windchest with all the bottom boards removed. Small pieces of paper are glued under the stop action floaters to keep them from falling down, when the bottom boards are removed. The vertical bar standing at the left is a duplex action bar, before the shifters have been installed, and the holes covered with heavy paper.

174

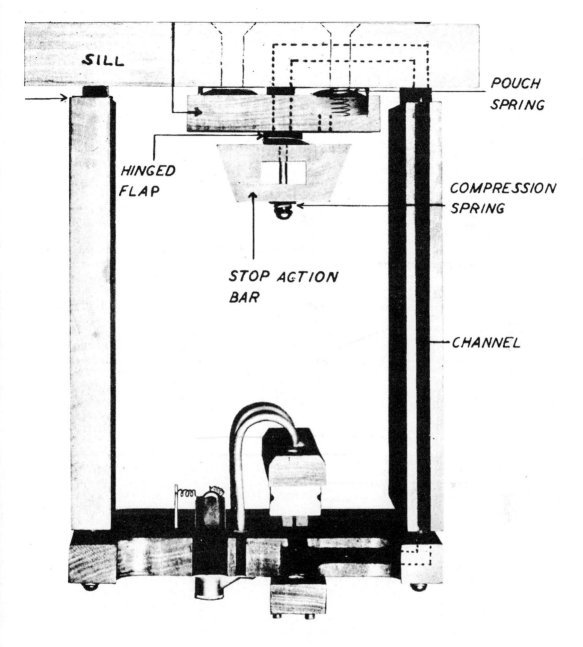

SILL

POUCH
SPRING

HINGED
FLAP

COMPRESSION
SPRING

STOP ACTION
BAR

CHANNEL

Figure 69.
Section of Wind Chest

Schantz Organ Company
Orrville, Ohio

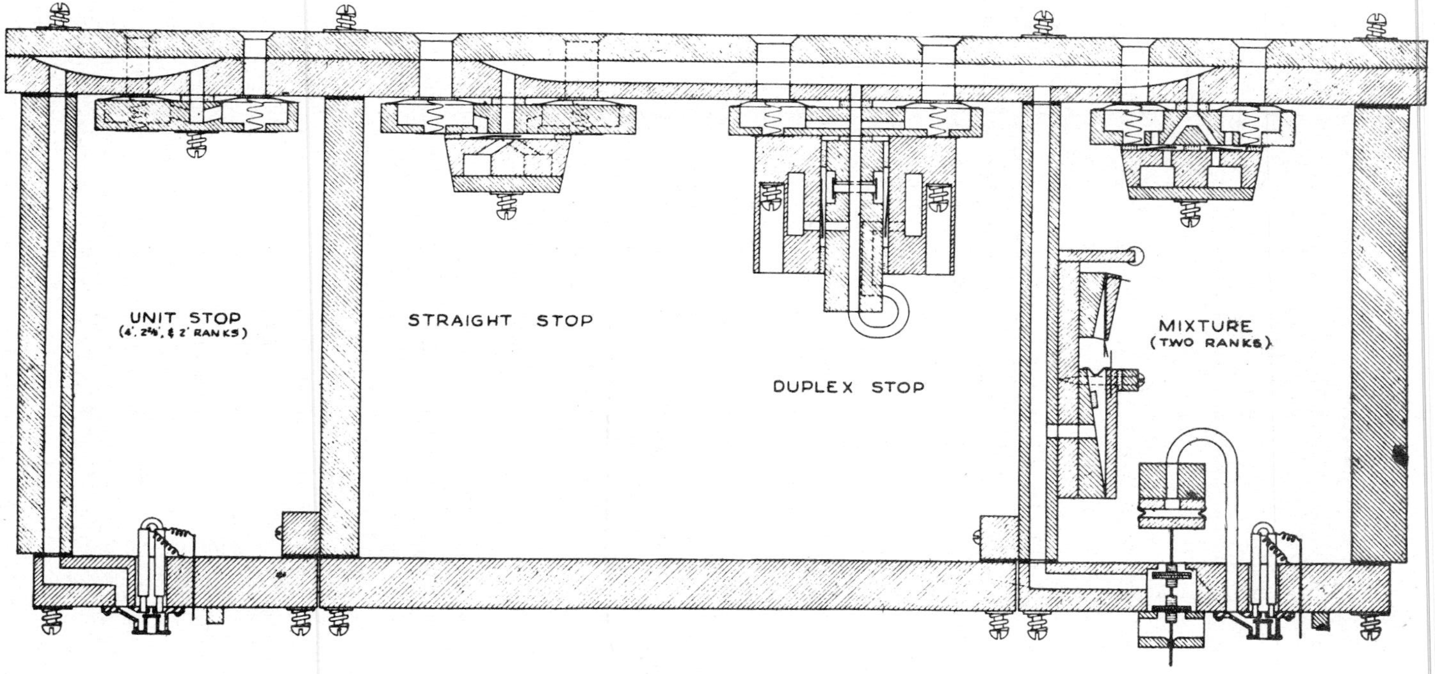

MIXTURE
(TWO RANKS)

DUPLEX STOP

STRAIGHT STOP

UNIT STOP
(4.2" & 2 RANKS)

THE SCHANTZ PIPE ORGAN COMPANY

Figure 70.

176

ism required is but a small fraction of that for a unit action.

THE VENTIL WINDCHEST WITHOUT INDIVIDUAL
PIPE VALVE PNEUMATICS

A windchest action that has some similarity to that made by the Austin Organ Co., though in other respects quite different, is that made by Hillgreen, Lane & Co., of Alliance, Ohio. It has for its basis the early type of ventil windchest made by Walcker in Germany some fifty years ago, though it has been simplified and improved by the American builders who use this action. Its similarity to the Austin system is in having one primary motor that draws the pipe valves open mechanically, by means of a tracker or wire, thereby not requiring individual pneumatics for each pipe valve. I am indebted to the builders for the drawing of their action shown in Figure 71. It will be noted by an inspection of the drawing that the windchest does not contain universal wind, as in the Austin air chest, but has separate air compartments under each series of pipes. This is a characteristic of all forms of the ventil chest.

Wind is admitted, by means of a ventil in the end of each stop compartment, in a similar manner to that described for the ventil windchest with individual pneumatics for each pipe. When the stop action is open, wind is admitted to the compartment under its respective set of pipes, so that the pipes will speak if the pipe valves are opened. With the ventil closed, no wind is admitted, so that the pipes will not speak, when the pipe valves are opened. Such stop action is simple and reliable. It certainly is a great advance on the slider stop action universally used for hundreds of years.

It will be seen by a further study of the drawing that the large primary pneumatic A upon being exhausted through the primary mechanism (in a similar manner to that previously described in detail for the Austin primary), draws with it a hardened steel wire CCC that passes through all the compartments of the windchest. To this wire are fastened the various pipe valve levers, by means of a collar with a set screw, so that the proper adjustments may be made. The pipe valve mechanism consists merely of felt and leather glued on a fibre disc, shown at B, which is fastened to one end of a pivoted lever, while the other end of the lever passes through the wire. A spring is provided to return the valve to its seat.

It is important that the wire CCC as it passes through the separate air compartments fit practically air tight. This is accomplished by passing it through a brass plate with a hole just large enough to allow the wire to move freely, without leaking wind from one compartment to another. The pulldown wires in the old tracker windchest passed through

177

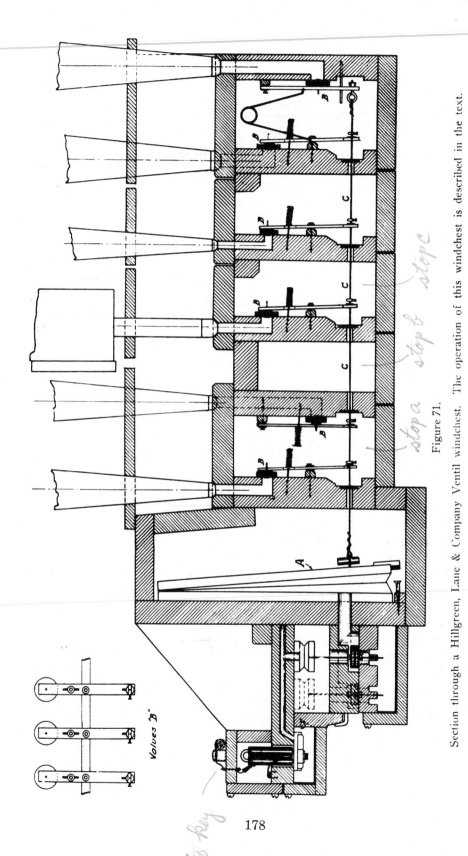

Figure 71.

Section through a Hillgreen, Lane & Company Ventil windchest. The operation of this windchest is described in the text.

178

similar brass plates where these wires emerged from the interior of the chest. A strong spring at the end of the windchest returns all of the mechanism to the "off" position immediately when wind is again admitted into the large pneumatic A.

The bottom part of each section of this windchest may be removed by taking out a few screws, which permits of ready access to the pipe valves for adjustments and replacements when necessary. It will be seen, from a careful perusal of this drawing, that the action requires a very small amount of boring of holes and other channeling as compared to the more usual type of modern windchest. When once carefully adjusted, this action should operate very satisfactorily.

A certain amount of play or lost motion is left at the point where the pipe valve levers connect with the wire CCC that is drawn by the primary pneumatic. Changes in atmospheric conditions, with consequent swelling or shrinking of the wood of the windchest will not cause the pipe valves to be drawn from their seats, with this additional play provided, which might otherwise occur, as the pneumatic might not open sufficiently wide to permit the pipe valves to seat properly. Thus the possibility of ciphering from this cause is overcome. Such a system of construction lends itself best to a small number of stops on each section, so that the hardened steel wire is not too long or does not have to pass through too many brass plates. In the case of large manual divisions, two or more windchests may conveniently be provided, which will serve both to speed up the action and to provide each section with steadier wind.

THE DIRECT ELECTRIC ACTION

An organ action, and windchest mechanism, known as the direct electric action has been invented by Louis J. Wick, of the Wicks Pipe Organ Co., of Highland, Ill. We are able to furnish drawings of this mechanism taken from the patent specification granted to Mr. Wick, November 19, 1929. The first patent was granted in 1922 and the first direct electric organ was built in 1914. No other system has been employed by Wicks since that time. J. S. & C. H. Odell Co., of New York, have also a direct electric action, as well as the Estey Organ Co., of Brattleboro, Vt., and Reuter Organ Co. which they sometimes employ in the case of small organs. Austin Organs, Inc. have a patent on a direct electric action. The Wicks Company is the only builder that has consistently employed such an action over a period of years. During the past 20 years they have developed and improved this action and former objections to it have been removed.

In the Wick's action the windchest mechanism has been brought to perhaps its simplest form. It consists merely of an electro-magnet which directly draws the pipe valve off its seat, thereby admitting air to the

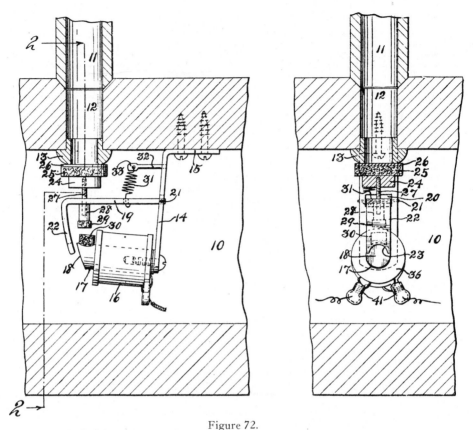

Figure 72.
Side and front views of the Wicks Direct Electric Action.

pipe. No pneumatics of any sort are required and electricity does all the work.

The operation of the action is as follows: We are referring to Figure 72. Upon the coil 16, being energized with current, the core of the magnet 18 becomes magnetic, and attracts the armature 22, which is pivoted at 21. This armature has connected to it the pipe valve disc 25 that is drawn away from the valve seat 13, as a result of this attraction. The spring 31 returns the armature and valve disc as soon as the coil is no longer energized with electricity, to their original position. This spring is used primarily to keep the valve seated. It must be borne in mind that all actions require a spring of some kind or other to accomplish this same purpose. The spring also serves to make the action very responsive by returning the valve without delay. A coil spring of this type will last indefinitely.

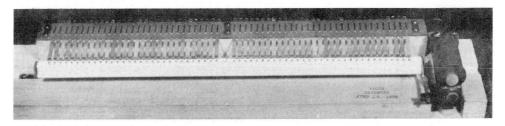

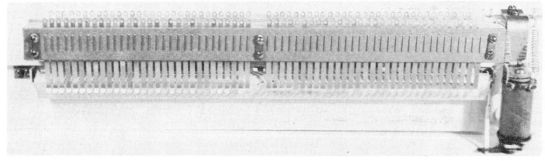

Figures 73 and 74

Top photo, side view of Wicks 61 note gang switch. Photo below, a top view of the same switch.

Figure 75.

Modern direct electric relay as used by Wicks. Note the wiping contact which cleans as it is used.

There are five sizes of magnets of the type just described employed in the Wicks action. Each size is designed to require the minimum current to open the various-sized pipe-valves. Pipe-valves up to $1\frac{1}{4}$" in diameter are opened by these magnets, with a surprisingly low current consumption. The very small valves are opened by magnets requiring much less current than the standard organ magnet. What is called their .oo coil consumes 2/100 amperes and experiments are now in progress whereby even this will be reduced 50%. In the case of stops requiring a small volume of wind, such as strings and reeds, where small openings only are necessary, these small coils are used throughout. The magnets for the larger valves consume more current, but still a surprisingly small amount for the work they do. Larger valves than $1\frac{1}{4}$" in diameter are open by an electro-pneumatic unit. The reason for this must not be misunderstood. These larger valves formerly were controlled direct by a magnet which did not consume an objectionable amount of amperage. The object of the pneumatic, however, is to retard the closing of the valve so that the pipe is given sufficient wind to develop its proper tone. There are a comparatively small number of these units required because not a great many valves exceed $1\frac{1}{4}$" in diameter.

Arcing at the contacts is overcome entirely by winding several turns of high resistance wire around the coil, which serves to absorb all sparks.

These direct electric units may be mounted on an air box in any position anywhere, as no boring of holes other than the pipe holes or any channeling is required. All other intervening mechanism is eliminated in smaller organs. Only a switch is required for the stop action, thus avoiding ventils, pitman valves, and all other stop action mechanism. The action is very quiet. A cable connects the magnets in the air box to a switch, which permits the pipes on each air box to be connected or disconnected with the key mechanism. By a series of switches a stop may be used at any or all pitches on any keyboard.

When there are more than fourteen stop keys on any one manual so that there will be more than fourteen contacts required with each key, a relay is introduced. A relay is also required on all organs with couplers. This is for the purpose of dividing up the current required into a series of contacts, so that no one contact will have an abnormally heavy load. If too much load were placed on any one contact, arcing and other troubles might result. The same is true of the electro-pneumatic organ. A series of contacts is provided for each key on the keyboard, with a contact for each magnet to be operated. This part of the action has been worked out with particular care.

The switches employed for the stop-action and couplers are of special Wicks design, and have two rugged contact-points for each note. The switches are also operated by a direct-electric magnet and no pneu-

182

Figure 76

Figure 77

The ingenious balanced valves employed by Wicks for supplying air to the large pedal pipes. Upper left, the valves are closed. Upper right, the valves are open. Lower photo shows how the valves are attached to the top board of a pedal chest. The feet of the pedal pipes stand in the holes on the top board, as they do on a pneumatic windchest. Note that the organ wind surrounds all sides of each of the balanced valve boxes. One valve disc must be pulled open by the direct electric magnet, against the air pressure, at the same time that the disc on the other end of the valve stem is being pushed open by the air pressure. The two discs are in balance with the wind. The valves are held closed by a light spring. The magnet has only to overcome the resistance of this spring to operate the valves.

matics, tubes, primaries and other mechanisms are required. These switches, so vital to the Wicks action, are notable for their simplicity, efficiency, and durability. An illustration appears on page 181, figure 73.. There are many switches required with this system, as each stop must have at least one switch, and if the stop is unified there must be a switch for each pitch at which the stop is used, (this last is the same in all organ actions). The Wicks system lends itself to unification or borrowing with the utmost ease, and slight additional expense. This will not appear an unmixed blessing to the "purists," but it certainly is in the case of small organs, and Wicks have built many of these.

Obviously, the direct electric action is at an advantage with low wind pressures. It will work perfectly successfully on wind as low as 2" pressure, because it is not dependent upon air pressure for its operation. This is something that the other types of modern organ action will not do. 4" is about the lowest pressure on which the majority of pitman windchest actions will operate satisfactorily. The Wicks factory has made use of an experimental air box, which may be entered with the wind on, whereby the operation of each of the valves, under wind-pressures up to 15" water-gauge, and varying voltages to 15 volts, may be observed. In this way it has been determined to a nicety by actual observation under normal working conditions just what size magnet is required to open a pipe-valve of a certain size at a given pressure and voltage.

Of course, the direct electric action requires a larger generator, because of the large number of magnets required, (not only for the pipe-valves, but all of the stop action switches, combination action motors, etc., are electrically operated) than the electro-pneumatic organ. The total power consumption is probably no greater however; a smaller blower will suffice, as no wind is required to operate the action. So long as the mains are heavy enough to carry the current from the generator to the relays, at which point this heavy current is divided up into many circuits, with no undue load on any one circuit, the system is electrically and mechanically sound, and there is no more danger of fire ensuing, or burned contacts, than in other organs. Thus there are no limitations to the size of the organ that may be built on the direct electric principle. A larger organ simply requires a larger generator and a heavier generator line than a smaller one. The actual electric load on any given contract or subsidiary conductor is no greater in the largest size organ than in the smallest.

The voltage or power factor in a Wicks is no different from that in any other organ. All coils operate on as low as 8 volts, however the operating voltage is 14. Some builders use as high as 15, which is the maximum permitted by the National Electrical Code. More amperage, or volume is used as the organ increases in size, just as one uses more volume when burning every light in a building. The voltage, however, remains the same irrespective of the number of lights in use.

Residual magnetism, the enemy of a floating disc type of armature is a benefit to the direct electric action, for the armature never touches the core and sufficient magnetism can not be formed in the coil to offset the force of the air pressure and spring. The armature is hinged and therefore always remains in position.

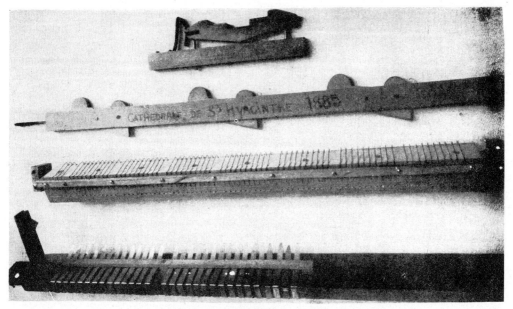

Figure 78.

The lowest portion of this photograph shows the original coupler switch used by Casavant in their first electric console at the Cathedral, Ottawa, Canada. The coupler switch above is the one used for the first time by Casavant in 1895 in St. Patrick's Church, Montreal, Canada. This is essentially the form of coupler switch used by nearly all American builders.

The upper portion of the photograph shows some combination rockers that were used for the first time in 1881 and in the Cathedrale de St. Hyacinthe in 1885. This was apparently the first adjustable combination mechanism installed in an organ. It was invented by Dr. Sallust Duval who was at the time associated with Casavant. Mr. Frank Roosevelt secured the patent rights from Dr. Duval in 1889 and modified the form to that shown at the top of the photograph, known as "the rocker and two pins" type. Casavant's original form is very similar to that which is now being used by several leading builders.

CHAPTER 12.

A HISTORY *of the* ORGAN CONSOLE

Previous to fifty years ago, it was not customary to have the console a separate or detached portion of the organ. In modern organs, however, it is almost invariably detached, and at a greater or lesser distance from the organ itself, in accordance with the circumstances. It should be placed where the organist can best hear his choir and organ. Small tubular-pneumatic and some electro-pneumatic organs were built with the console as a part of the organ proper. Occasionally tracker organs (or tracker organs with Barker lever) had a separate console, but this complicated the mechanism to such an extent that such a disposition of the console was rare, unless a very large or important instrument was built, or in other special cases.

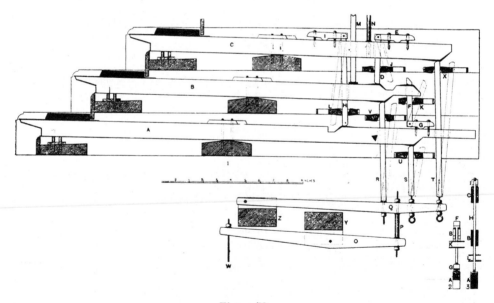

Figure 79.

View of the pedal couplers used in the tracker action. When a pedal key is depressed, it draws down the tracker, W, which moves the lever, O, in turn raising the lever, Q, which raises the Stickers, R, S, T, which raise the back ends of the manual keys. When the stickers are moved into the position shown in the dotted lines, they may be raised without affecting the manual keys. (Audsley, "The Art of Organ Building")

186

A HISTORY OF THE ORGAN CONSOLE

THE TRACKER ORGAN CONSOLE

In the typical tracker organ, the console consisted simply of the keyboards (both manuals and pedals), the draw stop knobs (with perhaps some combination pedals for moving a group of the draw stops at one time), and the couplers, for coupling the various keyboards together. There was also a Swell Pedal, inconveniently placed at the extreme right. All controls were ordinarily placed in a central position at the front of the organ case. The various motions of the keys and draw stops were transmitted directly to the pipe valves or sliders, as has been previously pointed out in our chapter on Organ Actions.

The only matter that should further be noted in regard to the tracker organ console (or, in reality, simply keyboards), is the means of coupling the various manuals together and the pedal keys to the manuals. This was accomplished as shown in Figure 79. It will be noted from the drawing that the pedal keys were coupled to the manuals by means of trackers and a system of levers;—the back ends of the levers corresponding with the manual key scale, and the front ends corresponding with the pedal key scale which is, of course, much greater. These levers were, therefore, arranged in the form of a fan, the back ends of which had a series of oblong strips of wood approximately one-half inch by three-sixteenths in thickness that passed through a perforated strip of wood. The back ends of the manual keys were bevelled so that by drawing this perforated strip forward the complete set of "stickers," as these oblong strips of wood were called, would come immediately under the tails of the keys. When a pedal key was depressed, with the stickers in this position the back end of the corresponding manual key would be raised at the same time. When the coupler was in the "off" position, the perforated strip was moved away from the back ends of the keys so that the pedal keys on being depressed raise the sticker without affecting the manual keys. In order to put this arrangement on the tail ends of the upper keyboard, they had necessarily to project further back than the lower keyboard. This involved drilling a hole through the top keyboard for the stickers of the lower keyboard to pass through, in order to transmit the motion of the lower keyboard to the windchest mechanism.

The coupler system between the keyboards was simply a series of jacks attached to a strip of wood, each jack moving independently with the motion of the key, with sufficient clearance between the two keyboards so that the lower keys could be depressed without affecting the upper keys when the series of jacks was in the "off" position. A small inclined block of wood was attached near the back end of each key of the lower manual covered with leather. The jacks could be brought up this incline by putting the manual coupler into the "on" position. Figure 80 illustrates this.

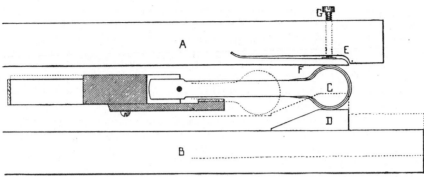

Figure 80.

The Swell to Great Coupler used in the tracker action. The coupler is shown in its On position. When moved in to the position shown by the dotted lines, it no longer acts on the Swell keys. (G. A. Audsley, "The Art of Organ Building.")

The distance between the back ends of the two keyboards with the jacks in this position was close enough to have the effect of joining the motion of the two keyboards. Upon depressing a key of the lower keyboard, it would immediately impart its motion to the upper key. In all these forms of tracker couplers, the keys themselves actually moved. When the pedal keys were coupled to a manual, the manual keys actually moved down when the pedal keys were depressed. This was a guide to beginners in learning to play the organ as to what pedal notes were being played. The modern organ action provides no such assistance.

The stop knobs, as has been indicated, operated the sliders on the top of the windchest, through a series of squares and levers. By arranging blocks of wood on a series of the stop rods, back of the point where the knob passed through the stop jamb, and providing a roller or fan with arms attached to it that would engage these blocks, with a suitable motion from an iron pedal to move this roller, a series of stops could be brought on with one motion of the pedal. The exact stops to be brought "on" by a combination pedal had blocks secured to the stop rods that were to be moved. Combination pedals were frequently made double acting, with two sets of rollers so that by one motion, stops that were wanted were pulled out, and the ones not wanted would be pushed in. In nearly all cases the combination of stops so drawn or pushed in had to be fixed permanently. It was a very difficult matter to make any changes.

It was usual for organs to have two or three combination pedals for each manual. These were permanently adjusted to draw progressively a soft combination, a mezzo combination, and all the stops on that division. Combination pedals worked well when the stop knobs themselves worked with moderate ease. When a series of sliders became damp, thereby causing them to work with considerable friction, a great amount of exertion was necessary to pull out or push in a group of such stops and an enormous amount of clatter and noise was generally entailed when such motion was accomplished. It should be obvious that these pedals were a great convenience to the organist, especially where the organ was of considerable size. The utter impossibility of changing a large group of stops entirely by hand rapidly, is quite evident to any one who has tried it.

This comprises about all the mechanism that was in the console of the old tracker organ and it was quite enough, when all the parts had to be made by hand. The author made entirely with his own hands such a console mechanism when he was a boy starting high school. The result of this labor has given him a very wholesome respect for the tracker organ. It has also given him a very intimate knowledge of such mechanism that could not possibly have been obtained in any other way.

While I would not for a minute wish to return to the tracker organ for steady use, I always have a feeling of being perfectly at home on such an instrument that I played for so many years, and a feeling of intimate contact with the pipes themselves that one never experiences in playing an electric organ. Undoubtedly for the lay reader not versed in organ mechanism, the tracker action is much the simplest to understand, as all the motions are purely mechanical and can actually be observed. Whereas, in the pneumatic and electro-pneumatic organs, a good part of the motion is accomplished by invisible means such as electricity and wind pressure.

The next stage in the development of the console occurred with the introduction of the Barker lever to the action. The manual couplers were attached to the lever mechanism, in this case. The weight of the touch was not increased when the couplers were drawn. Figure 44 shows this clearly. When the Barker lever was first introduced, the stop action remained tracker or directly mechanical.

THE TUBULAR-PNEUMATIC CONSOLE

With the introduction of tubular-pneumatic organs, the stop action became a modified form of the Barker lever, designed for the requirements of moving the sliders. This was accomplished by means of a pair of good sized pneumatics one of which, upon being inflated, would draw the slider out. The other would push the slider in. These pneumatics had necessarily to be made powerful, to overcome the resistance that would sometimes exist to moving the slider. The operation of the sliders from the keyboard was now made extremely easy. When a stop knob was drawn it merely opened the valve admitting air into the large stop action pneumatic. Figure 46 shows this. The hard work was done by the pneumatics.

At this stage of development a great improvement in combination action was possible, because the combination mechanism did not need

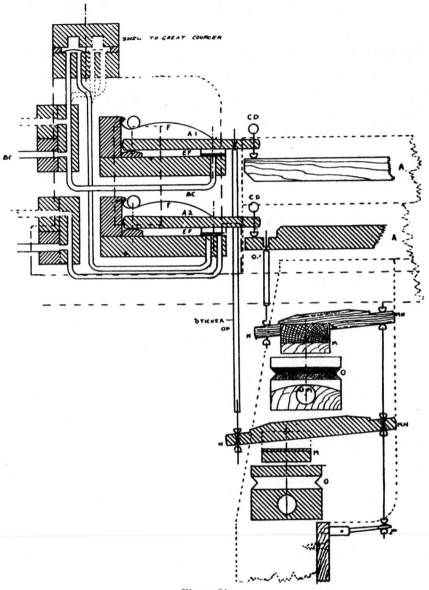

Figure 81.

Tubular pneumatic couplers. (From W. & T. Lewis, "Modern Organ Building.")

necessarily to be operated by pedals. Formerly with the great resistance of a series of stops or sliders to be overcome, it could only be done by means of foot levers. When the stop action was made pneumatic the action became so light that a thumb piston or small button introduced between the manual keys could be made to accomplish the result equally well, and much more conveniently.

Combination pedals are generally believed to have been invented by J. C. Bishop in 1809. Henry Willis introduced into his organs thumb pistons about the year 1851, so that both these systems of controlling stops are in reality quite old. The coupler system of a tubular-pneumatic organ is shown in our illustration, Figure 81. Another device came into use with the introduction of pneumatic stop action, the register Crescendo Pedal. This pedal makes it possible to gradually cause all of the stops to sound, or by reversing the motion of the pedal to gradually silence them. This is done without moving the stop controls on the console, nor upsetting any combination of stops that may be drawn. It is a convenience for certain effects, and has a limited legitimate usefulness. It is also the first and last refuge of the incompetent player. To "pump" a register Crescendo Pedal instead of drawing stops by pistons or by hand, is so inartistic and so inexcusable, that the late eminent organist, Mr. Edwin H. Lemare had this pedal permanently disconnected from any organ he played regularly. I have always contended, however, that the best the builder can do is to build a console with all conveniences. If some of them, such as Master Swell Pedals and Crescendo Pedals, Octave Couplers on the Great Organ, Tremulants and other devices are liable to abuse by the incompetent, it is unfortunate. If there are legitimate musical uses for these things, they should be furnished. An organ can scarcely be made fool-proof anyway. Nearly everything that an organ contains can be wrongly employed, and overdone.

Register Crescendos have been built with selective controls permitting of a Crescendo on Flutes, Strings, Diapasons or Reeds, or any combination of these qualities. This is a refinement that may be worth while in a large organ. I question its value.

Another pedal that is frequently duplicated by a piston (in each case both should be reversible), is the so-called "sforzando" or full organ pedal. One motion of the pedal or piston causes all stops and couplers in the organ that will produce a good full organ tone to immediately be brought on, without moving the registers. A second motion of the pedal or piston will re-establish the condition of pipes sounding to the registers as before. Sometimes two or more of these pedals are supplied, one drawing a mezzo organ and the other Tutti. Lights or other warning signals are usually provided to show when either the register crescendo or full organ pedals are in use, so that the organist will not think he is going to play softly with the stops he has drawn, and find that he is crashing down on the full organ unexpectedly.

The construction of these mechanicals is given in our chapter on Types of Organ Consoles.

THE ELECTRO-PNEUMATIC CONSOLE

Coming now to the consideration of the modern electro-pneumatic console, we discover that there are two general types in use. One contains all the coupler mechanism and combination action within the console itself. The other may contain the coupler mechanism but have the combination mechanism remote from the console, in which case the console can be made much smaller in size. Modern improvements have made it possible to provide a large number of combination pistons and to have their mechanism placed within the console without making the latter too cumbersome. All modern combination actions visibly affect the stop knobs, or stop keys themselves.

The controversy that raged a number of years past in both "The Diapason" and the "American Organist" as to whether this should be so or not has now apparently entirely died out and no one at present advocates any arrangement of combination pistons that does not visibly affect the stop controls in the console. During the development of the modern electro-pneumatic console, however, it was discovered that by means of a recorder board which enabled the organist to set whatever combinations he desired, the stops inside the organ could be moved, without visibly affecting the mechanism at the console, thereby greatly simplifying the console itself, so far as the combination action was concerned. There are perhaps yet one or two builders who advocate this system for the general pistons. It seems a step in the wrong direction.*

A console that was used by the Hutchings-Votey Organ Company was probably the smallest and lightest organ console ever built, the sides of which could be folded up. The combination pistons did not affect the stop knobs visibly, but changed the stops themselves, within the organ. As this mechanism is now practically obsolete, except for the few organs around the country that were made with this system, it seems scarcely worth while to describe it in detail. It was simply one of the phases of development through which the electric console passed. It was an extremely ingenious console, and the only one that was truly portable, and easily movable. Some of our larger movable consoles could be better moved with a five ton truck.

---

*When the controversy was at its height as to whether combination actions should actually move the stop knobs themselves or work "blind," Mr. Skinner, who entertained strong opinions in this matter, is credited with the remark "that he knew some 'ivory knobs' in the organ business that couldn't be moved with any kind of a combination action."

In connection with adjustable combination action development, the name of Hilborne L. Roosevelt, the eminent organ builder of New York, should be mentioned as the first to introduce the adjustable combination action, along with Casavant. To him, also, is attributed the invention of the windchest with individual valves for each pipe, or the chest known as the "Roosevelt windchest," which type is still in use to this day. We have remarked elsewhere that he was a pioneer in electro-pneumatic organs in this country.

I believe it is unwise in a work of this kind to enter the controversy that exists at the present time, for stop keys as against stop knobs in a console. Apparently the first stop control suggestive of stop keys was in use in Avignon Cathedral as early as 1804. Mr. William Horatio Clark of Reading, Mass., applied for a patent covering a certain type of stop key in 1877.

The present form of stop key in general use in consoles is generally credited, however, to Hope-Jones. Austin Organs, Inc. and others have greatly improved this form.

The Aeolian-Skinner Organ Company has persistently maintained the superiority of the stop knob console and has consistently built this type. Whereas, the Austin Organs, Inc. have advocated the stop key console and has usually built this latter type. Many other builders adopting the Austin idea will build both kinds of console. Having played both kinds for many years past, I am less than ever inclined to dogmatize upon their relative merits. I can be happy and satisfied and comfortable with either type. The principal thing about a console, as the late Mr. Lynnwood Farnam once remarked, is, "does it work?"

In general, I believe the stop knob console presents a more handsome appearance and is the more traditional form. Because of the disposition of the stops at both sides as well as over the top of the keys, the combination action is rendered more complicated than when stop keys are used. This causes the stop knob type to be rather more expensive to build than the other. These matters are largely ones of preference and individual taste and as either type of console has now been brought to a very high degree of efficiency by nearly all of our American builders, with every convenience provided for the assistance of the organist, there is in reality little to choose between them.

STANDARDIZATION OF MEASUREMENTS

A matter that is of considerable importance to organists, however, is the proper dimensions and distances between the manuals and pedals. This has never been standardized as it should be in America. I have come to the conclusion that there will never, for many years to come, be any standard system of stop control, nor any standard system of what the individual manual combination pistons will affect. It should be observed that combinations are of two classes—1. universal, or general pistons affecting all stops and couplers and other mechanicals of the entire organ, 2. individual manual pistons and pedal toe pistons which affect only the stops of their division. In 1928, a discussion of standards in the "American Organist," relative to combination actions, was engendered. Whether pedal stops should be affected by manual pistons or whether the couplers should be affected, and, if so, how and why, were the principal questions at issue. It is astounding, the different opinions that were expressed by many eminent people about this matter. I have my own preferences for one style, while other organists prefer something quite different. I do not believe that any substantial purpose would be served by getting into this controversy. The Kimball Company solved this problem by providing on and off switches, the same as several other builders, for causing the pedal stops to be affected or not, by the manual pistons. In addition, on their larger organs this company provided another set of on or off switches or cut-outs, whose purpose was to make it optional with the player as to whether manual or pedal couplers shall be affected by manual and pedal pistons. One switch cuts out all couplers, while the other cuts out only the inter-manual couplers. The General or Universal pistons affected all the couplers and stops of the entire organ, as is usually the case.

Certain measurements, however, should be recognized as standard, such as distances between manual keys, and the distance of the pedal keyboard from the manuals. Keyboards should be two and one-half inches above or below each other. A distance of four inches from the front edge of one manual to a perpendicular line touching the front edge of the one above or below is tending to become standard. In a three or four manual organ, it is desirable that the height from the top edge of the center pedal key to the top edge of the Great Organ keys, shall be two feet eight inches (which brings the Choir manual 29½ inches from this point). Also, the distance from the front edge of the center black note of the pedals should be 8½"-10" back of the front edge of the bottom keyboard. It is important that the pedal keys should be placed sufficiently forward under the manuals, otherwise the organist has a tendency to pitch forward when playing on the upper keyboard on a four manual organ, and his pedals must be played in an unnatural position. The modern pedal keyboard of 32 notes is properly placed in a central position with regard to the manuals, instead of C under C as was common with shorter compass pedal boards. It has been well stated that "the convenience of the organist should be made the first consideration of the organ builder regardless of fads, hobbies or economics."

It has always seemed to me that at least the keyboards themselves might be standardized. This has been very largely done in the matter of manual keys, for now the distances between key-centers are practically uniform. It is not the case with the pedal keys.

As far back as 1855 Henry Willis introduced in the organ in St. George's Hall, Liverpool, the radiating and concave pedal board slightly modified, that has now become standard in the United States. Seventy-five years ought to be a long enough period of time for the slowest of the organ builders to have gathered the necessary data on these dimensions and enabled them to reproduce the standard Willis pedal board. It does not appear to be so. Only recently I played a recital upon a new organ of a lesser known builder with what purported to be a standard concave and radiating pedal keyboard, whose measurements were so out of scale as to make it an extremely difficult matter to avoid playing many wrong notes (at least more than my usual percentage). It would require several days' practicing to become familiar and perfectly sure on this pedal keyboard, by which time the rather definite feeling of security which an organist may feel in playing on a standard pedal board would take several days more to reacquire. Such matters as this appear to me inexcusable and preposterous. Fortunately, all of our leading builders have at least agreed on a scale for the pedal board that is nearly enough standard as to cause no confusion in going from one of their organs to another.

As an example of the slowness with which improvements in organ construction are adopted, the matter of the radiating concave keyboard perhaps furnishes one of the best. It was fifty years after Henry Willis first introduced this pedal keyboard to organists and organ builders, in a very important organ where it would undoubtedly cause widespread attention, before this type of board was adopted to any extent in either England or America. Only as recently as forty years ago, it was discovered, by means of a questionnaire sent to one hundred of the leading organists in this country inquiring which type of pedal board they preferred, that the vast majority still preferred the old-fashioned, inconvenient and thoroughly unscientific flat pedal board. Why? Because they were used to it and did not wish to trouble themselves to learn anything new. As far as the organ builder was concerned, he could not be blamed for continuing to furnish the flat pedal board which was obviously cheaper to construct, particularly as that was what the organist thought he wanted.

Happily, this matter is now finally closed and not even the most obscure organ builder in this country would consider building an organ without a radiating, concave pedal board of some sort, though some of them have apparently not taken the trouble to learn the correct measurements. These are given in our drawing on page 219. 201

The compass of the manuals has been fixed at 61 notes from CC-C4. In older organs, the range was seldom higher than A3 or 58 notes. Some large English organs extended downwards to GGG. These have now been rebuilt to the modern compass. A Canadian firm is advocating a compass of six octaves, from GGG to G4. There is certainly something to be said in favor of extending the pedal compass downward to perhaps AAAA, or GGGG as on the piano keyboard. It is very valuable to have the BBBB, AAAA♯ and AAAA available on the pedal, especially where there is no 32' pedal stop. Mr. Lynnwood Farnam long recognized the unsatisfactory effect of the pedal, especially in compositions written in the key of G, A, B flat or B, where no bass sufficiently deep was available. He overcame this defect, without changing the compass of the pedal board, by installing the GGGG, AAAA, AAAA♯ and BBBB pipes of the Trombone on the organ he played at the Church of the Holy Communion in New York. These pipes are playable by special stop control, consisting of both stop knobs and reversible pedal (the latter Mr. Farnam considered of great importance for all 32' stops), and provide tone in the 32' octave, in the region where it is most valuable and effective. The cost of four of the smallest pipes is a small fraction of the cost of the entire 32' octave. Whether they are installed (as in this case) as partial 32' stops, or whether the pedal keyboard is actually extended to this compass is perhaps not so important as to have such pipes available. They are surely most useful, and make the rendition of music in the keys referred to even more effective than other keys, from the standpoint of a deep pedal. Here is something for organ builders and organists to consider.

Some organists are confused by reading specifications of organs that call for 73 pipes for each stop on the various manuals, while there are only 61 keys. When the manual keys are coupled an octave higher, if the stops have only 61 pipes, the octave coupler has no more pipes to act on for the top octave of the keyboard, and has therefore no effect. An additional octave of 12 pipes is usually provided so that the octave coupler may be effective throughout the entire upward compass of the manual keyboards. It is customary with some builders to provide no octave couplers on the great organ and therefore only 61 pipes are necessary for each stop on this division. To be perfectly logical an additional octave of pipes should be available at the lower end of the keyboard when the sub-octave coupler is used, otherwise this coupler has no pipes on which to act below tenor C. However, the top octaves of all the stops on a division will probably not cost as much as one bottom octave. To have any stop acted on in its entirety by both the sub and super octave couplers requires 85 pipes. Such construction is rare. The lower pipes are nearly always available on the pedal and to extend 8' manual stops would only serve to make the organ sound muddy if chords were played in these lower regions.

For the sake of completeness mention should also be made of a few of the many gadgets, touches, and attachments that have at one time or another been placed on organ consoles.

A HISTORY OF THE ORGAN CONSOLE

Mr. T. Scott Buhrman, the editor of the "American Organist," has for some years past kept for his own amusement a record of such alleged conveniences and attachments. A careful analysis of this list reveals the fact that most of the devices there enumerated are either not new, or are impractical, or both. To multiply "Trick" devices is a favorite practice of builders whose standard mechanism is deficient. The majority of organists, and among them the experienced recitalists, despise a console loaded with special devices.

When the console is provided with an adequate number of manual pedals and general pistons, the organ can be best controlled without the use of other devices, which only serve to complicate matters.

One or two special devices, however, should possibly be mentioned. First:—Double Touch or Second Touch: Pressing the manual or pedal key much harder than usual forces it beyond the first point of resistance and carries it on down to a second and lower point, called Second Touch. This lower and second point has its own set of contacts which operate precisely in the manner of an entirely new manual division. A special group of stops is selected for playing from this Second Touch, usually the heavier voices in the organ, and some of the couplers.

Second:—Melody Octave Coupler: A device, controlled by a stop-knob or stop-tongue, which when in operation automatically duplicates the top or treble note at the moment being played, and adds it an octave higher to the actual notes played by the hands. It is instantaneous in operation and arpeggios will result from it, if the chords should be carelessly struck in arpeggio fashion.

Third:—Melody Touch: A device used by the late C. Seibert Losh in a manner similar to Second Touch divisions of an organ, whereby a selected list of the normal stops of the organ is duplicated in a special set of stop-tongues which, when drawn, add themselves to the treble or melody notes only. In Second Touch, these supplementary stops come on only when any of the keys are pressed down harder to a lower point, whereas in Melody Touch no extra pressure is needed; the Second Touch and Melody Touch devices are similar in that both require the presence of certain selected additional stop-tongues to control the registers selected for Second Touch or Melody Touch use. On the other hand the Melody Octave Coupler does not require a supplementary group of stop-tongues, for it simply duplicates at the octave the melody notes of such registers as are at the moment being played.

Double or second touch was very popular with many theater organists. It enabled them to bring out a melody, not necessarily the top note played, against a suitable accompaniment on one manual, with one hand, allowing the other hand to be used for a counter-melody, or percussions. To utilize these facilities requires a somewhat easily acquired technique in playing. This has seemed to work against any form of double touch being generally accepted, though the idea was employed in theater organs for many years. Church organists want none of it.

In general, it is fair to say that a console is most satisfactory when it enables an organist to do the things he wants to do with the greatest speed and convenience. It will be able to provide these facilities when it has a liberal supply of adjustable combination Pistons (in some cases duplicated by Pedals that visibly move the Registers; conveniently placed Expression Pedals; Crescendo Pedal (properly adjusted); Full Organ Pedal; and some Pedal Coupler Reversibles, conveniently near their respective Manual Pistons. This is really all that is necessary or desirable. Here, of course, the question "Does it work?" is most weighty.

Some builders and organists prefer double touch manual pistons: first touch will affect only the manual stops, and the second touch, by pushing the piston harder, will move the pedal stops and couplers. This overcomes the difficulty of having pedal stops and couplers affected by manual pistons at all times, something which is very annoying to some organists, and yet leaves the pedal stops and couplers instantly available, when wanted, on the manual pistons.

Many other devices placed on a console serve only to distract attention from the fact that the standard and legitimate controls enumerated above are adequate. They cannot perform the work as well and serve only to confuse the visiting organist.

At the annual convention of the American Guild of Organists held in Boston in 1932, a committee was appointed for the purpose of making recommendations concerning console measurements and other matters. The author of this book was the chairman of the committee. For purposes of completeness the essential features of the report are reproduced below, and it is hoped that the measurements recommended will agree with what has preceded in this chapter.

All this is now standard practise.

A.G.O. REPORT

We herewith present the report of the console committee of the Guild. The committee's recommendations were officially adopted at the 1933 annual meeting. Arguments etc. have been eliminated and the findings of the committee rearranged so that the busy reader may grasp the measurements and recommendations in the most logical manner possible and at the minimum cost in time and effort. The manner of presenting these measurements is as they were given in The American Organist.

PEDAL CLAVIER

Compass: 32-note, CCC to G.
Radiation: 8' 6" radius. Maximum permissible, 9' 6"; minimum, 8' 6".

Concavity: 8' 6" radius. Maximum 8' 6"; minimum, 7' 6".

Length between heelboard and toeboard: 27".

Length of playing surface of sharps: 6½".

Height of sharps above naturals: 1" at player's end, slightly higher at the other.

Width of playing-surface of natural keys: 7/8".

Radius of curve of sharps: Fronts, 8' 6"; back, 9'.

Distance, center to center, of adjacent natural keys at front ends of sharps: 2½". This makes the octave 17½".

PEDAL TO MANUAL

Left to right location: Centralized under the manuals.

Front to back: Pedal DD-sharp's front end 8½'' to 10'' back of plumb-line dropped from front edge of white keys of lowest manual of 2m or 3m console; 11'' on a 4m.

Vertical: 29½'' between playing surfaces of natural keys of lowest manual and middle natural key of pedal.

PEDAL ACCESSORIES

Knee-panel and toe-board carrying the pedal accessories to follow the 9' radius curve of the distant end of the sharp keys.

Crescendo shoes: Heel end of playing surface of shoe to overhang sharp keys by 1¼'' maximum forward position, or be placed ¾'' maximum distance back of them, with shoes in closed position.

Swell shoe to be located directly in front of the E-F gap.

Choir shoe to left of Swell.

Solo shoe to right of Swell.

Register-Crescendo shoe invariably to the right of all others, and slightly raised.

Great shoe to displace Solo in three-manual organs. To the left of Choir in four-manual organs.

Bench: 20½'' above middle E of pedal clavier, adjustable in each direction.

MANUALS

Compass: CC to c^4, 61-note. But 16', 8', and 4' registers of divisions having 4' couplers on themselves shall extend an additional octave upward, with the exception of the Great Organ in large instruments.

Overhang: 4''.

Surface-to-surface: 2-3/8'' if possible; 2½'' maximum.

Inclination: On 4m consoles, bottom and two top manuals inclined gently toward center; other manual level.

Depth of touch: 5/16'' to 3/8'' scant.

Weight of touch: 4 ounces, with "tracker-feeling" recommended.

DEVICES RECOMMENDED

Swell Shoe Arranger: A device enabling the organist to couple any set of shutters at will to any shoe. Recommended when there are more than three chambers.

Crescendo Indicators.

Device coupling all shutters to master shoe. (Committee suggests placing it to right or left of the couplers so that it can be controlled by the combons.

Crescendo Percussion and Tremulant Cut-Out: To operate when shoe is 1/3 or ½ open, without moving stops.

Pedal Combons to Manual Combons: On-or-offs by which the organist may have the manual combons operate also the Pedal combons of like number.

Coupler control system on large organs so that one-section and two-section couplers can be operated independently at will from the manual combons.

At least four full-organ combons to be operated by duplicate toe-studs.

Pedal Organ combons shall be duplicated and exist as toe-studs and manual pistons.

Two ensemble pistons on large organs, ff and fff.

Capture System of combon setting.

ORDER OF STOPS

The order within each division is that already established: 16' flues, 8' flues, 4' flues, 2' flues, mixtures, 16' reeds, 8' reeds, 4' reeds. Stops not mentioned in the above take their normal position according to pitch in the respective flue and reed divisions. Loudest to softest is the order within pitch-groups.

Stop-tongue consoles, two rows over top manual: Top row, left to right: Swell, Choir, Solo or Echo, with couplers of each division following the stops. Lower row: Pedal, Great.

Stop-tongue consoles, stops in side jambs: Left: Pedal and Swell; right: Great, Choir, and Solo. One-section couplers may be located with the stops; two-section couplers in a row over top manual.

Recommended in 4m consoles that only one row of stops be located over the top manual, the others being placed in the side jambs, so that the music-rack may be kept low.

Stop-knob consoles: Left jamb: Pedal and Swell; right: Great, Choir, Solo. Order within the division as given, from bottom to top. Tremulants at top. One-section couplers above each division of stops.

Logical Sequence: Great, Swell, Choir, Solo, Echo. (This logical sequence is very wisely recommended in all cases where possible, "as the families are then in the same relative position, be the organ a 1m or a 4m." And this fundamental principle for couplers is one of the most valuable endorsements of the committee.

COMBINATIONS

Capture System preferred.

Absolute Combons only; if Duals are supplied they shall be in addition to the Absolute.

Tutti Combons: Shall operate full organ with no omissions. Pistons located under left Swell and Great manuals, or under left Swell, Great, and Choir.

Manual Combons: Shall control Pedal stops through Pedal combons operable from manual combons by onoroffs or by double-touch (with insistence that if a builder does not know how to make second-touch pistons the onoroff method is to be used).

The following chapter will consider in detail the action of the console of the modern electric organ as manufactured by the various builders of America.

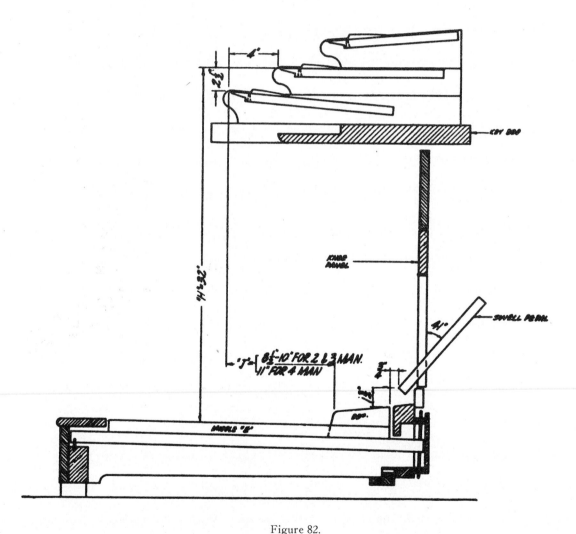

Figure 82.
A. G. O. Measurements for Console.

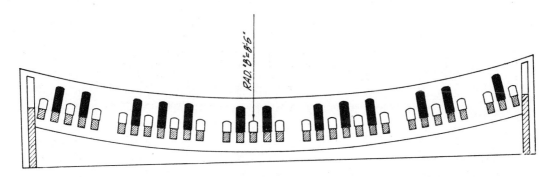

SECTION AT "X-X"

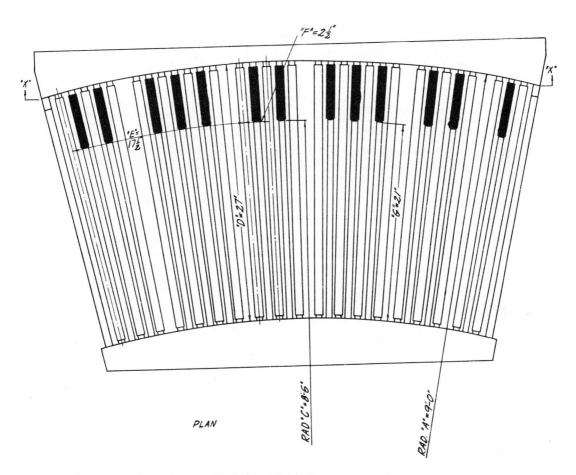

PLAN

Figure 83.

Measurements of Standard A. G. O. Pedal Board.

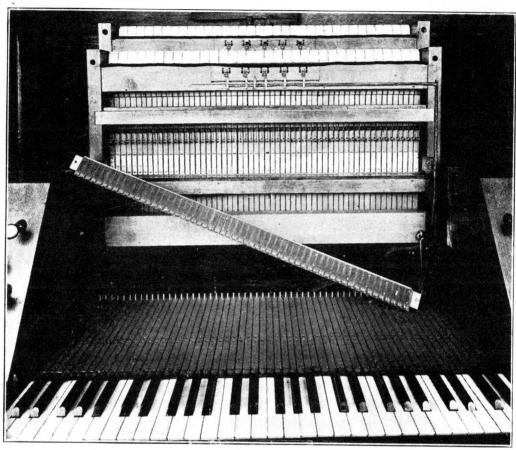

Figure 84.

Keys of the console in St. Patrick's Church, Montreal, Canada. One of the contact bars has been removed, which clearly shows the platinum-tipped contacts. Very few changes have been made in contact bars by builders who use these types to-day. This was built by Casavant in 1895.

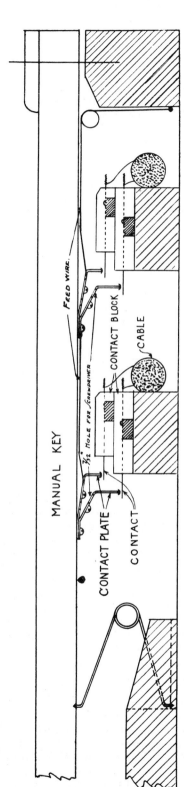

MANUAL KEY

FEED WIRE.

CONTACT BLOCK

CABLE

3/32 HOLE FOR SCREWDRIVER

CONTACT PLATE

CONTACT

Figure 85.

Side view of a Kimball manual key, showing the method of installing four contact blocks under a single key. In this manner as many as thirty-six contacts may be made by one key directly, without the use of a relay.

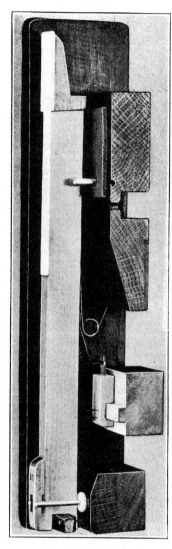

Figure 86.

Photograph of the Kimball manual key, showing the location of the contact block, at which point the circuits are closed that lead to the coupler switches for the various divisions. This type of contact is used by several other leading builders.

203

CHAPTER 13

SPECIFIC EXAMPLES *of* MODERN CONSOLE ACTION

KEY CONTACTS AND COUPLER ACTIONS

From our general description of the electro-pneumatic action, it should be clear that the movement of the keys, registers, and other controls, by the organist, results in "making" or "breaking" contacts, which in turn close or open one or more electrical circuits or complete paths of current between the contacts and the magnets in the organ. Figure 85 shows a form of contact block that is used beneath each key of the console. Aeolian-Skinner, Casavant, Estey, Hall, and Tellers Companies and several other builders employ this type of contact block with small modifications in each case. Wires of silver or phosphor-bronze are inserted in a series of saw cuts in a hard wood block in the manner shown in Figures 85 and 86. When a key is depressed all the separate wires make contact with a silver or phosphor-bronze plate that is connected with the feed wire.

From the contact blocks the circuit leads to the coupler switches. These are a series of additional contacts (one for each note) arranged in a row, as shown in Figures 73, 74 and 78. A circuit runs from a single contact under a given key to a corresponding contact on a coupler switch.

Considering Middle C on the Great manual for example, a wire will run from one of the contacts on this key to a point on a switch corresponding with middle C, where the circuit may be broken or made once more. From the switch the circuit runs to the middle C magnet on the Great windchest primary box. In other words when this switch is in action (that is, closed), the magnet operating the primary valve which permits all the middle C pipes on the Great windchest to sound, is energized. This action takes place every time the middle C on the Great manual is depressed, and the switch closed. Another contact on this same key will run to another switch. From this switch the circuit runs to the magnet on the Great windchest primary which operates the pipe valves of C above middle C or C below middle C; in other words, an octave higher or lower. The first switch is known as the Great Unison Coupler or Great to Great 8'. The other switches are the Great to Great 4' or Great to Great 16' couplers. Similarly other contacts on the same key will run to other switches, which in turn will continue circuits to the middle C magnet on the Swell Organ primary box for the Swell to Great 8' coupler and so on for all the couplers. The number of contacts under each key is governed by the number of coupler switches desired.

If no switches were provided, all these circuits would be closed by the series of contacts actuated by depressing the middle C key. In such a case all the middle Cs on all manuals as well as the octave above and octave below would sound. The switches permit the "making"

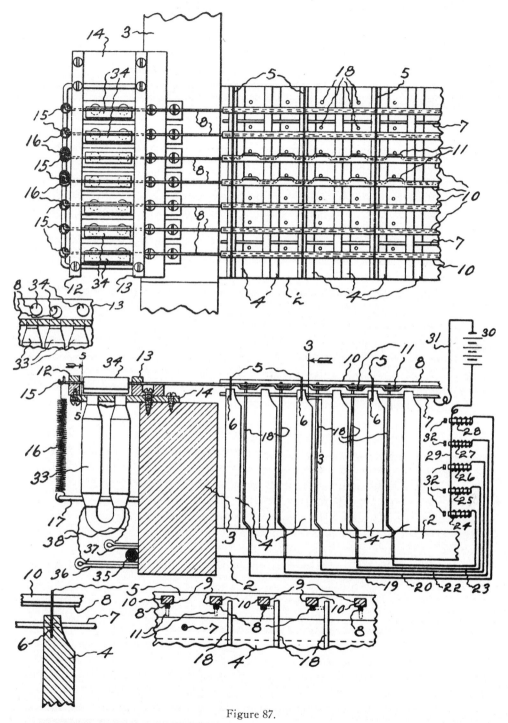

Figure 87.

Top and side views of the Austin key action (Coupler Rollers). The silver wire key contacts are shown in Figure 88 more clearly. They are here labeled, 18. The silver wire rollers themselves are shown by number 8. On the end of these rollers is soldered an armature, 34, that is attracted by the magnet, 33. The armature will cause the roller to rotate about a quarter circle, when attracted by the magnet, and cause the rollers to assume position shown at 11. When in this position, the contacts will make against the roller. When the magnet is not energized, the spring 16 pulls the roller back to position shown at 10, where the roller is inoperative, as the key contacts then merely strike against the wooden strips, 10.

205

or "breaking" of these circuits at will. They are therefore an indispensable adjunct of the action, and it is as important to be able to "make" and "break" the various circuits leading to the organ magnets through the switches, as it is at the key contacts.

The pedal key action is the same as the manual in nearly all cases. Figure 87 shows the Austin key action. In this case the key contacts and coupler switches are combined, resulting in a somewhat simplified construction. In this action, the key contacts only "make" (when a key is depressed) if one or more of the coupler switches are in position to permit contact to be made. If no switches are on, no contacts will be made when the key is operated. The circuits from the various switches run to a junction board on the console and there the circuit is completed to the magnets on the windchest as in the case of the switches where contact is not made directly by pressing a key. Further description of the Austin Coupler System is given under Figure 88.

Figure 89 shows the Moller key action. In principle it is similar to the Austin though the details of construction are quite different. The explanation of its operation is given under the drawing.

Figure 90 illustrates the Kilgen key action. This is so nearly like that of the Moller Company as to require no further statement in regard to its operation. In this action, however, silver contacts are used, whereas in the Moller flat strips of spring phosphor-bronze perform the same function in their standard action. Silver contacts are used when requested.

Another form of key action shown in Figure 96 is that made by Hillgreen, Lane and Company. Its principle is a modification of the Austin system also.

From the foregoing, it should be evident that there are two general types of key and coupler action. One has a contact block under each key on which all contacts are made whenever a key is depressed and then the circuit is "made" or "broken" as desired by means of independent switches not operated by the key contacts directly. The other type makes only the contacts desired directly on the coupler switches.

COMBINATION ACTIONS

The chapter on the History of the Organ Console contains historical information concerning the earlier development of combination actions.

The drawings furnished in the following pages show the various systems employed by some of the builders and are provided with explanations, so that it is only necessary to state that combination actions may be divided into two major groups: 1. Those that may be set by holding the piston in, on which the combination is desired, and at the same time moving the stop controls by hand. In this manner, the cams are moved

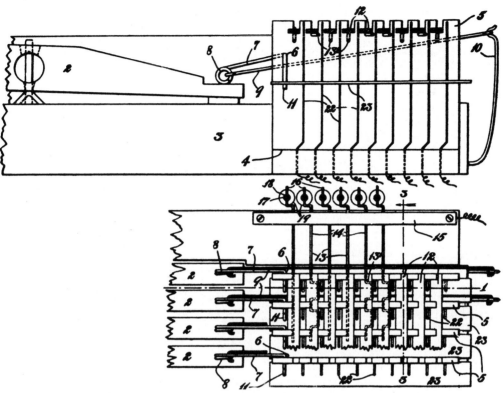

Figure 88.

Side and top views of the Austin key action. 2 is the back end, or tail of the key. When the tail of the key rises, it causes the strip, 23, to be drawn forward; this strip controls all the contacts, 22. The contacts will strike the wooden stops, 12, unless a coupler roller is in playing position, in which case the roller projects beyond the wooden stops, and allows the contacts to rub against it. The key spring is shown at 10, and with its attendant wire, 9, combines to form the "tracker" touch of the Austin, that is, a touch that is heavier at the beginning of the downward motion of the keys, than at the end.

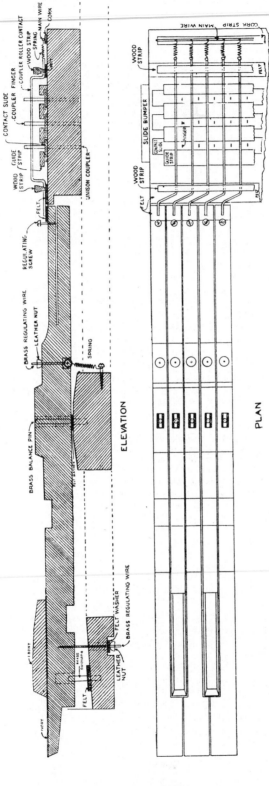

Figure 89.

Side and top views of the Moller key action. The explanation of the parts are given on the drawing. The coupler action operates the contact slides by means of a pneumatic, moving the series of contact fingers for the whole 61 keys into a position such that any key, upon being depressed will make a contact with the contact finger that has been brought into position by the contact slide.

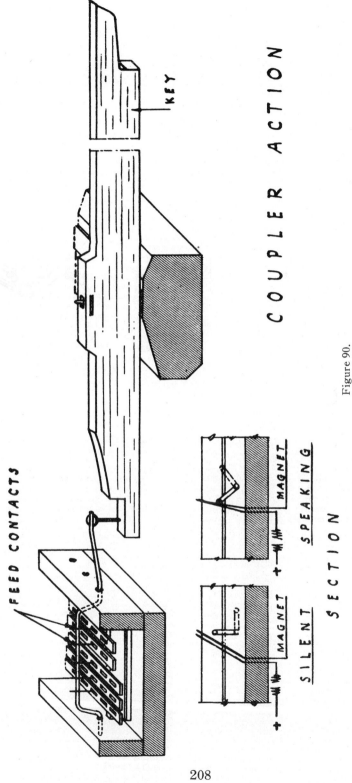

KEY

FEED CONTACTS

MAGNET

SILENT

MAGNET

SPEAKING

SECTION

COUPLER ACTION

Figure 90.

The key and coupler action employed in the Kilgen organ. The tail end of the key operates a roller that rubs against the feed contacts, provided they have been pulled toward the roller, by the movement of the contact strips to the right. The lower view shows the two positions of the contact roller, when making contact, and when in the "off" position.

good

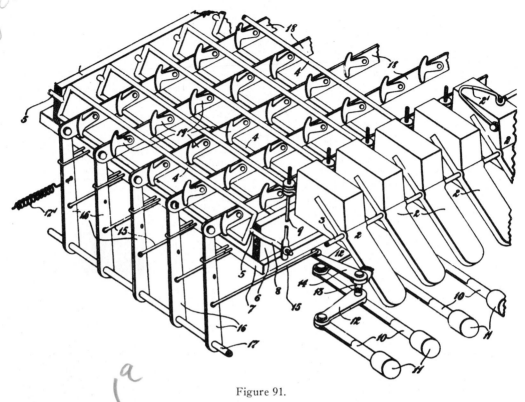

Figure 91.

a

General view of one of the original Austin combination actions. This at first was operated mechanically. When the combination piston 11 was pushed in, it drew the lever, 16, toward the right. The stop tongue, 2, operates a roller, 4, that permits of a series of traces being passed through. To these traces are attached a series of cams, 19, that can be shifted to either of two positions at the time the combination of stops to be drawn or shut off is set on the trace. When the cams are set in the down position, the stop key roller, 4, will be actuated and the stop key pushed down, because the trace is pushed to the right by the piston. The opposite result is obtained when the cams are set in up position. A trace is required for each piston. Cams are set on each trace to affect whatever stops are desired to be moved by each particular piston. General or universal pistons will require a complete series of cams for every stop and coupler on each trace. Manual pistons require only cams affecting stops on that manual. The roller 4 is arranged to "make" and "break" the stop action circuit, as it is rotated.

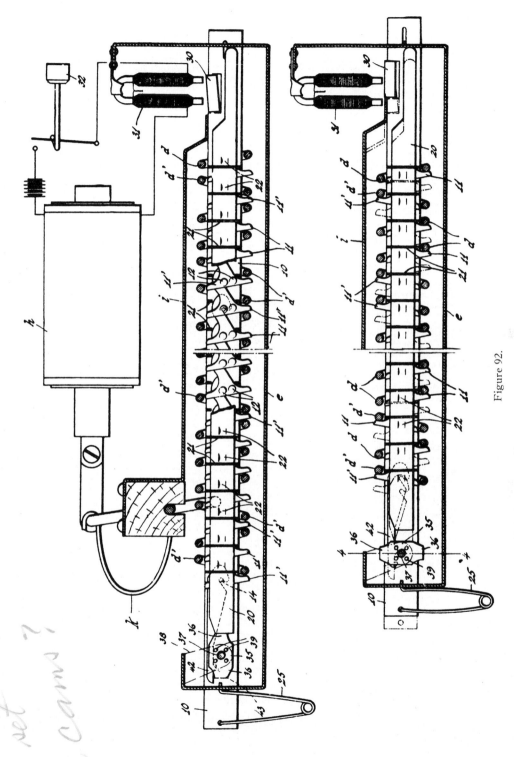

How set the cams?

Figure 92.

The present form of the Austin combination action. 30 represents the trigger, which is in reality an armature and is attracted toward the magnet 31 when a combination piston is actuated. This enables the fan, i, to push the trace 10. The large solenoid magnet h acts a little later than the magnet 31, so that the trigger 30 is drawn into position before the fan starts forward. This is essential to the operation of the action. To the trace are connected the series of cams 11, which in turn rotate the stop action rollers d to the right or left, in accordance with the way the cams are set on the trace, whether in position to draw the stop on or off. There is one trace with its series of cams for each piston. The series of traces may be placed compactly in the Austin console, passing through the stop action rollers. These rollers are more clearly shown in Figure 107.

210

into the desired position on the trace or roller. This is the Austin system, from which many other builders have departed only far enough to avoid conflict with the numerous Austin patents. The other system is to prepare the registration desired, and then, holding the setter piston, the piston on which it is desired to set this registration is pressed. The function of the setter piston is to adjust the cams, by means of pneumatics to the required set-up. This system is used by many builders, and has been developed from the original Casavant-Roosevelt adjustable combination action.

The Kimball Company for a time used an action that permitted the setting of combinations in either of the above ways, so that the organist could take his choice. An ingenious locking device (operated by the setter piston), locked all the stops in the position in which they were desired, and set this combination on whatever combination piston was then depressed. Combinations could also be set by merely holding in the piston desired by the organist, similar to the Austin system. When a general shifting of the stops was desired, the setter could be used. Small changes might more conveniently be made without using the setter.

Where there is a large number of combination pistons required, and the console may not be made too large, a remote control system is installed. In such a case the combination setting mechanism is located usually in the organ, and transfers impulses from this point to the console, and back again to the organ. This is an indirect and expensive system, and has nothing in its favor, so far as reliability, simplicity and economy are concerned. Where the console for a large organ must be of restricted size or made movable it must be used. Figure 98 shows such a setting mechanism. Remote control does operate silently, however.

In all combination systems, the movable cams must have sufficient spring tension to prevent the motion of the cams when not intended. The tension should be sufficient to safely move the stop rollers, but not too great, as then the cams cannot be readily shifted when setting a new combination.

RELAY ACTION

When a sufficient number of contacts cannot be conveniently placed adjacent to, or under the manual keys, to accomplish all that is desired, and especially when there are several unit stops in the organ, each of which requires a large number of contacts and switches, a relay mechanism is introduced. As relays are usually placed in the organ, and are operated either directly from the windchest channels, or primary valves, or by means of an independent primary they are not in reality a part of the console.

However, in a relay, as shown in Figure 97, used by the Kilgen

Figure 93

Above: Combination action for Stop Key consoles of The Kilgen Organ Company. Parts are precision made of die-stamped aluminum. The action requires no wind. Combinations are set by holding in piston and putting on and off stop keys.

Below: The Kilgen, precision-made combination action applied to the Drawknob console requires no wind for operation, and setting is the same as on Stop Key type. Drawknob chests are on rollers, preventing any jamming or sticking.

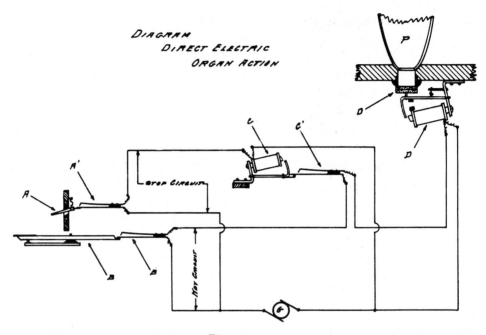

Figure 94.

The aim of the above diagram is to show the Direct Electric Organ Action in an elementary form pertaining to stop key and manual key action as it has been developed by and applied by The Wicks Pipe Organ Company.

Fig. 94, letter "A", represents a stop key, letter "A'" its relative contact. Letter "B" and "B'" the manual key and contact respectively. "C" is a magnetic gang switch (illustration of which appears on page 181) of which "C'" shows one of the series of contacts. Letters "D" and "D'" represent the magnetic valve action and pipe valve respectively. At "P" we find the pipe and at "G" the generator represented.

As it is shown, the action is in its neutral position; that is, with all circuits open. To operate, stop key "A" is depressed closing the circuit for that stop thru contact "A'". This causes the coil "C" to function closing in turn all the circuits of the gang switch thru the contacts "C'". The Action now is set up for operation of a single stop throughout the entire compass of the manual keyboard, as the gang switch "C-C'", has sixty-one individual contacts corresponding to the sixty-one keys of the manual. From the switch "C-C'" the circuits are carried through to the chest valve mechanism represented by "D-D'". It is evident that any key now depressed on the manual will cause the corresponding pipe valve in the chest to operate and the pipe to speak.

Additional stops may be brought on or others cancelled by manipulating corresponding stop keys at letter "A".

It should be understood that for each stop circuit there is a corresponding manual key circuit. For each stop in an organ there must be an individual circuit to each manual key. The key scale (about ½") determines the number of circuits that can be operated from one key. Practice has established the fact that by double banking (one series above the other) fourteen individual circuits can be operated. When more than this number of contacts are required, a relay is placed in the key circuit, where by the key circuit can be subdivided into as many circuits as may be required for any size organ.

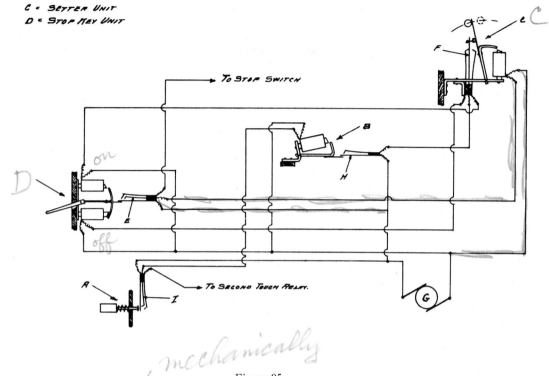

setter

A = PISTON
B = PISTON SWITCH
C = SETTER UNIT
D = STOP KEY UNIT

TO STOP SWITCH

on

off

D

B

H

E

TO SECOND TOUCH RELAY.

A

I

G

mechanically

Figure 95.

COMBINATION ACTION

The Wicks combination action is remotely controlled, all switching and setting mechanism being located in the organ proper or perhaps in an adjoining room. Stop-key unit "D" is the only part remaining in the console. By removing the mechanism in this manner the console parts are reduced to a minimum and also the noise of operation.

The combinations are set in the same manner as the majority of other combination actions. The stop keys or knobs desired are first drawn. Then by holding the setter button in, the combination is set on whatever combination piston these stops are wanted, by pushing the desired piston.

The operation of the various parts when setting a combination is as follows: All stop-keys or draw-knobs which are on, engage contact "E" attached to each stop-key, which causes the coil in unit "C" to become energized, thus pulling the armature to the core and bringing contact "F" (this is a make and break contact) to the closed position and in turn energizing the "on" coil in unit "D". When the setter piston is released the energized coils of unit "C" are held in position by a parallel bar until a new set-up is desired.

There is a setter unit "C" for each piston and a magnet with contact assembly for each stop-key or draw-knob. For draw knobs a different arrangement is used.

The foregoing explains the setting operation. Next we shall consider the movements when the pistons are pressed. When pushing thumb piston "A" (manual 1st touch and pedal 2nd touch) two contacts "I" are engaged. These contacts control two individual gang switches "B" each of which contain as many contacts as there are stop-keys in each division. The switches through their respective contacts "H" supply current to the center contact of the make and break "F" "On or Off" of unit "C" continuing to its respective coil to stop-key unit "D".

213

Company, one contact on each key is necessary at the keyboard to operate the relay magnets. It is possible to operate two or more magnets from the same contact, but this greatly increases the electrical load, and tends to cause arcing or burning at the contacts and should be avoided. Assuming that a contact is provided at the console for operating the magnets of the relay mechanism, it will be seen that the relay magnet operates every time a key is depressed. The relay magnet exhausts a motor pneumatic, which in turn works a roller, that will make contact with the various switches, in precisely the same manner, as when a key is depressed. In the case of the relay, the contacts are closed electro-pneumatically, while at the keyboard, the contacts are closed mechanically, by the motion of the key under the fingers.

Figure 96 is the electro-pneumatic relay used by Hillgreen, Lane & Company. Its operation is also like the key action of this builder. The only function of the relay is to provide and operate more contacts than can be conveniently operated otherwise.

The Kimball relay is shown in Figure 101. The similarity of the relay in principle to the Kimball key action is remarkable. This builder also attaches a relay mechanism to operate with the primary valve stems.

M. P. Moller makes both the electro-pneumatic relay similar to the builders mentioned, and also a relay that works pneumatically from the windchest channels. The manner of mounting the contact box on the windchest is shown in Figure 65.

This makes a simple and effective relay, when not too many contacts are required.

In all these relay mechanisms, the circuits from the contacts run to a series of switches. If the relay (as in most cases), is for a "unit" stop, the switches are arranged like the coupler switches in the console to complete a series of circuits. A choice is afforded the organist by these switches so that when middle C for example is depressed, not only middle C on the unit chest can be made to sound, but the C above or below, or in fact any interval, dependent on the number of switches, and the manner in which the circuits are wired. Obviously the separate relay and additional switches and wiring add greatly to the cost of a "unit" stop as compared to that of a "straight" stop. As much mechanism is required for this purpose as the entire key and coupler action of a whole manual division (if a "straight" organ). In fact the relay and its attendant switches is an independent key and coupler action applied to the operation of one or more unit stops.

There remains to be described the full organ and crescendo pedals in the console. The operation of the expression pedals is shown in Figures 39 and 40, and an explanation is there given of their function. Also toe studs usually merely duplicate the manual pistons, or if they

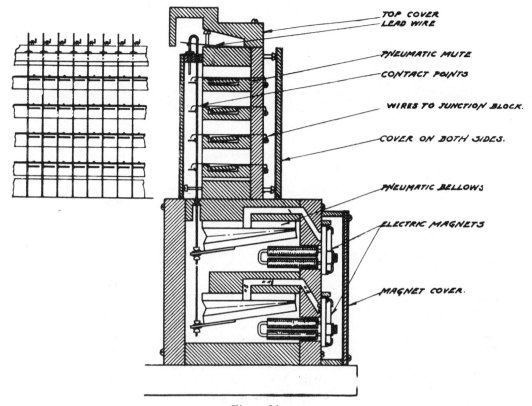

Figure 96.

Sectional view of the electro-pneumatic relay used by the Hillgreen, Lane & Co. The operation is similar to that described for Figure 117.

Labels for Figure 96:
- TOP COVER
- LEAD WIRE
- PNEUMATIC MUTE
- CONTACT POINTS
- WIRES TO JUNCTION BLOCK.
- COVER ON BOTH SIDES.
- PNEUMATIC BELLOWS
- ELECTRIC MAGNETS
- MAGNET COVER.

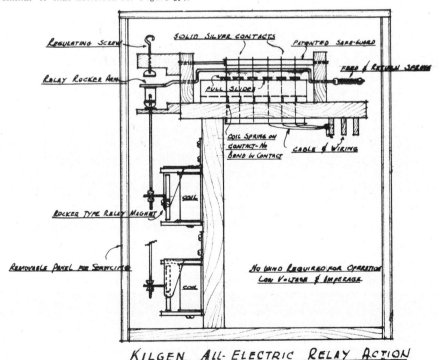

Labels for Figure 97:
- REGULATING SCREW
- SOLID SILVER CONTACTS
- PATENTED SAFE-GUARD
- RELAY ROCKER ARM
- FEED & RETURN SPRING
- PULL SLIDES
- COIL SPRING ON CONTACT—NO BEND IN CONTACT
- CABLE & WIRING
- ROCKER TYPE RELAY MAGNET
- COIL
- REMOVABLE PANEL FOR SERVICING
- NO WIND REQUIRED FOR OPERATION LOW VOLTAGE & AMPERAGE
- COIL

KILGEN ALL-ELECTRIC RELAY ACTION
THE KILGEN ORGAN COMPANY- ST. LOUIS, MO.   FIGURE 97

215

have independent combination traces, perform the identical operations that the manual pistons accomplish.

Ordinarily all the stop action contacts affected by the full organ pedal are either "made" without moving the register controls, as in the Austin system, or are governed by circuits run from these contacts to a point where they may all be closed at one time by the action of the pedal. The crescendo pedal in nearly all cases requires circuits from the stop action and coupler action, to be run onto a drum or roller, where, by turning the roller, the various contacts may be made progressively, in a predetermined manner (usually from soft to loud).

Figure 98.
Wicks remote control combination action.

216

CHAPTER 14

TRANSFERENCE of STOPS

"UNIFICATION"

Undoubtedly, what was one of the most highly controversial questions in organ building in America during the past half century was the one relating to the subject known as "unification." There have been endless arguments for and against "unification" published in "The Diapason" and the "American Organist" for many years past. The matter is still unsettled, with strong advocates for and against.

Before taking up the subject of "unification" and defining what we mean by this term, we shall take up the simpler matter of the transference of stops from one keyboard to another.

Until the introduction of the tubular-pneumatic action, it was seldom if ever possible to play a stop or set of pipes belonging to the Swell Organ, for example, on the Great Organ independently, and without the use of couplers. By means of a system of double stop action (which is described in our various chapters on organ action in detail), it is possible to play any or all sets of pipes perfectly independently on either one or both of two different keyboards. This plan should never be used simply in an effort to make an insufficient number of stops suffice for a large building. On the other hand, such a plan in the case of a small organ, or even in larger organs to render certain stops available independently, on more than one keyboard, is frequently of a very great advantage in adding to the number of tonal effects that are possible. No argument can be advanced that this practice can in any way upset the tonal balance of the organ, or in fact affect the full organ in any manner whatever. It is merely a plan for placing the tonal resources at the most convenient disposal of the organist.

Hope-Jones is usually credited with having developed this plan of transference of stops or "duplexing," as it is commonly called. Mr. Skinner refers to the idea as rendering a particular stop "interchangeable" between two manuals. So much then, for the plain duplexing of stops between manuals. To adopt such a plan certainly involves no artistic violations of any sort in the tonal scheme of the organ, but rather makes the limited resources of a small organ available to greater advantage. The only possible question of the advisability of this procedure that can be raised is whether the additional cost of the mechanism involved in doing this duplexing is worth as much or more than the additional pipes that might be purchased with the same amount of money. This is a matter for the designer of the organ to determine, when all the circumstances of the installation are known.

Coming now to what was the controversial matter of unification. Originally this term meant a scheme of treating the entire organ as a single unit and making it possible to draw any or all of the stops on all of the keyboards at any reasonable pitch. This plan was originally announced before the Royal College of Organists in London by Hope-Jones at his lecture delivered on May 5, 1891. Unification now may mean that only one or two sets of pipes in an organ are so treated.

Mr. John Compton, the eminent English organ builder, has apparently been about the only one in England to follow along the lines that Hope-Jones suggested. Mr. Compton is not only a voicer of organ pipes of the highest excellence, but an organ builder of extraordinary resourcefulness and skill. There is no question in my mind that if unification could ever be made to justify itself in a church organ, the examples Mr. Compton has produced in England, as for instance in the Liberal Jewish Synagogue, London, are the finest of this type of organ in existence. But the whole trend of modern thought in organ design is against unification in any form in a church organ, and I am afraid Mr. Compton is still waging a battle which is lost.

At this point, it should be observed that there is likely to be a certain amount of confusion in the minds of some organists as to the distinction and very real difference that exists between a unit organ and a straight organ with one or more unified stops.

A true unit organ has its registers available at practically all pitches on all keyboards, including the pedal, and therefore needs no couplers in the ordinary sense. The various sets of pipes have no "home" manual to which they belong. The organ with *some* unified sets is a regular orthodox straight organ for the most part with one or more stops available at various pitches, on perhaps, more than one manual and pedal, but with the unified stops having a definite "home" manual to which they really belong. This is important to realize. Controversy arises when a few unified sets of pipes are introduced in an otherwise straight organ scheme, because organists are not clear on this point. As soon as the term "unit" is mentioned to them, they think of the completely unified theater organ and make no allowances whatever for the unfinished and crude voicing that prevails in many theater organs. This combination is manifestly unsuited to church use and has been since its inception. On the other hand, a few soft unified voices do not destroy tonal balance or ensemble, but add additional color and flexibility.

So far as I know, Henry Willis in England, the Aeolian-Skinner Organ Company and Casavant Freres in this country are builders who are such "Purists" that they have always been unalterably opposed to unification of any sort in a church organ and have steadfastly refused to follow this practice, except in the smallest organs. I know of no other American organ builders who have not, at one time or another, accepted the arrangement, and made a practice of unifying at least one or more stops. It became nearly a universal custom in American building, sometimes rightly and more often wrongly employed.

I am sure we may grant at the outset, that, if space and money are ample, every artistic organist prefers the so-called straight organ, where every stop is represented by its own set of pipes, individually scaled and voiced to a nicety, to maintain a true balance and relation between the 16 and 4 foot registers and the 8 foot. There never was any argument about this. Unifying should never have been adopted in any form under these conditions. It was at best a compromise between insufficient 16' and 4' and other registers not at unison pitch, or an ample supply of these registers when unification of certain 8' registers was adopted. In the very nature of things, these derived stops did not exactly duplicate independent pipes.

The difficulty is, that in many cases neither space nor funds are ample, and it then becomes a serious question as to the best course of procedure. It must be obvious that twenty sets of pipes will require less room than thirty, and, if an organ of twenty sets is partly unified, it will have approximately as many tonal effects as could otherwise be obtained from thirty or more sets where they are all "straight" stops. "Approximately" is the correct word to use, as the effect will, of course, not be exactly the same. In our chapter on The Tonal Design of the Organ, we discuss at length an organ ensemble and how it is secured. A good ensemble is one of the most characteristic and desirable virtues a church organ may have. It is not important in a theater organ and not so important in a residence organ, though quite desirable. It should, therefore, be apparent that no stops should be unified, particularly in a church organ, that are going to tend to upset the tonal balance or create an imperfect ensemble. If the unifying is confined to only soft registers, such as Dulcianas, small scaled Flutes, and Gemshorns, and possibly a very soft mild String, then it is inconceivable that the ensemble of the organ will in any way be injured by such practise. When the more powerful toned stops are drawn, the tone of these lighter stops will be entirely swallowed up and practically inaudible, so what is done to them is of no consequence in the ensemble.

If unification is extended to powerful stops, such as Diapasons (even to the second Diapason on the Great Organ), or Chorus Reeds, such as Trumpet or Tubas, or large scaled Flutes, the ensemble is sure to suffer more. Even this faulty use of unification was practiced extensively. When unification is attempted intelligently and with discretion, it is not objectionable and permits of much greater tonal variety, even though it is freely admitted that such extended stops are not as good as independent pipes.

In reality, all that unification consists of, as applied to a single stop, is to furnish that stop with independent and individual octave couplers. Why it should be considered so inartistic and reprehensible to

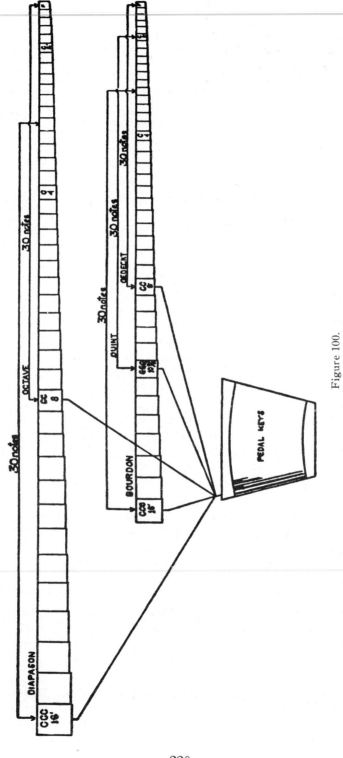

Figure 100.

The "Augmented Pedal." (From Skinner, "The Modern Organ.") The pedal compass is now 32 notes, but the same principles apply.

apply octave couplers to various stops individually, rather than being compelled to couple all the stops in use on a whole manual by means of the regular octave couplers, has never been quite clear to me. It is frequently more artistic and desirable to couple only one or more stops on a keyboard at 4' or 16', than to couple all the stops on the particular keyboard that happen to be drawn at 16' and 4' when the regular octave couplers are used.

Probably one of the chief objections to unification of the more powerful stops is, that the octave couplers are caused to affect stops that are already played individually at octaves, thereby in effect creating a coupler which plays this stop two octaves above unison or two octaves below unison or even greater extremes from the unison pitch, in cases where the stop is unified at more than three pitches (a common practice). This has the effect of upsetting the tonal balance of the organ seriously and makes the ensemble appear to have all top and bottom and no middle. Such inartistic use of unifying stops has been one of the chief reasons for their condemnation by artistic organists and builders. But organists should know more of the mechanics and should never fall into such traps—their ears alone could show them that the effect is wrong. No such objection can be advanced in the case of the softer toned stops recommended.

Unit stops, to be really successful, properly should diminish in power towards the top and increase in power toward the bottom, a condition which is almost the reverse of what obtains in the case of a stop used at one pitch only. If the bass of the unit stop is to be available on the pedal (as is nearly always the case), or otherwise the cost of unifying is not justified, it must necessarily be heavy in the bass portion to make a suitable pedal stop. Particularly the bottom octave must be heavy if the stop is of any great power on the manual. It is not desirable to have the four foot octave of a Flute as powerful as the eight foot unison tone and, therefore, the stop should decrease in power upwards. A unit stop, therefore, is somewhat of a hybrid or composite in scale and power when most artistically developed. These difficulties are not encountered in the case of soft toned stops, as already suggested, as they may be kept approximately the same strength throughout the compass without any modification, with reasonably good results.

Another type of duplexing that is very useful in some ways is that which is employed to make the same set of pipes available at octave and unison pitches or sub-octave and unison pitches on the same manual. Also, if a duplex chest is provided, a stop may be played at unison pitch on one manual and an octave higher or lower on the other. This can be accomplished with small expense and little mechanism as compared with that required for the actual unifying of a stop, and is frequently more justifiable from this point of view than to adopt unification.

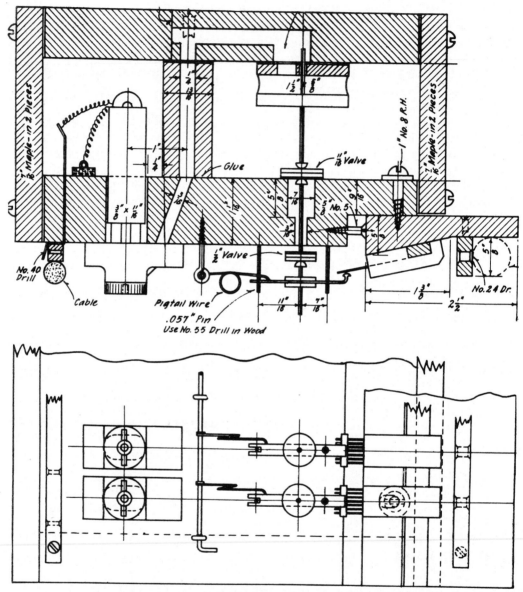

Figure 101.

Sectional and bottom views of the Kimball electro-pneumatic relay. Whenever more contacts are required than can be placed directly under the keys themselves a relay mechanism of some sort is required to give additional contacts. Referring to the upper drawing: the key contact operates the magnet which in turn exhausts the square pneumatic causing the wire attached to it to draw the bus bar against the series of contacts. This same mechanism may be employed for a much larger number of contacts than are here shown. In which case the contact blocks would have to be spaced farther apart.

222

Unless a stop is going to be used at least four different ways, as for example, unison pitch, octave above, octave below and on the pedal, it does not pay to unify it. The cost of additional mechanism for such limited use is as great as would be the cost of individual pipes, which are always preferable when space is available.

Another form of unifying though called by the euphemistic name of "Augmented Pedal," is almost universally practiced by American builders, as well as English. Mr. Skinner, in his work on "The Modern Organ," has this to say for the Augmented Pedal:

"The Augmented Pedal" is supposed by many, including a few organ builders, to be a makeshift or form of swindle intended to defraud the unwary. It is for this reason that the following explanation is given.

"The idea of the Augmented Pedal is not new. It originated in England and the idea is at least thirty years old, probably more.

"It consists of a construction that permits of drawing the pedal stops at either sixteen or eight foot pitch.

"There is a fundamental reason why this is good practice with regard to the pedal organ and radically wrong when applied to the manuals. The manuals are played in chords, the pedal idiom is one note at a time. In the common chord of "C" on the manuals, if a four foot stop be taken from an eight foot stop, there will be, if both are drawn, one "C" less sounding than if both stops were complete in themselves. In the event of larger chords, doublings and omissions are more pronounced. *This is, of course, the case with all manual octave couplers.*

"With the pedal organ, the conditions are wholly different as chords are seldom played on the pedals. It is, therefore, clear that the effect of an eight foot stop is not discounted by any probable use of its sixteen foot relative. In the construction of the Augmented Pedal, all the stops to be augmented are carried one octave higher in order that the scale of the stops of eight foot pitch may be complete."

The italics are mine, and are important to observe, for nothing more serious happens musically when an octave coupler is applied individually to a certain stop, than when an octave coupler is applied to a whole manual. All builders and organists seem to be agreed in the liberal use of manual octave couplers, except on the Great Organ. Intelligently unified stops afford greater variety and choice in the use of octave couplers than the manual octave couplers provide. This furnishes their justification and *raison d' etre*. It must be observed that they cannot wholly take the place of additional pipes. Unification obviously cannot change or in anyway affect the tone quality of the pipes so treated, though some builders have endeavored to make the unwary purchaser believe it can, in some mysterious manner. If the time ever comes when organ purchasers have even rudimentary knowledge of organs, it will be impossible to put across such absurd ideas.

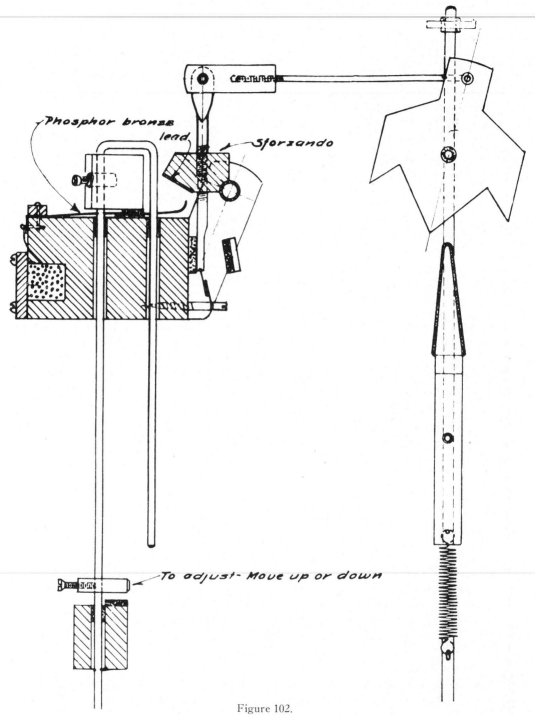

Phosphor bronze lead

Sforzando

To adjust - Move up or down

Figure 102.

On the right is shown the mechanism, whose principle is the same in all reversible actions, used for Great to Pedal couplers, Sforzando pedals, etc. The pedal actuates the pointed rod, which is pivoted and made to assume its normal position by the coil spring. Each time this rod is moved, it causes the mechanism at the top of the drawing to reverse its position.

224

TRANSFERENCE OF STOPS

Figure 100 is a diagram showing the principle of the augmented pedal and a wiring diagram for a unit stop.

With the increasing interest and respect for a true pedal ensemble there is more demand for independent pedal 8 and 4 foot stops, instead of "augmentation." It will, I believe, increasingly become the practice in the future to have more independent pedal stops of octave and super octave pitch, especially in large organs.

Mr. H. LeRoy Baumgartner, in the 1951 Aeolian-Skinner organ in the Church of the Redeemer, New Haven, Conn. has adopted a special type of unification, whereby the stop so unified is not affected by couplers. Such a stop is wired directly to the key contacts, and cables run from the console switches directly to the unit chests, thus obviating the expense of a relay. A pedal Bombarde, or big Solo Reed may be so treated, to make it available on both Choir and Pedal at unison and octave pitches, or on Choir and Great.

This type of unification may also be applied to a Spitz Flute, for example, which may be made playable at 16'–8'–4' from two or more divisions, without being affected by couplers. The idea is not new. I used it in my rebuild of the Johnson organ in First Presbyterian Church, Evanston, carried out by Walter Haltkamp. It is new that Aeolian-Skinner Organ Co. will go along with such ideas to a limited extent. These days of high prices have caused a somewhat thorough rethinking of what are the most important things we want in an organ. In Mr. Baumgartner's organ, a classic Positiv section was made possible by such unifying of a few stops. It is all the better that the unified stops are not affected by the couplers.

Figure 103.

Figure 104.

Two photographs of the Reuter key contact mechanism. Above, the stop keys and combination action parts have been lifted back on hinges, to expose the key contacts for adjustments. Below, adjusting a key contact, to make the action "fire" at precisely the right point, as the key is depressed. This point is normally about midway between the top and bottom of the key travel.

226

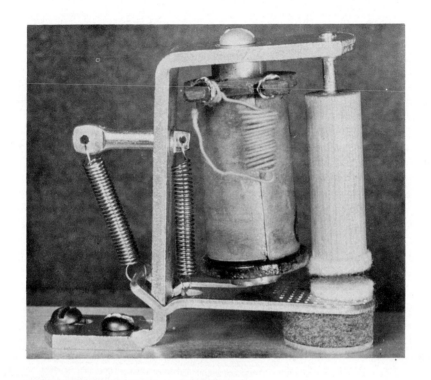

Figure 105.

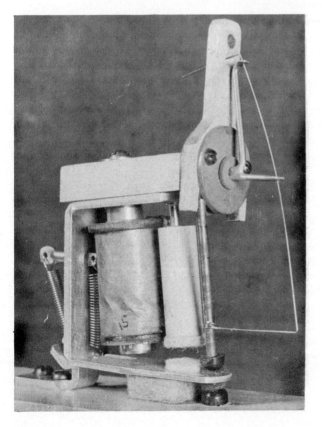

Above, the Reuter direct electric action. This is only used for the smaller pipe valves, in their small unit organs. It has proved to be extremely practical and economical when confined to this use only.

Below, the Reuter reversible action. One of the simplest and most effective reversible actions being produced. In combination with a Reuter direct electric magnet, the hair spring causes the small rod with the two buttons attached at the bottom of it to push one side, and then the other of the wooden piece with the two screws in it. The motion of this piece is transferred by means of a wire inserted in the hole at top of photo, to the stop key roller.

CHAPTER 15

A HISTORY *of* TONAL DESIGN

Present day interest in the organ of the classic or baroque period (approximately 1600-1750) has become so pronounced that I feel it is important that many more details of this period of organ building be furnished than were given in former editions of this book. Also 19th century organ building (as exemplified by Henry Willis and Edmund Schulze in England; Aristide Cavaille-Coll in France; and the Roosevelts, Johnsons, Jardines and others in America) has now more interest to organ lovers, than it had twenty-five years ago. Students want to know as precisely as possible, just what the organs of Bach's time were like, as well as those organs built a hundred years prior to his time. And again, the French organs available to the great 19th century French composers for the organ, such as Cesar Franck, and his contemporaries, are a subject of interest. While the English and American composers for the instrument in the 19th century are perhaps not so important, the best organs made in America and England during this century certainly contributed valuable and forward looking features, which may profitably be studied by any serious lover of the organ. These organs have great influence on our contemporary instruments.

For the assembling of this material, I have ferreted out facts from the following works: "The Modern British Organ," Bonavia-Hunt; "The Organ," Clutton & Dixon; "Bach, the Organist and His Works" by A. Pirro; "The Organ Students' 'Gradus ad Parnassam,'" Caspar Koch; and from a long list of specifications of 19th century American organs, compiled by F. R. Webber, an indefatigable student and collector of details about this period of American organ building. I feel that it is desirable that this knowledge be made accessible in one place, so that the earnest student may have in front of him, at a glance, the chief characteristics of the classic organ, as well as the 19th century organ in England, France, Germany and America.

From my trips to Europe in 1927 and 1932, I do have first hand knowledge of 19th and 20th century English, French and German organs, and can speak with considerable assurance about them. But my first hand knowledge of the 17th and 18th century French and German organs is confined to playing on two Silbermann organs in the Leipsig Museum and on some 18th century organs at Ottobeuren and Memingen. For this reason, to bring the organs of this period into focus, I have found it necessary to consult historians who write, at least, as though they had first hand knowledge of the subject, since we are dealing with history very largely. If I find several authors in substantial agreement on the facts, I think it safe to pass their information on to my readers, without verifying the original sources of the facts. As to the interpretation of the facts, I am leaving that to the reader's judgment and perspicacity.

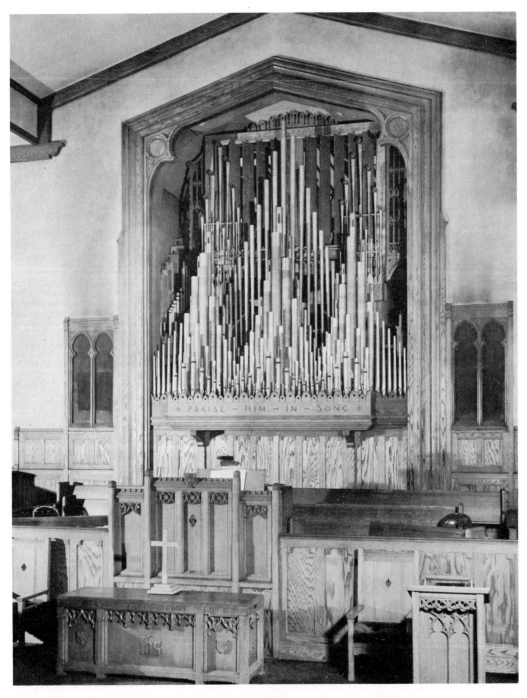

Plate XIV.

Holtkamp organ in **Miles Park** Presbyterian Church, Cleveland, Specification on page 258

229

Some enthusiasts think the organ of 17th and 18th century Germany and France should be slavishly copied for 20th century American churches. Others do not agree. But I believe that organs of this period have much to teach us of value, even if we would not want to use one of them in the Sunday morning church service.

To gain a background for the proper understanding of the various stop-lists which are to be presented, it is desirable that some general remarks be made concerning the pipe-work, the voicing characteristics, the method of combining the various ranks of pipes when actually playing these organs, and other details.

THE DEVELOPMENT OF THE DIAPASON

There have been at least three important stages in the development of the Diapason through the years. 1. The early German and English type was characterized by its thin, obtuse-angled languid, and in some German examples, by the inverted languid. Not over 2½" wind pressure was essential to this type of tone, in which the harmonics were not developed beyond the tenth or twelfth. Small scales were halved at every octave, so that the scale became relatively smaller in the upper portions of the register. The pipes had wide mouths, narrow windways and shallow nicking. The result of such scaling and voicing treatment left the trebles very weak, thus insistently requiring many ranks of Mixtures to bring the treble up to proper balance. These lightly winded, early types of Diapasons were said to have a peculiar, absolutely unforced charm to their tone.

2. The next type of Diapason was produced by the German builders in the baroque period (viz. 1600-1750 approximately). The chief and best known exponents of this type were Casparini, Arp Schnitger, Scheibe (Bach's organ builder), and the Silbermann brothers. Again, due to the inadequate wind supply, rather than from choice, the Diapasons made by these artist builders were very lightly winded, never more than 3¼" and usually, considerably less. The basses were furnished with small foot holes, while the trebles were more boldly treated. The tone was more foundational and flutey and softer than modern Diapasons, with very prompt speech, and as the trebles were opened up, they were relatively bold compared with the bass end, causing the stop to have melodic value.

Casparini's and Gottfried Silbermann's Diapason voicing was markedly bolder than anything earlier, using pressures up to 3¼" for the Great, and 4" on the pedals.

Edmund Schulze, another German, a century later, developed the pioneer work of Gottfried Silbermann and Casparini to the utmost. But more of this later.

The Diapasons of these builders differed somewhat; but all of them were smooth and mellow, and furnished a substratum for the magnificent upper work.

Plate XV.

Cadet Chapel, West Point, N. Y. East tanscept front. This is only the **smallest of** several cases for this organ, which were designed by E. Donald Robb, M. P. Moller, builders. The organ in the chapel owes its existence in its present enlarged form to the efforts of Frederick C. Mayer, the organist of the chapel for nearly forty years. It is certainly one of the largest, most unusual, and thrilling church organs in the world.

One of the characteristic features of Silbermann's Diapason work was the high percentage of tin used. Never less than 90% and up to 99½% pure tin. The "bloom" of these Diapasons was evident when played in chords, and particularly when combined with the rest of the Diapason chorus, which was given more brilliance than the unison rank. It is important that the chief features of the earlier and the later baroque style of Diapason be understood, for on this style of voicing was raised a whole superstructure of the Diapason chorus. In the baroque period and before, it should be understood that the chorus was the main consideration, and the unison rank was hardly more important than any other rank, merely a part of the chorus. The principal mission of the 18th century and earlier Diapason chorus was to enable polyphonic music to be heard with clarity and precision. All of the ranks of the chorus were practically identical in power.

The artistic use of Mixtures has been misunderstood during a good part of the century just passed. During the past twenty-five years the great revival of interest in 18th century and earlier organs has brought about a complete restudy and rethinking on the part of the more serious and scholarly builders of America, England, and Germany. We now find that no really successful organ has been made without upper work. Historically, Mixtures are probably a heritage of the mediaeval *vocal organum*, or singing in consecutive fifths, the organ following what was normal vocal practice. The fifth, and the octaves of the fifth, are part of the natural harmonic series of which every musical note is made up. Fifth sounding ranks have both a reenforcing and cohesive effect upon a Diapason chorus, when properly scaled and regulated.

Mixtures with the quint and octave sounding ranks, and octaves of the quint and octave, are the most useful and normal types of Mixture. When the third, or more normally, the tenth or seventeenth is introduced, it is generally better to have it as a separate rank.

The eighteenth century Diapason chorus may be summed up by stating that it contained a relatively large number of ranks, of slight power, and more or less flutey tone, all ranks being of about equal power. The numerous Mixtures did not produce an overpowering and unmusical scream or shriek. With little unison tone present, it was none the less reenforced by the resultant tones from the quint and octave sounding ranks in the Mixtures.

The German builders worked along lines essentially similar to the French builders only the Diapason chorus was more brilliant and powerful. The Germans placed little reliance on the Reeds for power. The French builders have always relied on the intensely brilliant Reeds for the greater part of the power of the organ, especially in a large building.

Plate XVI.   Indiana University Auditorium.   The great Roosevelt-Aeolian-Skinner organ is installed in the long triangular space between the outer wall of the building and the inner wall of the auditorium proper. It speaks from the four grilles shown in photograph. Description is given on page 186.

THE REED CHORUS

The 17th and 18th century French organ was the only one that made an attempt to develop a proper 16'-8'-4' Reed chorus. Francois Henry Cliquot, who did his best work in the third quarter of the 18th century, brought the French Reeds to a point where it remained for the great nineteenth century French organ builder Aristide Cavaillé-Coll to perfect them by increasing the wind pressure, and doubling the lengths (harmonic) of the treble pipes. The tone of the French Reeds was, and still is, intense and unbelievably prompt. All French chorus Reeds from the beginning had thin, unweighted tongues, and open, parallel shallots, thus emitting a perfect blaze of harmonics without any restriction or dampening.

These Reeds were not used with the Diapason chorus. The only flue pipes used with the Reed chorus were usually a Mixture V Ranks, and perhaps a Prestant 4'. We have here, of course, the beginnings of the Willis "full swell" effect, only the Willis Reeds were much better for an average type of church building.

I like to think of comparing the sound of the eighteenth century French Reeds to the more modern Willis Reeds, by likening their effect to the difference in sound between an 18th century Harpsichord and a modern Steinway grand pianoforte.

The great 18th century French builder, Cliquot, who in 1781 built the organ in St. Sulpice, Paris, will serve as a good example of the last of the baroque period in France. The Great organ consisted of the following:

Montre 32'	Tierce 1-3/5'
Montre 16'	Larigot 1-1/3'
Bourdon 16'	Cornet V
Montre 8'	Grosse Fourniture VI
Bourdon 8'	Cymbale VI
Prestant 4'	1 re Trompette 8'
Flute 4'	2 me Trompette 8'
Gross Tierce 3-1/5'	1 re Clairon 4'
Nazard 2-2/3'	2 nd Clairon 4'
Doublette 2'	Voix Humaine 8'
Quarte de Nazard 2'	

THE 17TH AND 18TH CENTURY GERMAN ORGAN

Before proceeding with the representative German classic organ stop lists and those of the 19th century French organ, I give an explanation of the German and French keyboard terminology. I give also

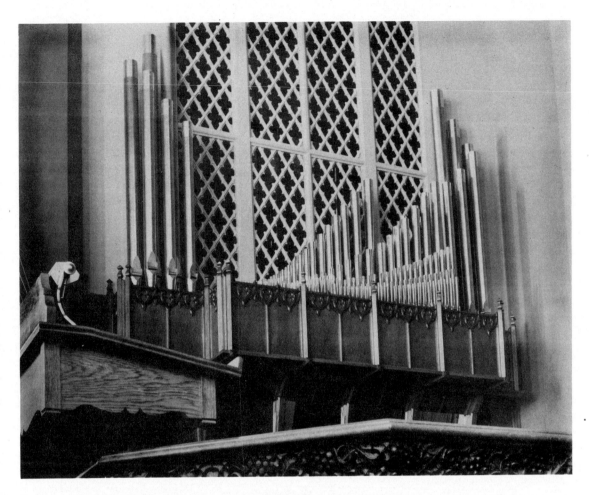

Plate XVII.

Portion of the Reuter organ in First Presbyterian Church, Rochester, Minn. Mr. Franklin Mitchell, tonal director for Reuter regards this organ as being truly representative of their present work.

To corbel out the Great and Positive sections on each side of the chancel walls, immediately in front of the grilles, is becoming a frequent practice of nearly all of our leading builders. The photograph shows left chancel wall only. The right wall is balanced by similar use of pipes in the open. Two advantages accrue by this arrangement. 1. The pipes so located are in a completely open position. 2. It saves space within the chambers for the other sections of the organ that require enclosure, and for the longer pedal pipes, that are too large to be exposed effectively.

the German and French stop names, ordinarily encountered in the classic and modern organs of these countries, together with the equivalent names usually used by English speaking people, and some particulars of voicing of the classic organ stops.

The various keyboards or divisions were referred to as follows:

(French)		(German)
Grand Orgue	–	Haupt werk, equivalent of Great organ
Recit expressiv	–	Brust werk, equivalent of present day Swell organ
Positif	–	Rückpositiv, equivalent of Choir organ, organ so named from the custom of placing this division behind the back (rücken) of the organist.
		Ober werk means literally the higher manual. In two manual organs, the stronger was, at that time, found above the other. The names are somewhat elastic in application, often being determined more by the location in the instrument of the various divisions.

STOP NAMES FOUND IN CLASSIC AND MODERN ORGANS
OF FRANCE AND GERMANY

BOMBARDE (French)—1. Reed of Trumpet type, 8'-16'-32'. 2. Manual division from which various pitches of Bombardes are played.

BOURDON (French), *GEDACKT* (German)—Stopped Flute.

CHALUMEAU (French), *SCHALMEI* (German)—Precursor of the Clarinet.

COR de NUIT (French), *NACHTHORN* or *WALD FLÖTE* (German)—Wide scaled flutes, usually of 4' and 2' Pitch. In classic organs, frequently found on the pedal division as solo stops.

CORNETT (German)—Flute-toned Mixture, containing the Tierce. Frequently containing five ranks, such as 8', 4', 2-2/3', 2', 1-3/5'. Used in the classic organ only as a solo stop, not in the ensemble. The Grand Cornet is, however, used with the chorus Reeds.

CROMORNE (French), *KRUMMHORN* (German)—Classic solo stop, of which the modern Clarinet is a more refined example.

CYMBALE (French), *SCHARF*, *ZIMBEL* (German)—Sharp (Mixture), a high

Plate XVIII

First Presbyterian Church, Kilgore, Texas. Aeolian-Skinner Organ Co.. The first modern instance in America where a Bombarde has been placed in an exposed position, horizontally, thereby directing the tone straight into the church auditorium. Such disposition of a big Trumpet stop was fairly common in the organs of France, where it is called "Trompette-en-Chamade." While the "Trompette-en-Chamade" arrangement is more picturesque and historic, almost the same musical results may be obtained by "hooding" the resonators of a big Bombarde. This was a common practice of Willis in England, and it is now being done in America by various builders.

pitched Mixture. It is the top Mixture of a brilliant ensemble.

CYMBEL STERN (German)—A toy star with little bells attached which sounded when the star was rotated. A favorite accessory of mediaeval continental organ builders. Foreshadowing the toy counter of the 20th century theater organs.

DOUBLETTE (French)—Fifteenth.

FLÛTE (French), *FLÖTE* (German)—Flute.

FLÛTE OCTAVIANTE (French)—Large scaled Harmonic Flute.

FOURNITURE (French), *MIXTUR* (German)—Mixture. Compound stop of two or more ranks, each sounding one of the harmonics of a given fundamental.

GAMBE (French)—General term for string-toned stops, such as Viols, Gambas, Salicionals.

GEDACKT (German)—Stopped Flute.

GEIGEN PRINCIPAL (German)—Violin Diapason. (from Geige - violin).

HOHLFLÖTE (German)—Clarabella.

JEUX de FONDS (French) *GRUNDSTIMMEN* (German)—Foundation stops.

KORNETT (German)—Ancient type of solo Reed, not to be confused with Cornet, chiefly found on pedal division at 2' pitch.

KRUMMHORN (German)—Classic organ solo stop, forerunner of the Clarinet.

MIXTUR (German)—See Fourniture.

MONTRE (French), *PRINZIPAL* (German)—Diapason.

MUTATION—A single rank of pipes sounding a pitch other than the fundamental or one of its octaves, such as Nazard 2-2/3' Nasat 2-2/3' or Tierce, 1-3/5'.

NACHTHORN (German)—See Cor de nuit.

NASAT (German)—See Nazard.

NAZARD (French) *NASAT* (German)—A flute toned stop sounding the 12th.

PRINCIPAL (German)—Diapason.

OCTAV (German)—Octave Diapason.

POSAUNE (German)—Trombone or Trumpet with heavy brassiness to the tone equivalent to the French Bombarde.

QUINTATON—Quintadena.

PLEIN JEU (French)—Full Diapason Mixture of at least IV Ranks.

PRESTANT (French), *OCTAV* (German)—Octave Diapason.

PRINCIPAL (Latin)—Diapason of 8' pitch. A Principal 4' was not the octave of an 8' fundamental, but the fundamental of a 4' series. Common on the Rück positiv division of the classic German organ.

SCHARF (German)—See Cymbale.

SCHWEITZERPFEIFE (German)—Literally, Swiss Flute, a delicate toned flute, between a flute or string tone.

SEPTIEME (French)—Mutation sounding the Flat 21st, 1-1/7'.

SESQUIALTERA (Latin)—A two-rank Mixture, consisting of the Nasat

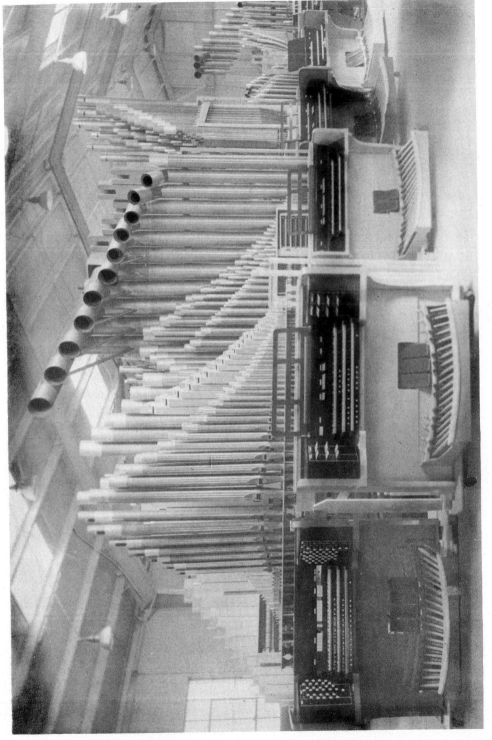

Plate XIX

A part of the erecting room of Wicks Organ Co. Note the various types of consoles that Wicks manufactures. Drawknob, stoptongue in oblique sidejambs, and standard stoptongue consoles, with the stoptongues in either a single or double row above the top manual. The notions and tastes of all organists may be suited by one of these styles.

2-2/3' and Tierce 1-3/5'. A Cornet could be made by adding the 4' and 2' flutes.

TERZ (German)—See Tierce.

TIERCE (French), *TERZ* (German)—The Seventeenth. The pipes may be either Diapason or Flute quality, depending on whether they are a component rank of a Diapason Mixture, or a single mutation rank. In the latter case, they are normally some type of open, or partly covered Flute.

TROMPETTE (French), *TROMPETE* (German)—Trumpet.

TROMPETE (German)—Trumpet.

WALD FLÖTE (German)—See Cor de Nuit.

ZIMBEL (German)—See Cymbale.

DESCRIPTIONS OF SOME "BAROQUE" ORGAN STOPS AS MADE TODAY
BY THE AEOLIAN-SKINNER ORGAN CO.

FLUEPIPES

KOPPELFLÖTE, 4'. Also used as a Nazard 2-2/3'.

2 ft. C. scale, 2½ in., mouth ¼. Slightly arched, cut ¼ to top of arch. ¾ inch opening at top of cone. Cone ¼ length of pipe, increasing as the compass ascends. 1 ft. C has a scale of 1-7/16 in. 6 in. C scale 13/16 in. The cut-up is lowered in treble. No flattening of upper lip. The canister top supporting the cone has the lower edge cut in a semi-spiral and a tit is soldered on the pipe, so the canister cannot slip. There is no packing, the top being fitted carefully to the pipe. The trebles are built up in power. The tone is very beautiful with a kind of transparent body. It is an excellent blender. Material preferably about 80% tin, spotted metal will do, but the tone suffers slightly.

KOPPEL GEDACKT AND SPILLFLOTE are modifications of the above. The former has a closed top and the latter has the cone portion half the length of the pipe body.

ROHRFLÖTE. 2 ft. C, scale 2-1/16 in. (cut up 2/7) (mouth ¼), slightly arched; no flattening of upper lip. Chimney ½ inch in diameter. Felt packing for canister. Spotted metal.

BOURDON. Similar to Rohrflöte, but with solid cap.

NACHTHORN. Open metal 30% tin. Scales, 4 ft. C - 3-7/16 in., 2 ft. C - 2¼ in., 1 ft. C - 1-7/16 in. 1/6 mouth cut up ¼. Full smooth flute tone.

BLOCKFLÖTE. 2 ft. C - 2-3/8 in. at mouth, 2/3rds diameter at top; mouth ¼ cut up ¼, slightly arched. Fine nicking; tin preferred. 1 ft. c - 1¾ in. at mouth; 6 in. C - 1 in. at mouth.

This type of stop is also used often for special types of mutations, such as 2-2/3 ft., 1-3/5 ft., and 1-1/3 ft. The Tierce has 1/6 mouth. The voicing is quite bold. An 8 ft. Gedackt, 4 ft. Nachthorn, 2-2/3 ft. Nazard, 2 ft. Blockflöte, and 1-3/5 ft. Tierce, create a Cornet tone of smooth

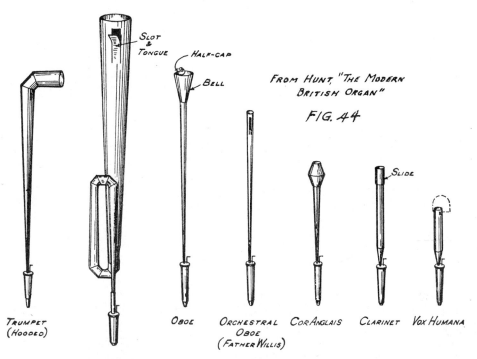

Slot & Tongue

Half-cap

Bell

FROM HUNT, "THE MODERN BRITISH ORGAN"

FIG. 44

Slide

TRUMPET (HOODED)

MITRED TROMBONE

OBOE

ORCHESTRAL OBOE (FATHER WILLIS)

COR ANGLAIS

CLARINET

VOX HUMANA

REED PIPES
(ILLUSTRATING PRINCIPAL EXAMPLES)

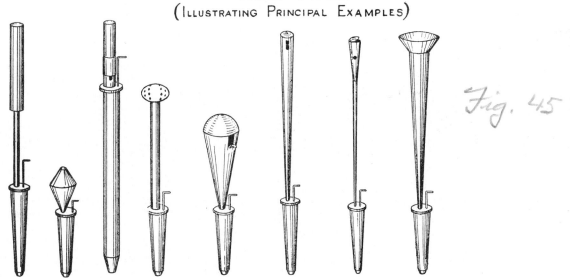

Fig. 45

ROHR SCHALMEI

BÄRPFEIFE

RANKET

APFEL-REGAL

EUPHONE

DULZIAN
FLÜGEL HORN
BASSOON
FAGOTTO

ORCHESTRAL OBOE (WALKER)

WALDHORN

IMITATIVE REED PIPES

Figure 106.

but powerful tone.

SIFFLÖTE 1 ft. Low C 1½ in.; 1/6 mouth, ¼ cut up; tin.

REEDS

CROMÔRNE OR KRUMMHORN. 4 ft. C of cylindrical resonator ¾ in., 2 ft. C - 5/8 in., 1 ft. C - ½ in. There is no inverted cone at the base of the resonator; not only does it go down to the block at the full diameter, but the latter is bored out so that the tube continues to the end of the shallot. The shallot is small, and tapered with a wide opening. Tongues are thin. Pressure 2½ in. to 5 in. The tone is powerful and similar to the Clarinet, with the fundamental greatly reduced in power and the characteristic harmonics greatly increased. It is a wonderful solo stop and is equally good as a chorus reed. One trick to make these pipes stable consists of giving the resonators plenty of "belly." In the treble they gradually flare at the top to keep up the power.

ROHR SCHALMEI. See Figure 45. Scale at 4 ft. C, 2¾ in.; body of pipe 8¼ in. long. Resonator, 2 ft. C, scale 1 in. Rohr, 3/8 in. brass. Tone more pure than Cromorne. Very lovely in solo or chorus use.

RANKETT. See Figure 45. Scale at 4 ft. C, 2¾ in.; body of pipe 8¼ in. long. Boot 2 ft. long. Notice that the cylindrical body extends down to the block and the tone issues through holes in the lower part of the body partially covered by a slide. The top of the resonator is closed. Internally there is a second portion of the resonator in the form of an inverted cone like a small-scaled Trumpet. This latter is open at the top and terminates about ½ in. from the cap of the main resonator. Note the unusual length of the boot.

CHORUS REEDS. Those preferred are refined versions of Cavaillé-Coll even to the Pedal 16 ft. and 32 ft. reeds in our later organs. No loading of tongues is employed. The speech of both 16 ft. and 32 ft. is much faster than the short loaded tongues usually used. No starters are necessary on the 32 ft. The objectionable "cough" in the speech of the low notes is entirely eliminated, and a much more even result is obtained. CCC of a Pedal 16 ft. has a vibrating length of 5-3/8 in., pressure 5 in. The tongues are draw filed so as to be thicker at the free end. This makes for an absolutely steady tone.

Professor Emile Rupp in his "Die Entwicklungsgeschichte der Orgelbaukunst" has the following to say concerning Silbermann organs:

"The cardinal principles of Silbermann construction and voicing are:

"1. Fullness and mellowness of tone by the use of large scales even in all harmonic corroborating stops.

"2. Homogenity of tone of each manual effected by permitting only small differences of scaling in the stops belonging to one manual.

"3. Strong contrast in the tonal character of each manual.

"4. Mild voicing of harmonic reenforcing stops (16' as well as upper-partials) so that these will not stand out as separate entities but are completely dissolved in the 8' foundation, thus strengthening the same mightily (by resultant tone).

"5. A complete set of harmonic corroborating stops on each manual."

Dr. Oscar E. Schminke has these comments to make on the principles stated above:

"Regarding No. 1, has not the great fault of upper-work in the past been its narrow scaling and faulty 'brilliant' voicing, which instead of reenforcing the 8' foundation caused a disagreeable, sour tone of ear-piercing quality? In the German organ of the nineteenth century the Mixtures were quite aptly nicknamed 'the screamers,' In a Silbermann the mutations are so voiced as to be used for coloring the 8' foundation and not merely to add brilliance. The latter is accomplished by the Mixtures. Even so, one can add Cymbel alone to the 8' foundation and still get a round, satisfying tone as this mixture is voiced very soft in the extreme treble. Yet this same Cymbel will cast a sheen like a spot-light over the full organ. Remember that after 1' the scale is kept very wide. A Silbermann ensemble in ascending from bass to treble reaches its maximum brilliance at about f^2 or g^2 and from there on gets milder as it goes up. This is quite contrary to the usual style of voicing which aims at a continuous crescendo up to the final note in the gamut. The ideal ensemble should to some extent combine these two principles, the former for Bach, the latter for Widor, using care however that the uppermost octaves do not scream.

"Regarding No. 2 and No. 3, unity and contrast of the different manuals, Gottfried defines his ideal as follows: Great, large and grave scaling; Oberwerk, brilliant, pointed scale and voicing; Brustpositiv, lieblich, delicate voicing; Pedal, strong penetrating voicing. We have at our command today a far larger assortment of colors than were ever vouchsafed the old masters, but we are still somewhat in the dark as to how the hues of the tonal palette should be grouped to the best advantage.

"Regarding No. 4 and 5, the subject of the blend of Silbermann upper-work with the 8' tone is one requiring the most intensive study on the part of any builder who desires to approximate the Silbermann ideal. The resultant 8' tone coming from such perfect blend is an important factor. The reason why the making of perfect harmonic-corroborating stops became more or less of a lost art is ascribed to various causes: a. Introduction of the tempered scale; b. Raising of the wind-pressure; c. Mania for excessively loud and raucous 8' and 16' tone. Rupp, an Alsatian, takes the French point of view and blames it all on Nietzsche and Wagner."

Plate XX

Kilgen Assembling Room
Organs are tested in factory before shipping, each one treated as an individual work of art.

A HISTORY OF TONAL DESIGN

We can now proceed to read more intelligibly and easily the stoplists which follow. First: The Schnitger organ.

Arp Schnitger, with whose organs Bach was familiar, (as his best work was done about the time of Bach's birth—1685) was probably the greatest of the baroque builders. His lifetime out put was about 40 organs, some of them up to 50 stops. Schnitger's work is characterized by being bolder and generally more distinguished than his contemporaries. The organ in Steinkirchen (20 miles from Hamburg) built 1685-7 has been recently restored by von Beckerath and is an excellent example of this builder's work.

HAUPTWERK	OBERWERK	PEDAL
Quintäton 16'	Gedackt 8'	Principal 16'
Prinzipal 8'	Rohrflöte 4'	Octav 8'
Rohrflöte 8'	Quinte 2-2/3'	Octav 4'
Octav 4'	Octav 2'	Nachthorn 2'
Nazat 2-2/3'	Spitzflöte 2'	Rausch quint II
Gemshorn 2'	Scharf III - V	Mixture IV
Mixture IV - VI	Krummhorn 8'	Posaune 16'
Cymbel III		Trompete 8'
Sesquialtera II		Kornett 2'
Trompete 8'		

Turning now to some of the organs upon which Bach played for the greater part of his life, we find at Arnstadt, where he first held the position of organist, an organ built in 1701 by J. F. Winder, of Muhlhausen.

HAUPTWERK	RÜCKPOSITIV	PEDAL
Quintäton 16'	Principal 8'	Sub bass 16'
Viola da Gamba 8'	Gedacht 8'	Octav 8'
Gedackt 8'	Spitzflöte 4'	Flötenbass 4'
Quinte 5-1/3'	Quinte 2-2/3'	Cornet bass 1-3/5'
Octav 4'	Sesquialtera II	Posaunen bass 16'
Mixture IV	Nachthorn 4'	
Gemshorn 8'	Mixtur II	
Cymbel II		
Trompete 8'		
Tremolo		
Cymbel stern		

The organ in the palace at Weimar contained the following:

HAUPTWERK	RÜCKPOSITIV	PEDAL
Quintäton 16'	Prinzipal 8'	Gross-untersatz 32'
Prinzipal 8'	Viol da Gamba 8'	Subbass 16'
Gemshorn 8'	Gedackt 8'	Violonbass 16'
Gedackt 8'	Klein Gedackt 4'	Principal Bass 8'
Octav 4'	Octav 4'	Posaunen bass 16'
Quintäton 4'	Wald flöte 2'	Trompeten bass 8'
Mixture VI	Sesquialtera	Cornett-bass 4'
Cymbel III		
Glockenspiel		

Plate XXI.

The organ built by the Austin Organ Company for the Sesquicentennial Exposition at Philadelphia in 1926, now installed in the Irvine Auditorium, University of Pennsylvania. The blowing plant is shown at the lower right. The re-enforced construction of the Austin Air chest is shown. The greater portion of the pipes are behind the horizontal shutters in the seven expression chambers. The organ was spread out across the stage for nearly one hundred feet in its original location.

A special feature of the organ at Cöthen was the pedal which boasted of two octaves and a half, from CCC-F'. The usual compass in Bach's time was CCC-D', 27 notes. Bach probably wrote the Toccata in F, after trying the organ at Cöthen. Bach made an expert examination (thereby becoming one of the first of that tribe known as "Organ architects,") of the organ in the University church at Leipsig. This was a remarkable instrument, which Bach was very fond of playing, and was a master work of Johann Scheibe, who also built the organ in the Thomaskirche.

1717, JOHANN SCHEIBE, UNIVERSITY CHURCH, LEIPSIG

HAUPTWERK	BRUSTWERK	RÜCKPOSITIV	PEDAL
Gross Prinzipal 16' (pure tin)	Prinzipal 8'	Gedackt 8'	Gross Prinzipal 16'
Gross Quintäton 16'	Viola d'Gamba 8'	Quintäton 8'	Gross Quintäton 16'
Klein Prinzipal 8'	Gedackt 8'	Flöte 4'	Octav 8'
Flute Allemande 8'	Octav 4'	Octav 4'	Octav 4'
Gemshorn 8'	Rohrflöte 4'	Twelfth 2-2/3'	Quinte 2-2/3'
Octav 4'	Nasat 2-2/3'	Hohlflöte 2'	Mixtur V-VI
Quinte 2-2/3'	Octav 2'	Viola 2'	Flöte 8'
Nazat 2-2/3'	Sedecimal 1'	Nineteenth 1/3'	Gross Quinte 5-1/3'
Octavina 2'	Schweitzerpfeife 1'	Weitpfeife 1'	Nachthorn 4'
Wald flöte 2'	Larigot 1-1/3'	Mixtur III	Octav 2'
Grosse Mixture V-VI	Mixtur III	Cymbel II	Second Prinzipal 16'
Cornett III	Cymbel II	Serpent 8'	Sub bass 16'
Zinkl, a species of Cornett of II Ranks			Posaune 16'
Schalmei 8'			Trompete 8'
			Hohlflöte 1'
			Mixtur IV

Thomas-kirche—built 1525, twice rebuilt during the 17th century, enlarged in 1670, and rebuilt in 1721 by Johann Scheibe. Stoplist below is as the organ was at the time Bach was playing upon it.

HAUPTWERK	BRUSTWERK	RÜCKPOSITIV	PEDAL
Prinzipal 16'	Grobgedackt 8'	Prinzipal 8'	Subbass 16'
Prinzipal 8'	Prinzipal 4'	Quintäton 8'	Posaune 16'
Quintäton 8'	Nachthorn 4'	Gedackt 8'	Trompete 8'
Speilpfeife 8'	Nasat 2-2/3	Klein gedackt 4'	Schalmei 4'
Octav 4'	Gemshorn 2'	Querflöte 4'	Cornett 2-2/3'
Quinte 2-2/3'	Cymbel II	Spitzflöte 4'	
Superoctav 2'	Sesquialtera II	Violine 2'	
Sesquialtera II	Regal 8'	Rauschquinte II	
Mixtur VI, VIII & X	Geigen regal 4'	Mixtur IV	
		Sesquialtera II	
		Schallflote 1'	
		Krummhorn 16'	
		Trompete 8'	

Plate XXII.

The organ in Emerson Richards' home in Atlantic City. Aeolian-Skinner Organ Co. More than

A HISTORY OF TONAL DESIGN

Although Bach played frequently upon organs built by Arp Schnitger and the Silbermann brothers, the organs enumerated above were the ones upon which he undoubtedly did the major part of his organ playing, during the course of a long life.

In contrast with the University organ in Leipsig, the pedal of which contained 17 independent registers, and 27 ranks, the one at the Thomaskirche contained only four Reeds and a Sub-bass 16'. No wonder Bach preferred the University organ. It should be said that the Reeds on the manuals of all German organs of the period amounted to very little.

Reeds were primarily reserved for the Pedal, where they were relied on to bring out pedal melodies against full organ, and to add weight and power to the Pedal.

To sum up the characteristics of the classic organ, whether German or French, we find that the registers were grouped according to their specific function.

There were three groups, as follows:

GROUP I DIAPASON CHORUS

	A	B	C	D
1. Principal	32'	16'	8'	4'
2. Octave	16'	8'	4'	2'
3. Twelfth	10-2/3'	5-1/3'	2-2/3'	1-1/3'
4. Fifteenth	8'	4'	2'	1'
5. Mixture	IV	IV	IV	III
6. Sharp	III	III	III	

GROUP II

Quintadena 16' — 8'
Gedackt 16' — 8'
Flute 4'
Nasat 2-2/3'
Tierce 1-3/5'
Larigot 1'
Piccolo 1'
Sesquialtera II
Cornet V

GROUP III

Trumpet 32' — 16' — 8' — 4'
Fagotto 16'
Oboe 8'
Regal 8'
Krummhorn 8'
Vox Humana 8'
Kornett 8'
Flute harmonique 8' — 4' — 2'
Nachthorn 4' — 2' — 1'
Wald flote 4' — 2' — 1'

Under group I, four distinct Diapason choruses are listed (A) of the 32', (B) of the 16', (C) of the 8', and (D) of the 4' harmonic series.

The registers of this group I form the Diapason ensemble. An inspection of the various stop lists given above will reveal this grouping on the various manuals. Take, for a good example, the University church, Leipsig organ. Here we have the Hauptwerk or Great with the Diapason chorus based on the 16' harmonic series: Principal 16', Small Principal 8', Octave 4', Quint 2-2/3', Fifteenth 2'. Grand Mixture V and VI. The

Brustwerk or Swell is based on the 8' harmonic series: Principal 8', Octave 4', Nasat 2-2/3', Octave 2', Mixture III. While on the Rückpositiv or Choir organ, the 4' harmonic series prevails, starting with Principal 4', Twelfth 2-2/3', Viola 2', Nineteenth 1-1/3' Weitpfeife 1' plus Mixture III.

Organum plenum, or full organ, originally consisted of any one or all the series of this group I. The term did not, therefore necessarily imply the use of couplers, since each manual was supplied with a full organ effect of its own. When coupling was used, it occurred between a 4' Manual and an 8' or between an 8' Manual and a 16' Manual, thus rendering unnecessary any octave couplers, unfortunately frequently necessary on the majority of modern organs.

Originally only the Diapason choruses were used in full organ, as outlined above. Later, in the Bach period, it had become usual to include foundation registers of Group II. The mutation and Mixture registers of Group II were not added, however.

Referring once more to the University church stoplist, and especially to the Rückpositiv, which lacks either 16' or 8' Diapason ranks. In such an instance, the 8' Gedackt might be used to supply requisite foundation tone. But the real point of the stop disposition in this organ is this: that so far as Group I or Diapason voices are concerned, the Hauptwerk is essentially based on the 16' harmonic series, the Brustwerk on the 8', and the Rückpositiv on the 4'. There are therefore three independent and complete Diapason choruses, with pitches averaging an octave apart, for contrast and variety, even though all manuals are played either separately or coupled.

Group II served for light ensemble and solo combinations. In ensemble use, the stops of Group II were used in regular, uninterrupted sequence, such as 8'-4'; 16'-8'; 4'-2'; 16'-8'-4'.

In solo combinations, regular order was avoided, and the stops were drawn in such a manner as to have at least two octave distance between the two flutes. For example, 8'-2'; 8'-1'; 16'-4'; 16'-2'; 16'-1'; 4'-1'; 16'-4'-1'. Either the above, or else a combination of unison or octave of unison plus a mutation pitch, such as 8'-2-2/3'; 16-1-1/3'; 4'-2-2/3'; 8'-2-2/3' 2'; 8'-2/23 1-3/5'. The Sesquialtera consisted of the 2-2/3' and 1-3/5' ranks. A cornet was formed by adding a 2' or 4'. The Sesquialtera was not included in the ensemble properly, as it was essentially used in solo combinations. Similarly other Mixtures such as Zimbel and Scharf, both of which contained a Tierce sounding rank were reserved for single line passages.

Group III is a typical list of solo stops of the baroque period. These Reeds were normally used alone for solo passages, rather than in combination with other ranks of this group. The Trumpet ranks were combined in groups of two or three, and occasionally added to full organ. Here, it should be noted that the German organ had comparatively few

Plate XXIII.

Small two manual Reuter organ, set up complete, in playing condition, on the erecting room floor. After thorough testing, the organ is dismantled and shipped. The organ will be installed permanently in a chamber, with only a shutter front required for the tone opening of the chamber.

Trumpets, and then only of 8' pitch, in contrast to the French organ of the same period, as made by Cliquot, for example. The French organ had well developed and important 16'-8' and 4' chorus Reeds, even before they became so all important to the ensembles of the nineteenth century Cavaillé-Coll organs. In classic French organs, the Trumpets were played separately, not added to the full organ, the same as was the German practice. The point is, that the classic French chorus Reeds were better and more important in themselves than the German.

To get more variety in solo effects, stops of Group III were combined with stops of Group II, and those of Group II with Group I. It should be noted carefully, however, that never were two 8' stops combined for solo passages. Always combined as in the following examples: Gedackt 8', Trumpet 4'; Gedackt 16', Vox Humana 8', Flute 4'; Gedackt 8', Octave 2'; Trumpet 16', Nasat 2-2/3', Cymbele III, etc.

Enough has been said to give the student an idea of the way in which the tonal resources were employed in the classic organ. The problem was one of selectivity. When the Diapason choruses were drawn, no flutes or Reeds were used, in ensemble passages, as they tended to obscure and thicken the polyphonic line. Also, they took additional wind. An ever present problem being to have sufficient wind, this may have had something to do with the custom also. I know that this statement is debatable, but the statement has good, common sense in its favor.

I have already said that Chorus Reeds were relied on primarily in the German classic organ, to give weight, solidity, and character to the pedal organ. At the Thomas-kirche, for example, there would have been no pedal without the Reeds, except a miserable 16' Sub-bass. This is an extreme example, as the normal classic German organ had many high pitched ranks of flue pipes, as in the University Church. But heavily winded 16' flue registers were distinctly not present, and I cannot but feel that this was primarily a wind problem. Reeds take about 10% to 20% as much wind to produce an equivalent volume of sound as flue pipes. In other words, Reeds are much easier on the blower, whether human, (inevitably the case in the classic organ) or the electric motor of the present day.

A recent interesting development of the German organ idea in America is the organ installed in 1937 in the Busch-Reisinger Museum of Harvard University. The organ has now been purchased by E. Power Biggs.

The pipe work is entirely exposed, no case.

Following his inclinations and convictions, Mr. G. Donald Harrison of the Aeolian-Skinner Organ Co. designed and finished this instrument which he chooses to call a "classic style" organ, for want of a better name.

The reader will notice that our stoplist indicates all pressures as

2½", and the Swell flues are tin (meaning, in organ parlance, 90% pure tin) while the Pedal and Great flue-work is spotted-metal. Also notice that there is no enclosure, nor is there a Tremulant. Mr. Harrison says further—

"The introduction of pneumatic blowing and mechanical action by Cavaille-Coll, the Frenchman, and Henry Willis, the Englishman, in the 19th century, increased the wind pressure and hence the volume of the organ, but decreased the original clarity of tone. In more recent years electrical blowers have again increased the pressure.

"Another embellishment was the increased use and invention of imitative stops such as the Celeste, the Harp, Chimes, Bells, Trumpets, French and English Horns. As a result of its transformation into an imitation symphony orchestra, the organ not only lost its original character but has come to be frowned on by every musician not an organist.

Neither Mr. Harrison, nor any competent organist believes "classic" organs capable of rendering modern music, such as the compositions of Karg-Elert, or of the modern French School satisfactorily. But as the Great and Choir divisions of a three manual organ, with addition of a modern Swell organ (with a Reed chorus, and soft Strings and Flutes, and an orchestral imitative stop or two, it could be made adequate for any type organ music. One most interesting observation I made while hearing Mr. Biggs play a Handel Concerto, some Bach Choral Preludes, and some of the precursors of Bach upon this organ, was that it was possible to get not only the clarity necessary for contrapuntal music, but some of the soft effects with the mutations and Sifflöte that were positively "ear tickling." Actually it equalled such vaunted modern solo effects as French Horns, Flute Celestes and other orchestral voices. I found this of extreme interest, and it no doubt will be to many another organist who may be misled by associating the term "classic" organ with such words as severe, austere and cold. It need not necessarily be so.

Finally, this instrument is no mere duplication of the Bach organs— the old principles are given the advantages of our times.

A CLASSIC ORGAN
Built by
Aeolian-Skinner Organ Co.
Designed & Finished by
G. Donald Harrison

HAUPTWERKE 2½" pressure: UNEXPRESSIVE		POSITIV 2½" pressure: UNEXPRESSIVE		PEDAL 2½" pressure:	
16	Quintade	8	Koppelfloete	16	Bourdon
8	Principal	4	Nachthorn	8	Gedeckt Bass
8	Spitzfloete	2-2/3	Nasat	8	Principal
4	Principal	2	Blockfloete	4	Nachthorn
4	Rohrfloete	1-3/5	Terz 61t	2	Blockfloete
2-2/3	Quinte	1	Siffloete	4	Fourniture 3r
2	Superoctave	½	Cymbel 3r	16	Posaune
1-1/3	Fourniture 4r	8	Krummhorn (brass)	8	Trumpet
				4	Krummhorn

Plate XXIV.

Liverpool Cathedral console. The photo from which our plate was made is from the excellent collection by Mr. Gilbert Benham. Stop-knobs are grouped, from left to right, in vertical rows: Swell, Bombarde and Echo, Choir enclosed and unenclosed, Couplers. Right side: Couplers, Solo (enclosed String tone, and unenclosed), Great, Pedal enclosed and unenclosed. In addition to the groups of nine Pistons centrally located under the respective manuals, and the Adjuster to the right of each, there are the Bombarde On and the Echo On, under the Echo treble, and the Solo Trombones to Great under the Great treble.

A more recent example of a "classic" organ which is carried a few steps further to provide the basis for a modern Swell organ is that which is given below. Plate XIII shows the disposition of the pipe work, mostly in the open, except for the two sections of the Swell organ. (This organ was formerly in the studio of Ernest White, Church of Saint Mary the Virgin, New York. Now in Ontario, Canada.)

Designed by: G. Donald Harrison.

Builder: Aeolian-Skinner Organ Co., Boston, Mass.

Wind pressure: three inches throughout. All stops are metal, with the exception of the Pedal Contre-Basse.

PEDAL			COUPLERS		
	16'	Contre-Basse		Swell Flues to Pedal	8'
	16'	Quintation		Swell Reeds to Pedal	8'
	8'	Spitz Prinzipal		Positiv to Pedal	8'
	4'	Rohrflote		Swell Flues to Pedal	4'
	IV	Fourniture		Swell Reeds to Pedal	4'
	II	Cornet		Positiv to Pedal	4'
	32'	Sakbutt		Swell Flues to Great	8'
	16'	Bassoon		Swell Reeds to Great	8'
	8'	Bassoon		Positiv to Great	8'
	4'	Bassoon		Swell Flues to Positiv	8'
				Swell Reeds to Positiv	8'
GREAT	16'	Quintaton		Positiv to Swell	8'
	8'	Bourdon		Great to Swell	8'
	4'	Prestant			
	2-2/3'	Quint	COUPLERS ON STOP JAMBS		
	2'	Octavin			
POSITIV	8'	Cor de Nuit		Sub Octave	
	4'	Koppelflöte		Super Octave	
	2-2/3'	Nazard			
	2'	Blockflöte			
	1-3/5'	Tierce			
	III	Cymbale			
SWELL				Sub Octave	
"Flues"	8'	Gambe		Flue Ventil	
	8'	Gambe Céleste		Super Octave	
	4'	Rohrflöte			
	III	Plein Jeu			
		Tremolo			
"Reeds"	16'	Bassoon		Sub Octave	
	8'	Trompette		Reed Ventil	
	4'	Cromorne		Super Octave	

The organ is basically of "classic" design, continuing a tradition of American classical organ construction started with the Busch-Reisinger Museum organ in Cambridge, further exemplified in Carl Weinrich's studio organ, the Tanglewood Shed and Worcester Art Museum organs, and culminating in this small, but tonally versatile instrument. In keeping with classical ideas, the Great organ is of eight-foot pitch, in which flue tone predominates. The Positive organ is also a flue ensemble, but of

Plate XXV.

St. Michael's, Hamburg. This console controls the largest organ in Germany. Note the old fashioned, flat pedal board which is still used in Germany. The register crescendo is operated by means of the large roller or drum immediately above the pedal keys. It is difficult to imagine why this arrangement should be more convenient than the ordinary register crescendo pedal. The large number of stop controls are conveniently disposed in somewhat elliptical fashion. The stop controls are a form of rocking tablet. The builder of this console, Walcker, has used a modern pedal board on the console for the Barcelona Fair organ.

four-foot, or octave pitch, and is of less dynamic power than the Great. The elaborate Pedal division is capable of adequate support of the upper divisions without need of resort to pedal to manual or octave couplers. All these features are found in the continental organs of the baroque period.

This remarkable organ also possesses a Swell division, further divided into two expressive boxes, one containing the flues, the other the reed stops of the manual. Couplers and ventils allow an extremely versatile use of this division, as it may be coupled in a number of ways to the rest of the instrument, as well as dynamically balanced against itself. This feature makes the organ useful not only for the classical literature, but also for performance of the 19th and 20th century music for organ, which usually presupposes an expressive division in the organ. The sheer versatility of this division would have given George Ashdown Audsley, the late organ architect, great joy, as it embodies a principle long fought for by him—the use of ancillary or floating expressive divisions containing stops of one tonal family, each in its own box.

The tonal scheme is complete without the use of sub or super-octave couplers. These have been added only to allow the easier performance of certain works, which may be facilitated by shifting the compass of the manuals to suit the music. As the instrument was primarily designed for teaching and recital work, clarity in tonal design has been the prime factor. Photograph and description by courtesy of H. Vose Greenough of Brookline, Mass.

Mr. Walter Holtkamp, of Cleveland, is an organ builder who has not only expressed dissatisfaction with the way organs have been built, but he is doing something about it. Along with Mr. Harrison and others he is quietly but persistently working and thinking in an intelligent way to bring forth tonally more satisfactory organs.

One of Mr. Holtkamp's strongest contentions is that organs should never be buried in chambers. For organs which he builds, he demands an open position with preferably no case work. He prefers that the speaking pipes themselves on their windchests, arranged symmetrically, should be seen in lieu of casework, grilles or dummy pipes. All advantage then is given to the organ, especially if on low pressure.

Mr. Holtkamp has carried into action during these past fifteen years the above theories of organ location in numerous examples. He has sent me a dozen photographs of organs built by him, each one with a good part of the pipes in the open. I have chosen three from these various examples which are shown in Plates XIV and XVII. One, a two manual in the Miles Park Presbyterian Church, Cleveland, has the following disposition of stops:

Plate XXVI.

The seven-manual console complete with adjustible bench removed. At top telephone set communicating with other console, orchestra pit, main chambers, etc. Next row crescendo indicator to left; ammeter to right. Next row indicator lights for each crescendo pedal. Music rack is adjustable and can be brought down over the sixth and seventh manual if desired. The stop keys are white, the intermanual couplers black with white letters, the other couplers and accessories grey with black letters.

PEDAL

Subbass 16'
Quintaton 16' From Great
Gedackt 8'
Gemshorn 4'
Trompette 16'
Fagott 8'

GREAT

Quintaton 16'
Principal 8'
Salicional 8'
Octave 4'
Rohrflöte 4'

SWELL (enclosed)

Geigen Principal 8'
Harmonic Flute 8'
Aeoline 8'
Hohlflöte 4'
Nazard 2-2/3'
Tierce 1-3/5'
Mixture IV
Cromorne 8'
Oboe Clarion 4'

Another in The First Church of Christ, Scientist, Cleveland Heights, is a small three manual with the following stop-list:

PEDAL

Subbass 16'
Quintaton 16' From Great
Octave Subbass 8' Extension
Octave Quintaton 8' Extension
Choralbass 4'
Fagott 8'.

SWELL

Harmonic Flute 8'
Salicional 8'
Gemshorn 4'
Flautino 2'
Plein Jeu V
Oboe Clarion 4'

GREAT

Quintaton 16'
Principal 8'
Copula 8'
Octave 4'
Gedacktflöte 4'

CHOIR (enclosed)

Gedackt 8'
Aeoline 8'
Aeoline Celeste 8'
Flute a Cheminee 4'
Nazard 2-2/3'

A much larger three-manual is in the Cleveland Art Museum. This organ is a more or less complete reconstruction of an early Skinner organ, which was originally installed in the same location. Although there are some of the pipes retained in their original state many others have been rescaled, and used at pitches other than their original pitches. A great many new sets have been added.

The present stop-list of this organ is as follows:

Plate XXVII. Unique console of the largest organ in the world in the Wanamaker Grand Court, Philadelphia. Designed by Charles M. Courboin and built in the Wanamaker Shops, under the supervision of George Till and William Fleming.

A HISTORY OF TONAL DESIGN

PEDAL

Contrabass 32'
Major Bass 16'
Subbass 16'
Quintadena 16' From Great
Lieblich Gedackt 16'
Octave 8'
Gedackt 8'
Quinte 5-1/3'
Choralbass 4'
Nachthorn 4'
Tierce 3-1/5'
Piccolo 2'
Mixture III
Contra Posaune 16'
Dulzian 16'
Trumpet 8'
Cromorne 8'
Schalmey 4' From Great

GREAT

Quintadena 16'
Principal 16'
Gedackt 8'
Salicional 8'
Grossoctav 4'
Octave 4'
Spitzflöte 4'
Quinte 2-2/3'
Superoctave 2'
Harmonics IV
Mixture IV
Dulzian 16'
Schalmey 8'

SWELL (Enclosed)

Geigen Principal 8'
Chimney Flute 8'
Quintation 8'
Gambe 8'
Voix Celeste 8'
Octave Geigen 4'
Bourdon 4'
Blockflote 2'
Octavlein 2'
Cornet Dolce III
Plein Jeu V
Fagott 16'
Trompette 8'
Clarion 4'
Vox Humana 8'

POSITIV—Open Section

Copula 8'
Principal 4'
Rohrflöte 4'
Nazard 2-2/3'
Doublette 2'
Tierce 1-3/5'
Fourniture III

POSITIV (Enclosed Section)

Concert Flute 8'
Dulciana 8'
Erzähler Celeste 8'
Fugara 4'
Flautino 2'
Flugel Horn 8'

Mr. Holtkamp has reconstructed a number of fine old organs, besides the Skinner in the Cleveland Art Museum. A notable one is the Johnson organ in the First Presbyterian Church, Evanston, Illinois. The author gave the rebuilt organ to this church in 1940, as a memorial to his aunt and uncle. During the reconstruction of this large three manual Johnson of some forty sets, (increased to fifty in the rebuild,) he became very familiar with the ideas of Mr. Holtkamp. I might say that there was not complete agreement on all points between us. This is natural and healthy. Mr. Holtkamp has been influenced in his thinking about organ design and the location of organs very largely by three men, who were all of them, at one time, located in Cleveland. All three of the following: Mr. Walter Blodgett, now the organist of the Cleveland Art Museum, Mr. Arthur Quimby, formerly the organist of the Museum and Mr. Melville Smith, now of the Longy School, Cambridge, have exerted all the persuasive powers at their command to induce Mr. Holtkamp to build the type of organs that are illustrated above. Besides this, I believe that

Plate XXVIII.

Riverside Church, New York City. Aeolian-Skinner Organ Co., Builders. This console controls one of the largest church organs in the world.

Mr. Holtkamp was following his own convictions, and would have gone a good part of the way he has, without the pressure exerted by these men.

A number of other builders, notably, Austin Organs, Inc., M. P. Moller, Inc., Reuter Organ Co. and Schantz Organ Co. have occasionally built organs copying in many respects the sound of the 17th and 18th century classic organ.

THE 19TH CENTURY FRENCH ORGAN

Continuing with our history of tonal design we shall skip about a century. We now turn our attention to the organ in France, as typified by the work of that great master builder, Cavaillé-Coll. After the French Revolution, there had been a hiatus in French organ building, and it wasn't until Cavaillé-Coll started building organs around 1840, that French organ building became important again. He dominated the French scene for nearly sixty years. Even to the present day, not only in Paris, where practically all of the important organs are his work, but in other parts of France as well, the influence and the tangible expression of his art are still heard. Cavaillé-Coll owed little to tradition or to his predecessors. He struck out along entirely new paths for the most part. This is little less than a miracle, for the French people are generally considered to be extremely conservative, and greatly opposed to change of any sort. They believe in venerating the past, and have the greatest respect for tradition. Once in a long time a man like Cavaillé-Coll arises, who does not believe like Elijah "I am not better than my fathers," and proceeds to change completely the traditions, customs and thinking of a whole art, such as organ building. The name for such a man is genius.

The flue chorus in the Cavaillé-Coll organ was built on a heterogeneous foundation; a radical departure from the 18th century notion of Diapason chorus plus flutes.

The 8' stops of a typical Cavaillé-Coll Great organ are a Diapason, Gamba, Flute harmonique and Bourdon. All four registers are of only moderate power and voiced with a view to good blending ability. The Gamba is more like a Geigen Diapason. The two flutes, though contrasting, one being double length, and the other stopped, are neither of them thick or tubby. The Diapason is also somewhat thin and of no particular substance. The outstanding feature of all Cavaillé-Coll organs were the chorus Reeds. These were always of considerable power, extremely fast attack, great brilliance and good regulation. On my visits to numerous examples of Cavaillé-Coll organs in Paris, I only once heard a French organ with these glorious Reeds in good tune. This is a matter of regret, and easily corrected by more frequent servicing. It has already been mentioned that Cavaillé-Coll took the excellent Clicquot style of Reeds and greatly improved them by raising the wind pressure and making the trebles

Plate XXIX.

The Austin Console in St. George's Church, New York City. The organ
is divided between the front and rear of the church. Hence the combination
pistons are divided.

harmonic, thus increasing the power and improving the quality in that portion of the compass where all Reed Stops are usually weak.

The organ in the church of Ste. Clotilde, Paris.

Cavaillé-Coll, 1859—Compass Manuals CC-F3, 54 notes. Pedals CCC-D-27 notes.

César Franck played this organ from 1859 until the year of his death, 1890

GRAND ORGAN	POSITIF	COUPLERS
Montre 16'	Bourdon 16'	Great to Pedal 8'
Bourdon 16'	Montre 8'	Swell to Pedal 8'
Montre 8'	Gambe 8'	Choir to Pedal 8'
Gambe 8'	Flute Harmonique 8'	Swell to Great 16'-8'
Flute Harmonique 8'	Salicional 8'	Choir to Great 16'-8'
Bourdon 8'	Prestant 4'	Great to Great 16'
Prestant 4'	Flute Octaviante 4'	Great Unison off
Octave 4'	Quinte 2-2/3	
Quinte 2-2/3'	Doublette 2'	
Doublette 2'	Plein Jeu III	
Plein Jeu IV-V	Clarinette 8'	
Bombarde 16'	Trompette 8'	
Trompette 8'	Clairon 4'	
Clairon 4'		

RECIT. EXPRESSIF.	PEDALE	VENTILS BY TOE STUDS
Bourdon 8'	Quintatön 32'	Reeds to Pedal
Flute Harmonique 8'	Contre basse 16'	Reeds to Great
Viole de Gambe 8'	Flute 8'	Reeds to Choir
Voix Celeste 8'	Octave 4'	Reeds to Swell
Flute Octaviante 4'	Bassoon 16'	
Octavin 2'	Bombarde 16'	
Bassoon-Hautbois 8'	Trompette 8'	
Voix Humaine 8'	Clairon 8'	
Trompette 8'		
Clairon 4'		
Tremolo		

It should be noted that the Reeds on all manuals and pedals could be drawn in advance, and disconnected from the various divisions, until wanted, by means of four ventils. When the ventils were opened by toe studs, the Reeds came into play. Except for this ventil system there was no equivalent for a combination action of any kind; no crescendo pedal, no full organ pedal, no registrational assistance to the organist. The limitations of control of the stops and couplers of the nineteenth century French organ were necessarily taken into account by the French composers of this period. Thus we find no pedal part ordinarily written in, where there is a rapid change from full organ to the Swell alone, and back to full organ, because of the impossibility of making such a rapid

Plate XXX.
The large Casavant console in the Royal York Hotel, Toronto, Canada.

change in the pedal stops and couplers. Gigout's, "Grand Choeur Dialogue" is a good example. We even can discover more or less barren spots in many of César Franck's more extended pieces for the organ, because he was taking time out to make a new registrational set-up. This does not necessarily detract from the greatness of the music, but it is surely interesting to know why some of it was written the way it was. No wonder nearly all of the French organists of the day needed an assistant to help with the registration. Actually they needed about three men and a boy, because the stop-knobs themselves pulled out by the yard, and it was impossible to manipulate them rapidly, as with a modern console, either with or without combinations. But the sounds that the French organists and composers heard from the Cavaillé-Coll organs in the superb, resonant churches, inspired some magnificent writing for the instrument.

It is interesting to note that the Positif was almost a duplicate of the Grand Orgue, lacking the 16' Diapason and 16' Reed. Naturally the total effect of the Positif is somewhat lighter, and there is a contrast between the two manuals in spite of an almost identical list of stops. The Swell to Great 16' coupler was perhaps justified as there was no 16' stop on the Swell. The French composers of the last half of the nineteenth century had a predilection for writing full organ effects at the top of the short compass keyboards, and in this region naturally, the 16' couplers added considerable sonority and fullness, and mitigated the 2' stops and Mixtures.

THE 19TH CENTURY ENGLISH ORGAN

The great English builder, Henry Willis, as early as 1855 demonstrated that he was fifty years ahead of his time, in the epoch-making organ which was installed in St. Georges Hall, Liverpool. This organ was, and still is today, after nearly a hundred years, a high point in organ building, tonally and mechanically. The present Henry Willis has brought the console and action completely up-to-date, and added some modern solo stops and mutations, but, generally speaking, the organ remains tonally in its original condition. It was built in 1855. This organ was so damaged in the air raids of 1940/41 that it has been in unplayable condition. There is consideration being given to its restoration.

Among other innovations, was the first modern concave-radiating pedal keyboard, devised by S. S. Wesley, and Mr. Willis. This is the pedal board now universally used in America and England, and other countries that do not live entirely in the past. But it was more than fifty years in gaining general acceptance in England and America. It will probably take another hundred years to have it generally used in France and Germany. By that time it will have become old enough to be of interest to the antiquarians.

Plate XXXI.

Plymouth Congregational Church, Lansing, Michigan.   Kilgen Organ Co.

A HISTORY OF TONAL DESIGN

To get back to our chief concern, the tonal innovations and improvements in this organ. Even though William Hill had introduced heavy wind pressure for solo Reed stops fifteen years earlier, it remained for Henry Willis I, (born 1821) to develope a whole series of chorus Reeds on heavy wind, with increased pressures in the upper portion of the compass. This latter idea undoubtedly came from Cavaillé-Coll, but Willis used partly closed shallots, rather than the traditional parallel open shallots of the French builders. By the methods of voicing Reeds developed by Henry Willis and his brother George, a purity and brilliance, combined with refinement and evenness of tone, plus a proper balance between treble and bass never before imagined, was produced. Henry's gifted son Vincent developed these methods still further. Here was inaugurated an entirely new school of Reed voicing, and one that contains all of the characteristics of the best of present-day work. However, present day voicers have found it possible to get excellent results with lighter pressures.

St. Georges Hall, Liverpool, began a renaissance of English organ building. That organ can still hold its own tonally against any present-day organ. The striking grandeur of the Willis Full Great, was matched by the superb 16'-8'-4' chorus Reeds of the Full Swell plus Mixture.

Here is the St. Georges Hall specification, as it is at the present day, after the 1931, Henry Willis, (III), rebuild. The additions consist of the series of choir mutations, the French Horn, and some additional pedal upper work.

GREAT	SWELL	CHOIR ORGAN
Double Diapason 16'	Double Diapason 16'	
Bourdon 16'	Diapason 8'	Contra-Viola 16'
Diapason I 8'	Geigen Diap. 8'	Diapason 8'
Diapason II 8'	Rohr Flute 8'	Gamba 8'
Diapason III 8'	Aeoline 8'	Hohl Flöte 8'
Tibia 8'	Salicional 8'	Stopped Diapason 8'
Viola 8'	Voix Celeste 8'	Dulciana 8'
Stopped Diapason 8'	Principal 4'	Vox Angelica 8'
Quint 5-1/3'	Geigen Octave 4'	Principal 4'
Octave 4'	Wald Flote 4'	Octave Viola 4'
Principal 4'	Twelfth 2-2/3'	Flute Harmique 4'
Octave Viola 4'	Fifteenth 2'	Nazard 2-2/3'
Tenth 3-1/5'	Piccolo 2'	Fifteenth 2'
Twelfth 2-2/3'	Seventeenth 1-3/5'	Harmonic Piccolo 2'
Fifteenth 2'	Doublette II	Tierce 1-3/5'
Seventeenth 1-3/5'	Fourniture IV	Larigot 1-1/3'
Doublette II	Clarinet 16'	Septieme 1-1/7'
Sesquiltera V	Clarinet 8'	Harmonic Piccolo 1'
Mixture 4'	Oboe 8'	Sesquialtera III
*Contra Trombone 16'	Clarion 4'	Bass Clarinet 16'
*Trombone 8'	Tremolo	Orchestral Oboe 8'
*Ophiclide 8'	*Trombone 16'	Trumpet 8'
Trumpet 8'	*Ophiclide 8'	Clarion 4'
Clarion I 4'	*Trumpet 8'	Tremolo
Clarion II 4'	*Horn 8'	

Plate XXXII.

SOLO ORGAN

Quintaten 16'
Tibia 8'
Violoncello 8'
Cello Celeste 8'
Tibia Clausa 8'
Violin 4' II Ranks
Flute Harmonique 4'
Piccolo 2'
Cor Anglais 16'
Bassoon 8'
Corno di Basetto 8'
Vox Humana 8'
Tremolo
Chimes
*French Horn 8'
*Double Tuba 16'
*Tuba 8'
*Tuba Clarion 4'
 Solo Diapason 8'
 Grand Chorus VIII
 Tuba Mirabilis 8'
 (30" pressure)

*Heavy Wind Pressure

PEDAL ORGAN

Resultant Bass 64'
Double open Bass 32'
Double Diapason 32'
Open Bass 16'
Contra Bass 16'
Diapason 16'
Violon 16'
Bourdon 16'
Salicional 16'
Quintaten (solo) 16'
Octave 8'
Principal 8'
Flute 8'
Octave Quint 5-1/3'
Fifteenth 4'
Viole (Violone) 4'
Octave Flute 4'
Fourniture VR
Mixture IIIR
Clarinet 16'
*Bombarde 32'
*Posaume 16'
*Ophicleide 16'
*Clarion 8'
*Octave Clarion 4'

An almost equally famous "Father" Willis organ is the one in St. Paul's Cathedral, London, built in 1872. The Full Swell is doubtless the most remarkable in existence of any Full Swell with only twelve stops.

GREAT ORGAN

Double Diapason 16'
Diapason I 8'
Diapason II 8'
Claribel Flute 8'
Quint 5-1/3'
Principal 4'
Flute Harmonique 4'
Octave Quint 2-2/3'
Super Octave 2'
Fourniture IIIR
(17-19-22)
Mixture IIIR
(24-26-29)
Trombone 16'
Tromba 8'
Clarion 4'

SWELL ORGAN

Contra Gamba 16'
Diapason 8'
Gedackt 8'
Salicional 8'

Vox Angelica 8'
Principal 4'
Fifteenth 2'
Echo Cornet IIIR
(17-19-22) ·
Contra Posaune 16'
Cornopean 8'
Hautbois 8'
Clarion 4'
Tremolo

CHOIR ORGAN

Bourdon 16'
Diapason 8'
Dulciana 8'
Violoncello 8'
Claribel Flute 8'
Gedackt 8'
Principal 4'
Flute Harmonique 4'
Flageolet 2'
Cor Anglais 8'
Corna di Bassetto 8'
Tremolo

SOLO ORGAN

Flute Harmonique 8'
Concert Flute 4'
Cornodi Bassetto 8'
Orchestral Oboe 8'
Tuba Magna 8'
Tuba Clarion 4'

PEDAL ORGAN

Double Diapason 32'
Diapason 16'
Violone 16'
Octave 8'
Violoncello 8'
Mixture III
(17-19-22)
 Contra Posaune 32'
*Grand Bombarde 16'
*Clarion 8'
*Heavy wind

Plate XXXIII.

Console of the large Reuter organ in the University of North Carolina at Chapel Hill.

A HISTORY OF TONAL DESIGN

Edmund Schulze, a contemporary of Henry Willis, was the celebrated organ builder of Paulinzelle, Saxony, who did his most important work in England. His work has already been mentioned. His Diapason chorus on 3-3/4" wind pressure was overwhelming in its grandeur, and needed no support from Reeds. In fact, the full Schulze Great was improved by omission of the Great Reeds. The best known examples of Schulze's work in England are at Doncaster, Tyne Dock, Armley, and Hindley. Apparently the big cities of England have no specimens of his work.

The boldest of the Schulze Diapasons is on the Great at St. Mary's, Tyne Dock. This is the Diapason which has caught the ear of many English organ builders, and more attempts have been made to imitate it than any other. Dr. Audsley quotes this example as the ideal Diapason tone for a large building. "A copious supply of wind on 3-3/4" wind pressure."

The Schulze organ in the Doncaster Parish church was built in 1862, following a fire in 1853 that destroyed the building and organ. Abbott and Smith of Leeds in 1894 installed a new console and action. The organ was further rebuilt in 1910 by Norman and Beard of Norwich. J. W. Walker and Sons did a restoration in 1935, including electrifying of the entire action and additional reservoirs and generally preserving the original Schulze character. The compass is apparently still only to A3 on the manuals (58 notes) and to F on the Pedals (30 notes).

GREAT ORGAN

Sub Bass, T.C. 32'
Double Diapason 16'
Bourdon 16'
Diapason I 8'
Diapason II 8'
Stopped Diapason 8'
Hohl Flute 8'
Principal 4'
Stopped Flute 4'
Gemshorn 4'
Quint 5-1/3'
Twelfth & Fifteenth II
Mixture V
Cymbel III & V
Cornet IV
Double Trumpet 16'
Posaune 8'
Trumpet 8'
Clarion 4'

SWELL ORGAN

Bourdon 16'
Diapason 8'
Terpodian 8'
Echo Gamba 8'
Voix Celeste 8'
Flute Harmonique 4'
Stopped Flute 4'
Principal 4'
Violed 'Amour 4'
Mixture VR
Scharf IIIR
Cornet IVR
Double Bassoon 16'
Trumpet 8'
Horn 8'
Hautbois 8'
Clarion 4'
Vox Humana 8'
Tremolo

CHOIR ORGAN

Lieblich Bourdon 16'
Geigen Principal 8'
Violda Gamba 8'
Gemshorn 8'
Salicional 8'
Flauto Traverso 8'
Lieblich-Gedackt 8'
Flauto Traverso 4'
Lieblich Flöte 4'
Geigen Principal 4'
Quintaten 4'
Flautina 2'
Trompette 8'

SOLO ORGAN

Gamba 8'
Gamba Celeste 8'
Claribel Flute 8'
Concert Flute 8'
Clarinet 8'
Orchestral Oboe 8'
Tremolo
(Mutations in Solo box)
Nazard 2-2/3
Piccolo 2'
Tierce 1-3/5'
Septreme 1-1/7'
Octave Piccolo 1'

ECHO ORGAN

Tibia Major 16'
Harmonica 8'
Vox Angelica 8'
Flauto Amabile 8'
Flauto Traverso 4'
Celstina 4'
Flauto Dolcissimo 4'
Harmonia Aetheria IIR
Tremolo

PEDAL ORGAN

Sub Principal 32'
Major Bass 16'
Principal Bass 16'
Open Bass 16'
Violone 16'
Dulciana 16'
Sub Bass 16'
Major Bass 8'
Flute Bass 8'
Violoncello 8'
Octave Bass 8'
Quint Bass 10-2/3'
Gross Tierce 6-2/5'
Quint 5-1/3'
Fifteenth 4'
Tierce 3-1/5'
Mixture II
Cymbell II
Contra Posaune 32'
Posaune 16'
Bombarde 16'
Contra Fagotto 16'
Bassoon (Swell) 16'
Trumpet 8'
Horn 8'
Fagotto 8'
Clarion 4'

A HISTORY OF TONAL DESIGN

Some of the other great English organ builders such as Harrison and Harrison, John Compton Organ Company, Rushworth and Dreaper, Hill, Norman & Beard, and the earlier pioneer, T. C. Lewis, should be mentioned. The examples of Willis and Schulze are cited in detail, as having more historic interest and particularly as having more influence on present day American organ building, with which this book is primarily concerned.

THE 19TH CENTURY AMERICAN ORGAN

We are now ready to turn to a brief history of American Tonal Design, before proceeding to the present day work of our leading builders. Here we must pause and pay our deepest respect to the work of a number of the best American builders of the latter half of the 19th century. With one or two exceptions, these firms are now out of existence, their founders and chief members having long since passed to their reward. After fifty or a hundred years, it is easier to give a fair estimate of the true worth of these builders. No element of competition or bias need warp our judgment.

Those organs built by Henry Erben, E. and G. G. Hook, Jardine & Son, Johnson & Son, J. H. & C. S. Odell, and Hilborne & Frank Roosevelt are especially noteworthy. These names are arranged chronologically. A little later than these, we find Steere & Turner, Steere & Son, George S. Hutchings, Farrand & Votey and Felgemaker.

I am selecting from a long list of specifications of organs by these builders a few representative ones, to enable the student to gain an idea of the characteristics of the best American organs of approximately a hundred years ago. A good many of the organs of these builders have been discarded for a modern electro-pneumatic organ, that is easier for the organist to play, but perhaps not so good for the listener's ears. Others have been rebuilt and modernized. If the original wind pressures have not been tampered with, a good part of the effect of the original organ may still be retained, and I have had personal experience with the sympathetic modernization of one of the last of the fine Johnsons, and the largest and most important of Roosevelt's work. As both of these organs were dated around 1890, they represent the last of the 19th century work.

What was the secret of these 19th century American organs, and their success as musical instruments? Take for example the organ built by Henry Erben in 1830 in Grace Church, New York City. It is still supporting the congregational singing of a large, wealthy congregation. Mr. Hilborne Roosevelt declared in print that it is "of singularly pure tone quality" and would not permit the congregation to dispose of it when he added a chancel organ in 1878. It is used to this day to accompany the hymns. What was Henry Erben's secret? The Great organ has nine stops, one of which is a III Rank Mixture, making eleven ranks. Seven of them are Diapason tone, and at seven different pitches. They blend into a glorious chorus. Two flutes and an 8' and 4' Trumpet complete the Great. Erben's famous gallery organ in Trinity Church, Wall Street, built in 1846 has ten stops on the Great, two of which are Mixtures, making fourteen ranks in all. Of the fourteen ranks, ten are of Diapason tone. These occur at 16', 8'-4'-2-2/3'-2'-1', with a 32' Pedal Diapason to support this chorus.

The work of Elias and George Hook, from 1827 to 1881 tells the same story: a good Diapason chorus in the Great division and chorus Reeds and more Mixtures in the Swell.

The Hook organ in Henry Ward Beecher's church, built in 1866 contained 52 stops and 64 ranks. Of these 30 were Diapason tone.

Four generations of the Odell family have been building organs from 1859 to date. The Gallery organ of the Collegiate church of St. Nicholas had Odell Diapasons which are still recalled with great warmth of feeling by all who attended Sunday afternoon recitals there.

Mr. F. R. Webber writes "within a few feet of me are some 2000 stoplists of organs by Goodrich, Appleton, Erben, Johnson, Hall & Labagh, the Odells, the Hooks, Hook & Hastings, the Roosevelts, the Jardines, Farrand & Votey, Hutchings, Steere & Son and several present day builders. Wherever there is a good organ, the story is always the same. It was no accident that the organs of the better builders were famed for their grandeur of tonal quality. They thought of an organ as a *good ensemble.*"

Fortunately today, in many quarters, where organs are considered intelligently, and with due respect and understanding of what the organ's history and tradition have been in this country, we are thinking along the same lines. This is after having gone rather far afield during the first three decades of the twentieth century when we thought in terms of unrelated, individual voices.

Here is a stop list of a Henry Erben organ, built a century ago.

EMMANUEL CHURCH, BALTIMORE, MARYLAND
Henry Erben, 1852
Rebuilt by Frank Roosevelt, 1892

GREAT ORGAN:

Double Diapason 16'
Diapason 8'
Gemshorn 8'
Gamba 8'
Doppel flöte 8'
Octave 4'
Dolce flute 4'
Mixture, IV Ranks
Trumpet 8'

SWELL ORGAN:

Bourdon 16'
Open diapason 8'
Spitz flöte 8'
Salicional 8'
*Voix celeste 8'
Stopped flute 8'
Harmonic flute 4'
Flageolet 2'
Cornet III Rands

Cornopean 8'
Oboe 8'
Vox Humana 8'
Tremulant

CHOIR ORGAN:

Geigen principal 8'
Dolce 8'
Concert flute 8'
*Unda maris 8'

*Roosevelt additions

Fugara 4'
Flute d'amour 4'
Piccolo 2'
Clarinet 8'
Tremulant

PEDAL ORGAN:

Open diapason 16'
Violone 16'
Bourdon 16'
Violoncello 8'

The organ was built for the west gallery. In 1914 a Chancel Organ of three manuals and 27 stops was added by the Austin Organ Company.

George Jardine has an example in the church of the Annunciation, New York City, just a year later than the Henry Erben. Note the Diapason choruses on each manual, complete from 16' to Mixtures on Great and Swell, and 8'-4'-2' on Choir. These old American builders were certainly carrying on the traditions of the 17th and 18th century continental builders. Only in the Pedal department were these organs much more limited than their European predecessors.

CHURCH OF THE ANNUNCIATION, NEW YORK
George Jardine, 1853

GREAT ORGAN: 9 Stops

Double Diapason 16'
Diapason 8'
Stopped Diapason 8'
Melodia 8'
Principal 4'
Twelfth 2-2/3'
Fifteenth 2'
Sesquialtera IV R
Trumpet 8'

CHOIR ORGAN: 8 Stops

Diapason 8'
Viola di gamba 8'
Stopped diapason 8'
Principal 4'
Flute 4'
Fifteenth 2'
Clarinet treble 8'
Bassoon bass

SWELL ORGAN: 10 Stops

Bourdon 16'
Diapason 8'
Stopped Diapason 8'
Dulciana 8'
Principal 4'
Fifteenth 2'
Mixture III R
Trumpet 8'
Oboe 8'
Clarion 4'

PEDAL ORGAN: 3 Stops

Diapason 16'
Bourdon 16'
Octave 8'

The organ in Tremont Temple, Boston, built by Elias and George G. Hook was a remarkable instrument for its day. It contained five Diapason choruses. Two on the Great, one each on the Swell, Choir and Pedal. There was not however the pitch differentiation in these various choruses as found in the German organ of a century or more earlier. There were, however, one chorus for the 32' Diapason series in the Pedal and two based on the 16' series on Great and Swell and the 8' series on the Choir. What could we have been thinking about in America, when we had such an example as this organ before us? For a fairly long period we not only abandoned any semblance of a Diapason chorus on any division but the Great organ, and at its worst there was no chorus on even this manual.

A HISTORY OF TONAL DESIGN

Unfortunately, Tremont Temple burned three times, each time being rebuilt. The present organ is a 1922 Casavant. Naturally, for the past three quarters of a century, no one knew or cared about this 1854 E. & G. Hook organ. It remained for Mr. Webber to preserve the record of this fine American instrument. I had no idea of it, until I went over Mr. Webber's stop lists. It is interesting to note the number of chorus Reeds, also, that this organ contained.

TREMONT TEMPLE, BOSTON
E. & G. Hook, 1854

GREAT ORGAN: 15 Stops

Double Diapason 16'
Grand Diapason 8'
Diapason 8'
Melodia 8'
Stopped Diapason 8'
Grand Principal 4'
Principal 4'
Twelfth 2-2/3'
Grand Fifteenth 2'
Fifteenth 2'
Sesquialtera II R
Mixture III R
Fourniture IV R
Trumpet 8'
Clarion 4'

SWELL ORGAN: 15 Stops

Sub bass 16'
Double Diapason 16'
Viol di gamba 8'
Stopped Diapason 8'
Principal 4'
Nighthorn 4'
Twelfth 2-2/3'
Fifteenth 2'
Sesquiltera III R
Double Trumpet 16'
Trumpet bass
Trumpet treble 8'
Hautboy 8'
Clarion 4'

CHOIR ORGAN: 10 Stops

Diapason 8'
Dulciana 8'
Stopped Diapason 8'
Principal 4'
Fifteenth 2'
Mixture III R
Hohl Flute 4'
Viol d'amour 4'
Clarinet 8'
Bassoon 8'

SOLO ORGAN: 6 Stops

Horn Diapason 8'
Gamba 8'
Clarabella 8'
Wald flöte 4'
Piccolo 2'
Trumpet 8'

PEDAL ORGAN: 10 Stops

Double Diapason 32'
Diapason (metal) 16'
Diapason (wood) 16'
Bourdon 16'
Octave 8'
Violoncello 8'
Quint 5-1/3'
Principal 4'
Posaune 16'
Trombone 8'

A HISTORY OF TONAL DESIGN

BAPTIST CHURCH, SHELBURN FALLS, MASS.
William A. Johnson, 1858, Opus 76

GREAT ORGAN: 12 Stops	SWELL ORGAN: 10 Stops
Diapason 8'	Bourdon 16'
Stopped Diapason treble 8'	Open Diapason 8'
Stopped Diapason bass 8'	Stopped Diapason bass 8'
Clarabella 8'	Viola da gamba 8'
Viola d'amour 8'	Dulciana 8'
Octave 4'	Principal 4'
Waldflote 4'	Celestina 4'
Twelfth 2-2/3'	Twelfth 2-2/3'
Fifteenth 2'	Fifteenth 2'
Seventeenth 1-3/5'	Oboe 8'
Mixture III R	Tremulant
Trumpet 8'	

PEDAL ORGAN: 1 Stop

Open diapason 16'

This is, in many respects, the finest of all existing Johnson organs. Of its 21 actual voices, no less than 13 are of the Diapason family; and so artistically are they voiced, and so carefully regulated in relation to one another that the full ensemble of the 13 Diapasons welds into a magnificent whole; solid, brilliant, and with silvery quality so characteristic of Johnson's best work. It is impossible to spoil this majestic ensemble even when the flutes are drawn. As in many of Johnson's organs, there is but one Pedal stop, but this weakness is characteristic of nearly all organs of this period, both here and abroad, with the exception of some of the continental organs. This organ has 23 stops, 19 actual voices, 21 ranks of pipes and a total of 1017 pipes. The compass of the Great Organ is 56 notes, that of the Swell Organ 38 notes, and the Pedal Organ but 17 notes. The Viola and the Waldflote have a stopped diapason bass. So skilfully were the Johnson organs designed that these shortcomings of tonal structure are hardly apparent except to the keenest ear.

ST. PAUL'S CHAPEL, TRINITY PARISH, NEW YORK
J. H. & C. S. Odell & Co., 1870, Opus 92

GREAT ORGAN:	SWELL ORGAN:	CHOIR ORGAN:	PEDAL ORGAN:
Bourdon 16'	Bourdon 16'	Geigen Diapason 8'	Diapason 16'
Diapason 8'	Diapason 8'	Dulciana 8'	Bourdon 16'
Viol di gamba 8'	Salicional 8'	Melodia 8'	Keraulophone 16'
Stopped Diapason 8'	Stopped Diapason 8'	Principal 4'	Quint 10-2/3'
Principal 4'	Principal 4'	Flute 4'	Violoncello 8'
Twelfth 2-2/3'	Fifteenth 2'	Fifteenth 2'	Trombone 16'
Fifteenth 2'	Mixture IV R	Oboe 8'	
Mixture III R	Cornopean 8'		
Trumpet 8'	Oboe 8'		

A HISTORY OF TONAL DESIGN

CHURCH OF ST. VINCENT FERRER, NEW YORK, N. Y.
Hilborne L. Roosevelt, 1874, Opus 7

GREAT ORGAN:	SWELL ORGAN:	CHOIR ORGAN:	PEDAL ORGAN:
Double Diapason 16'	Bourdon 16'	Doppel flöte 8'	Double Diapason 32'
Double Gemshorn 16'	Diapason 8'	Gamba 8'	Diapason 16'
Diapason 8'	Rohr flöte 8'	Dolce 8'	Gamba 16'
Violin 8'	Keraulophon 8'	Concert flute 8'	Bourdon 16'
Melodia 8'	Principal 4'	Viol d'amour 4'	Violone 8'
Flute 4'	Flauto traverso 4'	Rohr Flote 4'	Bombarde 16'
Principal 4'	Mixture IV R	Piccolo 2'	Tuba 8'
Wald flöte 2'	Cornopean 8'	Clarinet 8'	
Mixture IV R	Oboe 8'		
Cornet IV-V-R	Vox Humana 8'		
Trumpet 8'	Tremulant		
Clarion 4'			

Mr. Roosevelt considered this organ as one of his best.

ROOSEVELT-AEOLIAN-SKINNER ORGAN
INDIANA UNIVERSITY, BLOOMINGTON

One of the outstanding large organs of the country was the great organ in the Auditorium of Chicago, which was installed by Hilborne L. & Frank Roosevelt in 1889. For their day, the Roosevelt firm was acknowledged to be a leading builder. This was their master-piece and largest and most important work.

The organ had fallen on evil days, and needed major repairs. The owners of the Auditorium were not able to maintain the organ. In July, 1942, all of the furnishings of the Auditorium Hotel and Theatre were sold at auction, including the organ. The author bought the organ, in order to preserve one of the great musical art works of the nineteenth century. It was dismantled and stored in the basement of the First Baptist church in Evanston, where the author was Minister of Music for twenty-four years.

Indiana University had just completed before the second world war a magnificent auditorium, and wanted an organ. After considerable study and negotiation, it was agreed that the author would present the organ to the university with the stipulation that they should pay for its complete rebuilding, modernization, and enlargement. The work was entrusted to the Aeolian-Skinner Organ Company. Mr. G. Donald Harrison and the author worked out the new stop list, which is given below.

More mordant Strings were substituted for the old ones, and new orchestral voices were substituted, notably, French Horn, English Horn, Orchestral Oboe and Chimes and Harp. Also a twelve stop Positiv section, and more pedal stops were added.

A HISTORY OF TONAL DESIGN

The essential character of the Diapasons and Flutes and the twenty-eight ranks of Mixtures was retained. The principal change in the Mixtures was the elimination of the Tierces. A separate Tierce was added to the Great organ. One of the chief glories of the old organ was the battery of 16'-8'-4' French Trompettes on both the Great and Solo organs. The pipes of these six stops are made of pure tin, with typical open French eschallots. Those on the Great speak on 4½'' pressure, and those on the Solo on 8''. While not known for certain, it is believed that these six sets were made and voiced by Cavaillé-Coll. At least they were imported from France by Roosevelt, and they are unbelievably magnificent in a large auditorium. There is considerable weight and ground tone present as well as a blaze of harmonics, due doubtless to the large scale and very high tin content of the resonators.

Originally all manual divisions were enclosed separately, except six of the Great stops. This met with the unqualified approval of Dr. Audsley. In its new location, it was impossible to enclose the Great organ effectively, and so it was left in the open.

It is a source of satisfaction to the author to have been able to preserve this important organ for many years to come, where it will play a major part in the musical life of a great university. The stop list as printed below indicates the new pipes, and changes and substitutions from the original scheme.

AUDITORIUM INDIANA UNIVERSITY,

GREAT ORGAN

Contra Geigen Diapason 16'
Quintaten 16'
First Open Diapason 8'
Second Open Diapason 8'
Principal Flute 8'
Doppel Flöte 8'
Viola de Gamba 8'
Gemshorn 8'
Quint 5-1/3'
Principal 4'
Octave 4'
Flute 4'
(Harmonique)
Octave Quint 2-2/3'
Super Octave 2'
Tierce 1-3/5'
Mixture (4 & 5 Ranks)
(Tierce omitted)
Scharf (3 & 4 Ranks)
Ophicleide 16'
Trompette 8'
Clairon 4'
Chimes (Solo)

SWELL ORGAN

Bourdon 16'
Open Diapason 8'
Violin Diapason 8'
Clarabella 8'
Stopped Diapason 8'
Spitzflöte 8'
Spitz Flöte Celeste 8'
Viole-de-Gamba 8'
Viole Celeste 8'
Aeoline 8'
Unda Maris 8'
Octave 4'
Gamba 4'
Flute 4'
(Harmonique)
Rohr Nazard 2-2/3'
Flageolet 2'
Plein Jeu Mixture
(4 & 5 Ranks)
Acuta Mixture
(3 Ranks)

Contra Fagotto 16'
Cornopean 8'
Oboe 8'
Vox Humana 8'
Clarion 4'
Tremulant
Harp 8'
Celesta 4'

CHOIR ORGAN

Double Melodia 16'
Geigen Principal 8'
Viola 8'
Viola Celeste 8'
Lieblich Gedackt 8'
Flauto Traverso 8'
Dulciana 8'
Unda Maris 8'
Octave 4'
Flute d'Amour 4'
Nazard 2-2/3'
Piccolo 2'
(Harmonique)
Tierce 1-3/5'
Dolce Cornet (5 Ranks)
Euphone (Free Reeds) 16'
Trompette 8'
Clarinet 8'
Tremulant
Harp 8'
Celesta 4'

POSITIV ORGAN

Gedeckt 8'
Quintadena 8'
Principal 4'
Koppel Flöte 4'
Nazard 2-2/3'
Octave 2'
Block Flöte 2'
Tierce 1-3/5'
Larigot 1-1/3'
Sifflöte 1'
Cymbel (III Rks.)
Cromorne 8'

The above division to play from either Great or Choir manuals and provided with the following couplers:

Positiv on Great
Positiv on Choir
Positiv on Pedal

SOLO ORGAN

Contra Gamba 16'
Grosse Gamba 8'
Gamba Celeste 8'
Doppel Flöte 8'
Octave 4'
Gamba 4'
Flute Octaviante 4'
French Horn 8'
Orchestral Clarinet 8'
Cor-Anglais 8'
Orchestral Oboe 8'
Tuba Major 8'
Tuba Mirabilis 8'
Tuba Clarion 4'
Tremulant
Chimes

PEDAL ORGAN

Double Open Diapason 32'
Contra Bourdon 32'
First Open Diapason (Wood) 16'
Second Open Diapason (Metal) 16'
Violone (Wood) 16'
Dulciana 16'
Stopped Diapason 16'
Echo Lieblich (Swell) 16'
Quint 10-2/3'
Octave (Metal) 8'
Violoncello (Wood) 8'
Flute 8'
Still Gedackt (Swell) 8'
Octave Quint 5-1/3'
Super Octave 4'
Nachthorn 4'
Blockflöte 2'
Mixture (3 Rks.)
Bombarde 32'
Trombone 16'
Bassett Horn 16'
(Old Solo Bassett Horn)
Trumpet 8'
Clarion 4'
Chimes (Solo)

BARNES RESIDENCE ORGAN, EVANSTON, ILL.

The organ which has been in the author's home for the past thirty years has been heard by many hundreds of organists, so that its design may well be the subject of general inquiry and interest on the part of other organists. Many years ago, Mr. Gruenstein, the editor of The Diapason described it as a "thoroughbred residence organ of mongrel antecedents." It has been rebuilt, altered, changed, and experimented with on many occasions, during the past quarter century. This organ has been used as a "trial" organ for the author. It started as a modest three manual. A fourth manual was added some years ago, along with additional stops, stop-keys and gadgets until there was no more room. The Solo organ contains the only unit stops, outside of the Pedal, which has some extensions and borrows. In fact the Pedal organ would not suit the "baroque" enthusiasts. It relies on the various pedal couplers for its upper work, obviously. The 32' Bourdon is worth its weight in silver, at least, if not gold. It has an accommodating way of fitting under the soft stops as well as under the full organ.

The five Roosevelt stops from the old Auditorium organ in Chicago are perhaps the most distinguished voices. They were the choicest ones out of that great organ of 100 stops. Pipes have been tried and moved from one division to another so often, that the rackboard holes are now all practically interchangeable. Any stop can be placed anywhere, without enlarging the holes in the rack boards any further. The specification as it stands as this edition is being printed is as given below. There is no guarantee that it will remain this way in all respects, for too far in the future.

Note that there are two IV Rank Diapason Mixtures, a Dolce Cornet and some Flute Mutations (unit). The Great Trumpet is very bright, as is the Solo Trumpet. The full Swell is extraordinarily effective, clean, clear, bright, and thrilling. The two Swell Strings when coupled at 16'-8'-4' to Choir, with the three Choir Strings at 8' and 4', plus Vox Humana, with the two soft 16' pedal stops plus 32' Bourdon, give a String Chorus of remarkable character. It is one of Virgil Fox's favorite effects on this organ. The Solo Reeds, and Flutes are all distinguished. The variety, contrast, ensemble, and versatility of this organ are a never failing source of joy and satisfaction to the author, as well as to the many organists who play it.

It simply goes to prove that the work of a dozen or more builders may be successfully combined in the same organ, and sound harmoniously together. It is only the builders' representatives who do not always work together so harmoniously on the same prospect.

There are two expression chambers, each 16' long by 10' wide and 11' high. The pipes of the 32' Bourdon are laid horizontally, outside the chamber, and speak through a hole cut in the wall at the back of one of the chambers. The blower and relays are in a separate adjoining room, with two blower reservoirs.

A HISTORY OF TONAL DESIGN

ORGAN IN WILLIAM H. BARNES' RESIDENCE, EVANSTON, ILLINOIS

55 Stops—4 Manual

Ranks: Great ..... 9—5''   wind pressure
Swell ..... 16—4''   "   "
Choir ...... 10—4¼''   "   "
Solo .... 2—6''   "   "
Pedal ...... 4—6''   "   "

41 Ranks

GREAT	BUILDER
Diapason 8'	Kilgen
Doppel Flote 8'	Roosevelt
Octave 4'	Roosevelt
Flute Harmonique 4'	Roosevelt
Fourniture IV Ranks	Reuter
(12th-15th-19th-22nd)	
Trumpet 8'	Dennison
Chimes 20 Tubes	Deagan
Tremolo	

SWELL	BUILDER
Bourdon 16'	Hall
Diapason 8'	Moller
Gamba 8'	Gottfried
Voix Celeste 8'	Moller
Spitz Flute 8'	Gottfried
Spitz Flute Celeste	Gottfried
Stopped Flute 8'	Hall
Geigen Octave 4'	Moller
Flute 4'	Hall
Spitz Flute	Gottfried
Nazard 2-2/3'	Hall
Plein Jeu IV Ranks	Moller
Contra Fagotto 16'	Roosevelt
Trumpet 8'	Kimball
Cor Anglais	Gottfried
Clarion 4'	Austin
Vox Humana 8'	Pierce
Tremolo	

CHOIR	BUILDER
Contra Salicional 16'	Kimball
Viola 8' (Broad Scale)	Reuter
Viola Celeste 8'	Aeolian-Skinner
Clarabella 8'	Roosevelt
Flauto Dolce 8'	Gottfried
Flute Celeste 8'	Gottfried
Claribel Flute 4'	Roosevelt
Flauto Dolce 4'	Gottfried
Fugara 4'	Meyer
Dolce Cornet	Odell
II Ranks (No. 1-36—12th-	
15th. No. 37-61—15th-17th)	
Clarinet	Gottfried
Vibra Harp (49 Bars)	Maas-Rowe
Tremolo	

SOLO

Bourdon (Sw) 16'-8'-4'-2-2/3'-2'-1-3/5'

	BUILDER
French Trumpet 16'-8'-4'	Kimball
French Horn 8'-4'	Gottfried

PEDAL

	BUILDER
Contra Bourdon 32'	Moller
Principal Bass 16'	Moller
Bourdon 16'	Reuter
Gedeckt 16'	Moller
Salicional 16'	Kimball
Flute 8'	Moller
Trombone 16'	Kimball

Console	Austin
Windchests	Moller
Swell shades	Casavant
Blower	Zephyr
Rectifier	Orgelectra

283

Before closing this chapter on The History of Tonal Design, we unfortunately cannot ignore the concept of tonal design as advocated and as practised by Mr. Robert Hope-Jones. There are too many organs either built by him, or built by others under his influence, that are still very much in existence in this country and England. Mr. Hope-Jones came to America in the early nineteen hundreds from England.

Mr. Henry Willis, in a recent article in the "Organ Institute Quarterly" has this to say about the tonal ideas of this gentleman:

"In the 1890's, the tonal monstrosities by Hope-Jones were perpetrated, coupling the practical abolition of mixture work, over-developed quintadenas and diapasons of undue foundational tone with repressed harmonic development, huge scale and hooting flutes, dull and heavy-toned chorus reeds, with little harmonic development, so called "strings" of tiny scale producing thin and scratchy tones and other weird departures from the older and formerly accepted basic designs which, for many years, had given such fine service and superb results. Perhaps the most deplorable result was the impression upon even the leading organists of the period that mixture work in itself was undesirable; that this was so is made evident by the specifications of instruments designed and constructed in that period. The over-emphasis on big and fundamental diapason tone, made on the absurd and wholly illogical grounds that such constituted the best tonality to accompany and back up congregational singing, was another unfortunate factor resulting, in so many instances, in the first Diapason on the Great Organ bearing no relation at all to the Diapason Chorus but sticking out like a sore thumb—so much so that the knowledgeable organist will never use such a stop in full ensemble. Readers will be aware of scores of cases where this kind of unbalance is present and of the necessity of cutting such a stop off the combinations."

Reference has been made from time to time in this work to Mr. Robert Hope-Jones and the remarks we have quoted above are rightly disparaging to him. I was impressed, in reading over the "Dictionary of Organ Stops" by Mr. Wedgwood, with the remarkable number of stops that are there attributed to Mr. Hope-Jones. Nearly all organists and builders are familiar with the voices that have been freely copied and introduced in organs that are generally attributed to Hope-Jones, namely the Phonon type of Diapason, the smooth Tuba Sonora, the Diaphone, the Oboe Horn, the Tibia Plena, Tibia Clausa, etc. He appears, however, to have invented a large number of other less known stops. I by no means share the intense dislike of Hope-Jones that many builders entertain for his ideas, both tonally and mechanically.

It is a curious circumstance that the three companies with which Mr. Hope-Jones was associated in America for a greater or less length of time, notably, the Austin Organ Company, the Ernest M. Skinner Company and the Wurlitzer Company, all were remarkably successful in their respective fields of organ building. Whether it is because Mr. Hope-Jones was associated with them at one time, or because they let him go, in each instance, that they were successful, is a matter that can only be surmised. There is no doubt but that his influence has waned and that many of his ideas and theories on tonal design have been exploded, and abandoned, as being incorrect. On the other hand, we cannot, in all fairness, by any means overlook the widespread influence of his mechanical inventions on the development of the modern electric organ. Silver wire contacts, more efficient magnets, individual swell shutter motors, a systematic adoption of the method of unifying an organ, and many other mechanical improvements are due to Hope-Jones. Some of these things are not considered an unmixed blessing, particularly the matter of unification, which was treated in an earlier chapter. Nevertheless, though he may not justify the words that have been used concerning him, that he was the "greatest mind engaged in the art of organ building in this or any other age," the truth concerning him doubtless lies somewhere between this statement and the judgment of those who utterly condemn him. This is where I am inclined to place my estimate, viewing the matter in as impartial a light as possible. That he was a mechanical genius, who came into organ building with the fresh viewpoint of the outsider, not being satisfied to do things as they had always been done, cannot be denied. Along many lines he was an idealist. He made many mistakes which, had he lived longer, he might have been the first to correct. In doing as much pioneer work as Mr. Hope-Jones did, there were bound to be mistakes and misapprehensions. That he exerted a profound influence on organ building for thirty years, some of it for the better, and some of it for the worse, is at least recognized by anyone acquainted with the facts.

He had the faculty of stimulating thought in his associates, who in many instances carried out and developed his ideas.

Not only were the tonal designs of organs built in America from around 1900-1930 influenced by Hope-Jones, but the rise and fall of the theater organ took place during this same period. In the typical and most popular form of theater organ, pungent voices predominated. There were Strings that sounded like frying bacon, hooting Flutes, tubby Diapasons, honking Reeds, and no semblance whatever of ensemble or cohesion of these prima donna solo voices. Public musical taste was debauched by these sounds, which seemed to intrigue them greatly. It was inevitable that some of these abnormal and exaggerated voices would be introduced into church organs during this period.

Along with these pungent solo voices, Mr. Ernest Skinner and others were developing a whole series of orchestral imitative solo voices. Notably, the French Horn, English Horn, Corno di Bassetto, Flügel Horn, Fagotto and other stops were made available which had surprising fidelity to their orchestral prototypes. Organists became so carried away with the joy of using these voices, as well as being aware of the popular success of the theater organs, that the church organs of the period became too often a mere collection of solo voices, and had little more ensemble and cohesive quality than theater organs. Happily this period is definitely at an end, and the pendulum has swung to the other extreme in the thinking of many good organists.

Organs of the period under discussion were termed "romantic" for no very good reason, except that "romantic" music could be more readily played on them than on the organ of tradition. The next chapter of this book will outline a plan for combining the best features of the "romantic" organ with the "classic" organ, to produce a versatile organ, suitable for playing properly and adequately all types of organ music.

I should like to sum up the lessons to be learned from this chapter, by quoting Mr. Edward B. Gammons.

Mr. Gammons, Musical Director of Groton School, Mass. is a man like the author, who has spent a lifetime in studying organs and organ design from the point of view of the practical organist. Many years' experience in playing the organ in church has taught us both what is necessary and desirable. But more important than that, the experience gained by analyzing, testing and playing all kinds of organs of all types of design, both in this country and abroad has taught us to compare and evaluate. Any organist with many years' experience playing in church would get to know what he liked or didn't like about the organ he played. But unless this experience was supplemented by a wide knowledge of what other organs were capable of doing, he would have no basis for comparison. For this reason many very competent organists are unable to design a good organ. Mr. Gammons can. His tastes are eclectic, and he speaks from wide knowledge of the whole history of organ building in this country and Europe, and is thoroughly conversant with present-day tendencies in American Organ Building. It is therefore distinctly a pleasure and privilege to be able to reproduce a part of a paper termed "Some Modern Tendencies in the Tonal Design of the Organ" which he read before the Music Teachers' National Association in Boston.

This brings us to a place where we may profitably survey the present tendencies in organ design and perhaps point a few morals. While we may be amused at some of the excesses of the cinema organ, we do not have to attempt a literal re-creation of the 17th century baroque organ. It is by a study of the underlying purposes in organ design that we gain a perspective so that a twentieth century instrument may be created on which the best organ literature of all periods may be performed. We must guard against indiscriminate electicism and exclude ideals that are mutually contradictory.

At present we find several streams of thought and I shall briefly enumerate them. One school plans to copy faithfully the organ as described in Praetorius in 1619, action and all. Another subscribes to the limitations of the pure baroque organ in a small instrument for special restricted use. When such an instrument is built for a museum, college or conservatory for the express purpose of playing period music it seems there is a little we can cavil at, but such an organ can hardly be honestly advised for general adoption. In passing I should say that while a true baroque organ may be built today, you need have no fear that its tone must be harsh, irregular or unpleasant. Brilliant, intense and sharply differentiated, yes, but it still is musical and useful as is the harpsichord for music conceived for that medium.

We further find a school which tends to exalt the glories of the Willis type of organ, the Schulze or the Cavaillé-Coll and wishes to follow faithfully every detail of tone and control found in the work of these masters. It would seem to me that this again is something to be somewhat wary of. We do find that there are certain excellencies in each of the types of organ here alluded to, but to adopt all the details of one specific school without viewing the picture as a whole seems an unwise course.

Then too, there are those who were brought up on the more or less restrictive romantic organ and they find that any change in instrument entails a new orientation and in many cases a completely new style of music and playing. Where such is the case it is far easier to insist that any of the demands for change today is but a fad or passing fancy. These good folks will have none of the ensemble organ, no unenclosed divisions, no independent mutations or mixtures, and they point to the pleasures they give with hefty Diapasons, booming "Pedal Opens" and shimmering masses of acid string tone. What they fail to do is to ask whether or not they are honest with themselves as musicians or their auditors who in many cases are supposed to be worshippers of God himself.

Finally, what may we look toward at this juncture when we have no lack of really fine organists, artist builders, a plethora of sound musicologists and a rising group of able composers.

I should say that the post war American organ design must appraise every organ installation with an eye which sees the true glories of the contrapuntal idiom as the organ's highest function, but does not blind itself to the demands of other intervening periods.

In other words, we must see the innate rightness of the principles current in the baroque and classical period. It is up to us as teachers and organists to, see that the organ is presented in its best literature. In order to do that we must enlist the aid of the clergy, university and school heads, architects and physicists to see that once more the organ is brought out into the open, where tone may freely approach the listener in churches and auditoria where the acoustical environment is helpful to organ tone. Then we can see that the tonal forces of the organ are disposed so that the intrinsic character of our splendid organ literature may be heard to best advantage. The contrasts between properly located Great, Swell, Pedal and Choir organs tell far more effectively when these conditions are met.

Then we may combine the best assimilable ideals of the baroque and classic organ with many of the useful colors of the romantic organ and the flexible and instant control of modern mechanism. Lest I be considered indefinite about all this I would say explicitly that after we have our organs out into the open once again, then we must demand the use of fine materials, low wind pressures, so essential to unforced natural tone, the provision of a real ensemble on each division, and if possible two unenclosed sections as the Great, Rückpositiv sections, and a varied independent pedal that will maintain its own line, not by brute weight and force but by clarity of line. And as Schweitzer has demanded we too, can ask for a well apportioned Swell organ to give a tonal grouping subject to swell shutters. As he put it, the organ must be a musical Trinity, with the Great in one location, a Swell organ of equal power but different accent, and then the Ruckpositiv located apart from the main case.

From this point one may go forward as far as space and funds will allow. But, before frills and stops of limited utility are permitted we should satisfy the imperative demands of the primary function of the organ and its music. The outcome will be a school of design marked by adaptability to varied uses and environments, but all organs then might have clarity, majesty, flexibility and musical fitness.

When organs are built along these lines people as a whole will know and love the organ as an instrument and appreciate its vast literature and we as organists will play the organ to the greater glory of God and for the edifying and joy of our fellow men.

CHAPTER 16

GENERAL REMARKS *on* TONAL DESIGN

In designing an organ for a church, its chief purpose must be kept foremost in mind. Before all other purposes, the organ must aid in creating a religious atmosphere in the services of the church. If it fails in doing this, the organ is a failure as a church organ, no matter how well constructed, or how classical its design. Dr. A. T. Davison, the organist of Harvard University for many years, in his book on "Protestant Church Music in America," analyzes the reasons for having music in church. Among the many reasons which are sometimes given, he considers the most valid as being the reason that church music should be an oblation to God. If we agree, as I certainly do, that this is the chief justification for music in church, a good many other considerations fall by the way. It then becomes of small consequence whether or not the congregation *likes* the music, or whether their ears are tickled by sweet and intriguing sounds, either from the organ or choir. The first question to be answered, must be, is the music being produced a worthy oblation to God. It naturally follows that the cheap, the theatrical, the stereotyped, and the obvious are unworthy, and should be avoided by both the organ and the choir.

So to design suitable church organs, with which this chapter concerns itself, that this primary purpose of an organ may be realized, is something which requires a great deal of thought and experience. Fortunately we have the past to draw upon for guidance and help.

If the best possible specification were given to a score of builders, the result would be a like number of organs dissimilar in tone and ranging in quality from excellent to quite the reverse. In the same manner, if a score of artists were asked to reproduce some photograph or line drawing in colors, very different results would be secured.

To design an organ should involve a great deal more than writing a list of stops. In such a case, the balance of the details must be settled by the organ builder. To conceive in one's mind a finished instrument and to prepare clear notes of this conception for the organ builder's guidance and then to assume the responsibility of seeing that the original ideas are properly carried out, requires many years of varied experience on the part of one who undertakes the tonal design of any organ. He must have analysed the cause of the various effects he has noted, and have carefully sought the reasons why apparently identical pipes sound very differently in different surroundings. A competent designer should have both practical and experimental knowledge of organ building. He must also be able to refer particular instances to general principles. Certain rules of tonal design must be followed, regardless of tastes, fads, or fancies.

Mr. G. Donald Harrison, president of the Aeolian-Skinner Organ

Company, in speaking of the work of three of the greatest European builders, viz.: Cavaillé-Coll, Father Willis, and Schulze, says:

The student who cares to live with and thoroughly investigate the great works of these old masters of the past may discover the laws which are in common between them. Briefly they may be summed up as follows:

1. All stops employed, whether Diapasons, Octave, Mutation, String, Flute or Reed, are strictly musical in character. That is to say, the harmonic development is neither under nor overdone, but lies within well-defined limits, and the complete series of harmonics is in "phase."

2. The stops maintain such harmonic development throughout their compass.

3. The relative power of Octave and Mutation ranks to the Unison lies within definite limits and follows a certain logical order in all cases.

If these rules are adhered to and the tonal scheme is correct, it is almost impossible to go wrong. Beauty of the individual ranks, blending qualities, clarity in the ensemble are all assured, and yet an infinite variety in timbre is possible. The treatment can be exceedingly bold if desired without giving offense.

On the other hand, the breaking of one of these rules is fatal. Some little time ago I examined a large four-manual organ in which the tonal scheme was about perfect for its size. The builder had followed rules 1 and 3, but had largely disregarded rule 2. The treble of the whole Diapason structure faded away to weak flutes. In other words, the harmonic development had not been maintained throughout the compass. The result was lack of blend in the treble and with the octave coupler drawn the effect was really excruciating, and yet I understand the fear of this mechanical device led the builder to make this error.

I remember another instance in England where a certain organ builder had been entrusted with the rebuilding of an T. C. Lewis organ. Mr. Lewis was a disciple of Schulze, and the Great Organ of this particular instrument had a most beautiful color. The rebuilder, however, was not content to leave well enough alone and had added a high-cut heavy-pressure leathered Phonon. "I have given to it the foundation it needed," he said with pride in his voice. In reality he had broken our rule 1. The harmonic development of this stop was below par and consequently it just stuck out like a sore thumb and ruined the ensemble and the general clarity of the effect. Happily, however, it was not necessary to use the stop, and I noted with much satisfaction that the organist had omitted it from his combination pistons.

The artist organ builder will not slavishly copy either individual stops or departments from the old masters. "Stunts" of this kind rarely come off. Rather should he endeavor to give the fundamental laws his own interpretation.

Naturally I can only touch the fringe of these subjects. The design of Mixtures alone, with the various breaks arranged to suit the particular specification in hand is one which would require several volumes.

The poor organ has suffered more than any other instrument from the whims of amateurs, experimenters and dabblers. Tones are allowed and even heralded as great achievements which would not be tolerated in any other musical field. "Well, it's all a matter of opinion" is heard far too often. For an opinion to be worth anything it is necessary that the person offering it has reached the final stage of tonal appreciation. As my old friend the Rev. N. Bonavia-Hunt has said, "many people never go beyond the second stage of tonal appreciation in which they revel in harmonicless or unmusical tones."

One may have personal preference for the Willis or Cavaille-Coll or the Schulze organs referred to, since they are all artistically correct, but the man who likes better than any of these an instrument having fundamental errors cannot expect to have his criticisms or opinions taken seriously.

Finally, the ideal instrument seems to be a combination of the properly designed, produced and finished classical organ with the new, beautiful and subtle tones which have been produced in this country.

Austin Niland, writing in "The Organ" lists these qualities as essential if an organ is to be aesthetically satisfying. He says "no organ is musically tolerable in chorus or lesser effects unless the following are present to a certain degree:—

(a) BALANCE: The stabilization of all the pitches in satisfying proportions, no particular pitch predominating unduly.

(b) BLEND: A reaching out of a given register to embrace any one or more drawn with it. Thus, Viola & Flute or Gedeckt give a new composite colour, not merely string and flute sounding together.

(c) CLARITY: The clear revelation of inner parts in polyphony. This is of great importance in all but FF climaxes when only the broad chordal outline is important enough to be apparent.

(d) GRANDEUR: The unique majestic quality of good organ tone. It is possible to construct a baroque organ embodying blend, balance and clarity only. But without grandeur it would

be intolerable musically even though it would be possible to hear every note distinctly in polyphony.

(e) RESTRAINT: The quality of being within reasonable limits of power, so as (a) to avoid monotony and (b) increase the general utility of full chorus effects.

If we are to try to approximate the effects obtainable from the classic organ, we must first plan the organ to get the pipes in the open position demanded by low wind pressures.

This "pipes in the open" method of building organs, unquestionably has real merit. It should be followed whenever conditions make it possible. Such construction does not necessarily mean that the organ must be located in the chancel or pulpit end of the church. Frequently a transept or rear gallery location will prove to be better. A rear gallery location, unless the church is very small, practically presupposes the location of the choir in the gallery also, so that they may hear the organ properly, and so that the choir and organ may be in proper balance.

Pipes in the open naturally have a great bearing on tonal design. More especially when we are aiming at the free, unforced, natural tone produced by pipes on 3" wind pressure, an open location is essential to obtain these results.

At this point, some general statements should be made concerning wind pressures, unenclosed Great and Choir organs, and other matters to help to clarify present ideas concerning organ location and design.

When an open position for the organ can be found (and it must be found, if low pressures are to be used), which gives us the advantage of that special bloom and unforced quality obtainable only with low pressures, we must surely keep the Great and Pedal unenclosed. Low pressure flue-work will not stand enclosure; low pressure Reeds will. It is therefore more important that ever before that we realize the limitations and necessities of the low-pressure organs.

Because a Diapason chorus on $3\frac{1}{2}$" wind pressure sounds marvellously in an open gallery in a resonant church, it emphatically does not follow that it will prove anything but an utter failure when buried in a non-resonant auditorium. These statements may sound elementary or perhaps self-evident. But when one sees as I have, organists so carried away with the low-pressure idea that they want a low-pressure organ even though it must be buried in such deep chambers as to almost require a shipping clerk, to get the tone out, it doesn't seem as though the problem were so evident to them.

There are obviously some situations where low pressures cannot be made effective. This must be thoroughly understood. It should also be understood that the mere question of wind pressure is not of itself of such great importance. To suggest that the wind pressure be raised or lowered when designing an organ will not of itself make the organ good or bad. The question whether the wind pressures be high or low is merely a contributing factor in obtaining certain tonal results. So many other factors enter in, such as acoustics of the building, location of the organ in an open or remote position, general voicing treatment, and proportionate scaling of the pipes themselves to secure a satisfactory ensemble, that the matter of wind pressure must after all be considered in its proper relation to all these other factors. The secret of building a good organ surely does not lie in the simple procedure of reducing the wind pressure from that commonly employed for many years (for example 7½'') to say 3½''. To produce a good ensemble is a much more complicated and difficult matter. It has been found, however, that Mixture work definitely can be made to blend better and to be more cohesive with low wind pressure.

The controversy which has raged in the pages of the "Diapason" for some years past between the two opposing schools of thought in organ design as represented in their extreme by the labels "classic" vs. "romantic" may advantageously be resolved by a midway position, which I should like to set forth.

In a letter from the Rev. Tyler Turner, who is an Episcopal clergyman, as well as organ architect (and perhaps this may give him a more philosophic approach) he makes the following statements:

"There do not seem to be very many in the organ world who will buck up against a fad. We all like to be on the winning side."

"There seems to be a notion current that because the baroque organ should be revived, it must be revived with all the limitations of the prototype, and with an ivory-tower abhorrence of modern advantages. I think the passion for distinctions is typical of the adolescent mind. Either this or that. Which is right? Shall we have this, or shall we have that? And so on. A good baroque organ—complete, lock, stock and barrel—can fit into one corner of many contemporary instruments. But instead of building versatile instruments, the idea seems to be to make them as exclusive and restricted as possible. This, of course, is the way of respectability!"

In the final series of excellent translations of Louis Vierne's memoirs, printed several years ago in The Diapason, this very illuminating and, it seems to me, pertinent statement was made:

"Another tendency also reigns which would substitute for the excesses of the nineteenth century those of the seventeenth."

This seems to me to sum up some of our present-day organ designs with the minimum number of words and the maximum amount of discernment.

Fortunately, it doesn't have to be "either this or that," as Mr. Turner says we like to think it must be. An organ design doesn't have to be pure "baroque" or eighteenth century any more than it has to be merely a collection of fancy solo reeds, with some soft "pretty-pretties" such as flute celestes, voix celestes and similar effects. M. Vierne, after a lifetime of hearing and trying all sorts of organs, has the following to say in the memoirs quoted above:

"I will subscribe to these points of view when grand pianos have been done away with in favor of the clavecin and the violins in the orchestra replaced by ocarinas, when it is established once and for all that Beethoven, Weber, Schumann, Wagner and other geniuses were idiots, that Franck was an old fool and Widor an imbecile. As always, the truth, if there is any truth, lies in the happy medium. Art, to be really alive, must evolve. Let us not renounce any achievements of any era, but let us use them judiciously and disinterestedly, for the best good of art, without any preconceived system.

"Do you not realize how fragile a system is, whether definitely accepted or not, which seems old at the end of a few years? Contrast to even the most ingenious innovators the two-hundred-years' enduring popularity of a Sebastian Bach, who cared about as much for systems as a fish does for an apple! You will see the difference provided you are neither a snob nor prejudiced. For the specifications of an organ one must assemble foundation stops, mixtures and reeds in well-balanced proportion. Upon an instrument reasonably drawn up one should be able to play all kinds of music. Those who are called upon to preside over the construction of new instruments must have taste and good judgment. Arbitrary preferences, strictly personal sympathies and antipathies have no place in the matter. Impulsiveness is a fine thing; reason is without doubt a finer. I shall believe that until it has been proved to me that it is more practical to walk with feet in the air and head down than in the normal position."

This all seems so common-sense and reasonable to me that I feel it is distinctly worthwhile to review and call attention again to what M. Vierne has so well said. It is truly a philosophic approach. In spite of everything, many organists are so inclined to follow the lead of a few "high-brows" who have gone to extremes that they are afraid of being thought to be "old fogey," "unprogressive" and out of the running if they don't immediately jump on the band wagon and, like all converts, become more rabid protagonists for the fad of the moment than the actual leaders of the fad. This is naturally more true of the younger organists than of the more mature players who have seen and heard more organs of all types of design.

It is all very well to clarify the ensemble of an organ by the elimination of thick flutes, tubby diapasons, and muddy 16-ft. tone and the addition of sufficient upper work, so that contrapuntal music may be played with sufficient clearness so that the inner voices may be heard.

This is all to the good, provided the quint and octave quint sounding ranks are not so loud as to create the impression of a single note being actually a fifth. If contrapuntal music is to be played, and it certainly should be, as the greatest organ music ever written is in this style of writing, we must provide an organ first on which this type of music can be played effectively. To be effective all the voices must be heard, and this requires a clarified ensemble which all of our builders now know how to build. But when we carry this idea to the extreme of omitting all 8-ft. stops, to say nothing of 16-ft., and then don't use even the 4-ft. stops, but content ourselves with a dozen or so ranks of mixture, as I have heard one well-known recitalist do in playing contrapuntal music, we have reached the height of something. The pendulum has swung to the excesses of the seventeenth century at least.

I think some of our baroque enthusiasts have never stopped to realize or to analyze how these excesses came about. Until the beginning of the twentieth century the foremost problem of organ building was an adequate wind supply. The problem of producing sufficient wind for a large organ was especially formidable. It was discovered that high-pitched ranks could produce a lot of sound and take very little wind. The "wind-eaters" were large-scaled 8-ft. diapasons and flutes and, of course, the bigger pedal pipes. Thus, organs in Germany of the seventeenth century relied on mutation stops and mixtures for most of their volume, whereas in France the excessively brilliant open eshallot reeds were found to produce great volume with comparatively light wind requirements. I am entirely satisfied in my own mind that the limitations of the wind supply had more to do with tonal design than artistic or musical ideals. Practical considerations required either a great many high-pitched ranks or freely-voiced trumpets to get an adequate amount of sound in a large building, with the smallest volume of wind.

Today, as long as the public service companies of our cities can supply any amount of energy to any sized blower the organ may require, the wind supply problem is non-existent and certainly should not be included as a factor in designing an organ, as it certainly was in the seventeenth century. Let us by all means have a clarified ensemble in even a small organ, but let us have something more. Cesar Franck, Karg-Elert, Vierne himself, not to mention a host of lesser modern composers for the instrument, also wrote music which many organists will want to play and do play. Some of us are not content to confine our repertoire to Bach and his precursors. The music of these latter-day composers simply cannot be be played effectively on an organ which is pure "baroque." A few 8-ft. and 4-ft. flutes, with a complete set of mutations ending in a sifflöte, 1 ft., and a dozen ranks of mixtures with a krummhorn will not be adequate or satisfactory, no matter how perfect or well-balanced such voices may be. If one can't play contrapuntal music satisfactorily on a French horn, English horn, harp, chimes and flute celeste, to take the outstanding features of the so-called "romantic" organ, neither can he play modern organ music on the outstanding features of the "baroque" organ enumerated above. It seems to me that what must be done—and it is so obvious that that is probably a sufficient reason for its not being done—is to design an organ with the best features of each school of thought—a blending and union of the baroque-classic with the "romantic."

Immediately I will be told by the classicists that this can't be done, especially in a small organ. You must have either *this* or *that*. You can't have both. There must be no compromise. Just to prove that it can be done in an organ of thirty-two sets, certainly not a big organ, even in this day of small organs (now the general rule), I submit the following:

Here are the minimum great organ requirements for a clarified ensemble and classic build-up.

1. Gemshorn, 16 ft. 2. Diapason, 8 ft. 3. Octave, 4 ft. 4. Twelfth, 2-2/3 ft. 5. Fifteenth, 2 ft. 6. Fourniture, 4 ranks. Here are six sets. Minimum swell organ requirements: 1. Fagotto, 16 ft. 2. Trumpet, 8 ft. 3. Clarion, 4 ft. 4. Plein Jeu, 4 ranks. 5. Geigen octave, 4 ft. 6. Geigen Diapason, 8 ft. Another six sets. Note the above swell is not the baroque type of swell at all, but the minimum requirement for the orthodox English type of full Swell.

Suppose we have both an enclosed and unenclosed Choir division. The former, a typical Choir organ of the romantic period, the latter a Positiv of the classic period consisting of 1. Gedackt, 8'; 2. Nachthorn, 4'; 3. Nasat, 2-2/3'; 4. Block flöte, 2'; 5. Terz, 1-3/5'; and 6. Cymbel, III Ranks. The pedal minimum is 1. Contre Basse, 16'; 2. Bourdon, 16'; 3. Octave, 8'; 4. Mixture, III; 5. Trombone, 16'.

We now have twenty-three straight sets out of our thirty-two sets, which may all be classified as ensemble stops, or to be used in various combinations or groups for ensemble effects of lighter or heavier character. The full swell, as stated before, is more characteristic and more of a contrast to the great and choir and is much better adapted for that reason for playing modern French music. This is all we need as I see it for playing contrapuntal music, Bach and his precursors, or certain modern French music. The other nine stops, which have nothing to do with the ensemble, and which may be entirely omitted from it, if desired (as they will contribute little if anything to it) I want to do with as I please. These are added to make the organ capable of playing adequately romantic music and for the pretty soft effects, which are of first importance in making the public care to listen to an organ in church. If I want to make all nine of them unit stops I should be allowed to do so. I have given the "classic" organ its innings with nearly three-fourths of the total stops, and so the last quarter I want to be free to handle to the best advantage anywhere in the organ where they will increase the flexibility and be the most useful.

Here is the list of romantic voices.

Great 1. Hohl Flote 8'. Swell: 2. Gamba 8', 3. Voix Céleste 8', 4. Rohr Flöte 8', 5. Vox Humana 8', Choir: 6. Viola, 8', 7. Unda Maris 8', II Ranks, 8. Orchestral Flute, 8', 9. Clarinet, 8'.

With these nine stops added, let us see what can be made out of our combined classic and romantic organ, when some of the romantic voices are either unified or octave duplexed as detailed below. Here is the list:

GREAT (4" pressure)

1* Gemshorn, 16'
 * Diapason 8'
2 Hohl flöte 8'
1 Gemshorn 8'
 * Octave 4'
2 Flute 4'
 * Twelfth 2-2/3'
 * Fifteenth 2'
 * Fourniture IV

SWELL (5" pressure)

3 Rohr Flute, 16'
 * Diapason 8'
3 Rohr Flute 8'
 Gamba 8'
 Voix Celeste 8'
 * Geigen Octave 4'
3 Flute 4'
3 Nazard 2-2/3'
3 Piccolo 2'
 * Plein Jeu IV
4* Fagotto 16'
 * Trumpet 8'
4 Fagotto 8'
 Vox Humana 8'
 * Clarion 4'
 Tremolo

CHOIR (4" pressure enclosed)

 Viola 8'
 Unda Maris 8', II Ranks
5 Orchestral Flute 8'
5 Flute, 4'
 Clarinet 8'

POSITIV (3" pressure, enclosed)

 * Gedackt 8'
 * Nachthorn 4'
 * Nasat 2-2/3'
 * Block flote 2'
 * Terz 1-3/5'
 * Cymbel III

PEDAL

 * Contre Basse 16'
6* Bourdon 16'
1 Gemshorn 16'
3 Rohr Flute 16'
7* Octave 8'
6 Bourdon 8'
1 Gemshorn 8'
3 Rohr Flute 8'
7 Super Octave 4'
6* Flute 4'
 * Mixture III
8 Trombone 16'
8* Trumpet 8'

*Classic ensemble stops. 1. Gemshorn plays at two pitches on Great and on Pedal. 2. Hohl flöte plays at two pitches. 3. Rohr Flute plays at five pitches on Swell and two pitches on Pedal. 4. Fagotto plays at two pitches on Swell. 5. Orchestral Flute plays at two pitches on Choir. 6. Bourdon plays at three pitches on Pedal. 7. Octave plays at two pitches on Pedal. 8. Trombone plays at two pitches on Pedal.

GENERAL REMARKS ON TONAL DESIGN

The above scheme offers a compromise, which in reality is not a compromise, because both factions get the kind of organ they want. On it any kind of organ music can be played effectively. There are good characteristic ensembles on all manuals and pedals, and sufficient softer registers for music of an impressionistic nature where colorful quality (but not too pungent, such as produced by mutations) is absolutely necessary in the registration for proper effectiveness.

It seems to me that with thirty-two sets of pipes (counting each complete mixture as a set) one could scarcely do better in designing an organ to suit the divergent tastes of present-day organists. (Actually there are forty-two sets if each rank of each mixture is counted as a set.) In this scheme we do not have *this*, to the exclusion of *that*, but we have both. The scheme avoids the excesses and exclusions of valuable voices of both the seventeenth and nineteenth centuries and makes adequate use of the best features of design of both schools.

I offer this scheme as a working model for those organists who, like myself, believe that there is both good and bad in both the extreme baroque or extreme romantic type of organ, but who believe that the best features of both can be combined in an organ which will be an instrument of versatility, and a good deal better than the extreme type of either baroque or romantic organ.

CHAPTER 17

SPECIFIC EXAMPLES *of* GOOD TONAL DESIGN

MODEL SCHEMES OF VARIOUS SIZES

After much deliberation, I have come to the conclusion that to be of the most practical help to intending purchasers of organs, I cannot do better than to put down before such troubled and perplexed persons a series of designs for organs ranging from six sets of pipes to thirty sets. Two types of schemes are suggested in the smallest, largest, and intermediate sizes. One style having a considerable amount of octave duplexing, and one or two unified stops. The other type except for organs of ten stops or less, being entirely "straight" so far as manual voices are concerned. A choice is thus offered, with explanatory comments.

Not all builders do octave duplexing economically. Moller, Schantz & Reuter do this for about 10% the cost of a set of pipes. Ordinarily it does not pay to unify, a set of pipes unless such a stop is used at not less than six pitches, or at least six different uses are made of the unit stop, between manual pitches, and pedal pitches, combined.

As to costs; the various schemes will run as follows: Scheme No. 1 and No. 2 will cost between $6,000 and $7,000 at today's prices, depending on the builder.

Schemes No. 3 and No. 4 will cost between $10,000 and $12,000.

Schemes No. 5 and No. 6 will cost between $15,000 and $17,000.

Schemes No. 7 and No. 8 will cost between $25,000 and $30,000.

The various additions of stops suggested between schemes 1 to 8 inclusive, viz. the six; ten; sixteen-eighteen and twenty-five-thirty stop schemes may be averaged to cost $1100 to $1200 per additional stop.

We have been told, and I have said so many times, that every organ should be designed especially for the type of service, the size of the church, its acoustical conditions, and other factors. In my experience, however, this is true to only a limited extent. Certainly a small organ, if it is to fill a large church must have all the scales of the various stops somewhat larger and voiced on higher wind pressure than a large organ in a small church. Then too, an organ in an acoustically treated church (almost invariably rendering it poor for sound) will require somewhat different voicing treatment from that of one in a resonant building where a reasonable amount of reverberation is permitted. A well designed organ should be adapted to any type of service and to any style of playing. Naturally, a strict liturgical service might first require those voices in the organ best adapted to liturgical use. But there is nothing to prevent the use of such frankly romantic voices as soft strings, and even Vox Humana, at certain places in an austere, ritualistic, and formal service.

The schemes which are about to be presented will probably not suit the taste of all organists. I am satisfied that it is quite impossible to design any organ of more than ten sets where some organist can't think of something else he would rather have first than what is given. I do present these schemes with a great deal of assurance that they are first and foremost practical, useful and reasonable for the various sized organs being considered. There are no extreme ideas, no fads or fancies. They have proved themselves by actual tests to be good. Secondly, they are offered as the most economical and best use of the money expended. This is almost as important as the first quality that they have, in my opinion.

Outside of the three or four stop unified organs, which a number of our builders have been offering for the past fifteen years to compete with the electronic substitutes at about the same price range, one really has to have six sets of pipes to secure an organ with sufficient variety of soft and loud stops to be worthy of the name of organ. The three or four stop unified organs usually made in stock sizes, a dozen or so being put through the factory at the same time to secure economy in manufacture. Usually these organs do not have couplers, as they are sufficiently unified so that all stops may be played at all necessary and useful pitches on both manuals and pedals. Consequently there is not much use for couplers. However, when such organs are used for practice purposes, couplers are usually added to give the student organist practice in the use of couplers.

SOME SPECIFIC EXAMPLES OF GOOD TONAL DESIGN

SCHEME No. 1		or this	SCHEME No. 2	
GREAT	PLAYABLE AT		GREAT	PLAYABLE AT
1. Diapason	8'-4'		1. Diapason	8'-4'
Chimney Flute	8'-4'		2. Bourdon	8'-4'-2'
2. Dulciana	8'-4'		3. Dulciana	8'
Trumpet	8'			
			SWELL	
			4. Contra Salicional	
SWELL			T.C.	16'-8'-4'
			Bourdon (No. 2)	8'-4'-2'
3. Chimney Flute	16'-8'-4'-2-2/3'-2'		5. Voix Celeste	8'
4. Salicional	8'-4'		Dulciana (No. 3)	8'-4'-2-2/3'-2'
5. Trumpet	8'		6. Oboe	8'
Tremolo			Tremolo	
			PEDAL	
PEDAL			Bourdon	16'-8' (from no. 2)
			Salicional	8' (from no. 4)
6. Bourdon	16'-8'		Dulciana	4' (from no. 3)
Chimney Flute	16'-8'-4'		Bassoon	16 extension of no. 6

The Chimney Flute runs in metal all the way down to 16' CCC. Only the actual, full and complete stops are numbered in all cases.

298

SPECIFIC EXAMPLES OF GOOD TONAL DESIGN

SCHEME No. 1 has full couplers as follows:

Great to Pedal	8'-4'	Swell to Great	16'-8'-4'
Swell to Pedal	8'-4'	Swell to Swell	16'-4'
		Great to Great	16'-4' Total 11

SCHEME No. 2 requires no couplers, however they might be added as in SCHEME No. 1, if organ is to be used for practice purposes.

Coming now to additions to Scheme No. 1.

SCHEME 1-a Voice No. 7 should be a Voix Celeste 8' to go with Salicional.

SCHEME 2-a Voice No. 7 Pedal Bourdon 16'-8'.

SCHEME 1-b Voice No. 8 should be a Geigen Diapason 8' for Swell.

SCHEME 1-c Voice No. 9 Hohl Flute, or Melodia or Clarabella or Metal Bourdon or Doppel Flote, or Flute Harmonique. Some type of Flute for the Great organ which contrasts with Swell Chimney Flute. My preference is for the Hohl Flute as being close to the Flute Triangulaire in quality. Both stops have an unusually wide mouth for the area of the pipe, like a Doppel Flote. A singularly clear tone is produced which is most useful and interesting. Whatever Flute is chosen, it might well be made playable at 8' and 4' pitches on the Great.

We come now to ten stops, in which case the tonal forces may profitably and justifiably be placed in two chambers. Total enclosure for all of these small organs is a practical necessity for flexibility and and greatest usefulness of all the voices. It is time now to recapitulate and set forth our ten stop scheme to see how it looks.

SCHEME No. 3

GREAT (Separate expression)

1. Diapason 8'
2. Hohl Flute 8'-4'
3. Octave 4'
4. Dulciana 8'-4'

SWELL

5. Chimney Flute 16'-8'-4'-2-2/3'-2'
6. Geigen Diapason 8'-4'
7. Salicional 8'
8. Voix Celeste 8'
9. Trumpet 8'
   Tremolo

PEDAL

10. Bourdon 16'-8'-4'
    Chimney Flute 16'-8'
    Geigen Diapason 8'-4'

SCHEME No. 4

GREAT (Separate expression)

1. Diapason 8'
2. Hohl Flute 8'
   Chimney Flute 8'-4' (no. 5)
3. Octave 4'
4. Dulciana 16' T.C.-8'-4'-2-2/3'-2'

SWELL

5. Chimney Flute 16'-8'-4'-2-2/3'-2'
6. Geigen Diapason 8'
7. Salicional 8'
8. Voix Celeste 8'
9. Trumpet 8'
   Tremolo

PEDAL

10. Bourdon 16'-8'-4'
    Chimney Flute 16'-8'

SPECIFIC EXAMPLES OF GOOD TONAL DESIGN

The above organs both require couplers as listed for Scheme No. 1. Scheme No. 4 requires no octave duplexing but has two unit stops. Coming now to additions to Scheme No. 3.

SCHEME 3-a Voice No. 11 Extend Great Diapason 12 pipes to make a Pedal Diapason 16'.

SCHEME 3-b or 4-b Voice No. 12 Add Great Mixture II Ranks (12th & 15th).

SCHEME 3-c or 4-c Voice No. 13 Add Great Unda Maris 8' (Tapered).

SCHEME 3-d or 4-d Voice No. 14 Add Swell Plein Jeu III Ranks (15th-19th-22nd).

(For an organ to be used for liturgical purposes, this voice should probably be added before Unda Maris.)

SCHEME 3-e or 4-e Voice No. 15 Swell Oboe or Fagotto played at 16' TC-8'.

SCHEME No. 5	SCHEME No. 6

Such a scheme looks like the following, combining all the additions as outlined above:

GREAT (Separate expression)	GREAT (not enclosed)
1. Diapason 8'	1. Diapason 8'
2. Hohl Flute 8'-4'	2. Hohl Flöte 8'
3. Dulciana 8'	3. Dulciana 8'.
4. Unda Maris 8' (Tapered)	4. Octave 4'
5. Octave 4'	5. Rohr Flöte 4'
6. Mixture II Ranks (12th-15th)	6. Mixture II Ranks (12th-15th)
Tremolo	Tremolo

SWELL	SWELL
7. Geigen Diapason 8'	7. Geigen Diapason 8'
8. Chimney Flute 16'-8'-4'-2-2/3'-2'	8. Bourdon (metal) 16' T.C.-8'
9. Salicional 8'	9. Gamba 8'
10. Voix Celeste 8'	10. Gamba Celeste 8'
11. Fugara 4'	11. Flauto Traverso 4'
12. Plein Jeu III Ranks (15th-19th-22nd)	12. Mixture III Ranks (15th-19th-22nd)
13. Trumpet 8'	13. Trompette 8'
14. Oboe or Fagotto 16' T.C.-8'-4'	14. Oboe 4'
Tremolo	Tremolo

PEDAL	PEDAL
15. Diapason 16' (extension no. 1)	15. Contre basse 16'-8'
16. Bourdon 16'-10'-2/3'-8'-4'	16. Bourdon 16'-8'
Chimney Flute 16'-8'	17. Principal 8'-4'

With more than 16 stops, we may now consider the smallest three-manual scheme that is practical. It is as follows:

SPECIFIC EXAMPLES OF GOOD TONAL DESIGN

SCHEME No. 7

GREAT (enclosed with Choir)

1. Diapason 8'
2. Hohl Flute 8'
3. Octave 4'
4. Mixture III Ranks (15th-19th-22nd)
   Tremolo

SWELL

5. Geigen Diapason 8'-4'
6. Melodia 16'-(T.C.) 8'-4'
7. Salicional
8. Voix Celeste
9. Plein Jeu III Ranks (15th-19th-22nd)
10. Trumpet 8'
    Tremolo

CHOIR

11. Viola 8'
12. Chimney Flute 8'-4'-2-2/3'-2'
13. Dulciana 8'
14. Unda Maris 8' (Tapered)
15. Clarinet 8'
    Tremolo

PEDAL

16. Diapason 16'-8' (metal)
17. Bourdon 16'-8'-4'
    Melodia 16'-8'

Additions to the above should be as follows:

SCHEME 7-a Voice No. 18 Choir Nacht horn 4'

SCHEME 7-b Voice No. 19 Swell Flute Harmonique or Flute Triangulaire at 4'-2.

SCHEME 7-c Voice No. 20 Swell Contra Fagotto at 16'-8'.
In which case Swell Trumpet may be duplexed to play at 8'-4'. Fagotto will also play on pedal at 16'-8'.

SCHEME 7-d Voice No. 21 Vox Humana 8' to Swell.

SCHEME 7-e Voice No. 22 Great Gemshorn 16'-8' playing on pedal at 16'-8'.

SCHEME No. 8

GREAT (separately enclosed)

1. Gemshorn 16'-8'
2. Diapason 8'
3. Hohl Flute 8'-4'
4. Octave 4'
5. Mixture III Ranks (12th-15th-19th)
   Tremolo

SWELL

6. Chimney Flute 16'-8'
7. Geigen Diapason 8'-4'
8. Viole de Gamba 8'
9. Viole Celeste 8'
10. Flute Triangulaire 4'-2'
11. Plein Jeu IV Ranks (15-19-22-26)
12. Contra Fagotto 16'-8'
13. Trumpet 8'
14. Vox Humana 8'
15. Clarion 4'
    Tremolo

SCHEME No. 9

GREAT

1. Diapason 8'
2. Bourdon 8'
3. Gemshorn 8'
4. Octave 4'
5. Flute Harmonique 4'
6. Mixture III Ranks (12-15-19)

SWELL

7. Geigen Diapason 8'
8. Rohr Flute 8'
9. Viole de Gamba 8'
10. Viole Celeste 8'
11. Geigen Octave 4'
12. Flute Triangulaire 4'
13. Mixture IV Ranks (15-19-22-26)
14. Contra Fagotto 16'
15. Trompette 8'
16. Oboe 8'
17. Clarion 4'
    Tremolo

SPECIFIC EXAMPLES OF GOOD TONAL DESIGN

CHOIR

16. Principal or Viola 8'
17. Concert Flute 8'
18. Dulciana 8'-4'
19. Unda Maris 8'
20. Rohr Flute 4'-2'
21. Mazard 2-2/3'
22. Tierce 1-3/5'
23. Clarinet 8'
    Tremolo

PEDAL

Grand Cornet VII Ranks, 32'
(see later explanation)
Diapason (Great extension No. 2)

24. Bourdon 16'-8'
    Gemshorn 16'-8'
    Chimney Flute 16'-8'-4'
25. Octave 8'-4'
    Double Trumpet 16'
    (Swell extension No. 13)
    Contra Fagotto 16'

CHOIR

18. Koppel flöte 8'
19. Dolcan 8'
20. Dolcan Celeste 8'
21. Nachthorn 4'
22. Rohr Nasat 2-2/3'
23. Block Flöte 2'
24. Terz 1-3/5'
25. Krummhorn 8'
    Tremolo

PEDAL

26. Contre Basse 16'
27. Bourdon 16'-8'
28. Gedeckt 16'-8' (SW)
29. Principal 8'-4'
30. Bombarde 16'-8'

Couplers for each of the above, and the three manual scheme No. 7 include the following:

Great to Pedal 8'-4'
Swell to Pedal 8'-4'
Choir to Pedal 8'-4'
Swell to Great 16'-8'-4'
Choir to Great 16'-8'-4'

Swell to Choir 16'-8'-4'
Swell to Swell 16'-4'
Choir to Choir 16'-4'
Great to Great 16'-4'

Combination pistons are really not required on the smallest schemes No. 1 and No. 2. Schemes No. 3 and No. 4 should have at least 4 pistons each on Great, Swell and Pedal and 4 generals. Schemes No. 5 and No. 6 should have 6 pistons each on Great, Swell, Choir and Pedal. Schemes No. 8 and No. 9 should have 6 pistons on Great, 8 pistons on Swell, 7 pistons on Choir, 5 pistons on Pedal, and preferably 8 general pistons.

Scheme No. 8 is a three manual of 25 complete sets, (counting each of the two Mixtures as a set) plus two 16' extensions from Manual 8' stops, plus eight octave duplexes. Such an organ from a good builder, at today's prices would cost about $30,000.00.

Scheme No. 9 is practically a straight organ, with the equivalent of an enclosed Rück positiv, for the Choir organ. This scheme may be purchased for about the same price as Scheme No. 8 and may appeal more strongly to some organists. There are more "effects" possible on Scheme No. 8, but perhaps not all of them are necessary. The two schemes are presented side by side to demonstrate what may be done with some octave duplexing and unifying as against the straight scheme. The number of actual sets is less, because of the additional cost of relays and switches. With an organ of this size, it is debatable whether or not it pays to do anymore but a little unifying on the manuals. In the "straight" scheme No. 9, only one manual borrow is suggested, and this may be done at a nominal cost as the Rohr Boundron plays on the pedals at 16' and 8' anyway, and it may play on the manuals at these two pitches for the cost of two switches.

Regarding the pedal organ of Scheme No. 8. There is sufficient weight of tone, something which a good many completely independent pedal organs lack. This is an unfortunate lack, so far as I am concerned, and this feeling is shared by a good many other organists I have discovered. Please note the composition of 32' Grand Cornet on the Pedal.

Grand Cornet VII Ranks Composition on Note CCC
Bourdon 16' — 10-2/3' — 8'
Gemshorn   10-2/3' — 5-1/3' — 4' — 3-1/5'

This has proved itself to be a remarkably good substitute for a 32' stop.

This is as far as it is necessary to carry our model schemes. Beyond this point, we enter into the realm of individual taste as to what additions should be provided. The more romantically inclined might like to add some more Solo Reeds to the Choir such as English Horn 8', French Horn 8', Harp and Chimes. The classically minded would perhaps next want an independent 12th 15th plus Mixture III Ranks on Great. Independent 4' Flute on Great. Independent Oboe on Swell and so forth. Schemes No. 8 or 9 offer all that any average sized church should reasonably require from an organ, in my opinion.

SPECIFICATIONS OF RECENT AMERICAN ORGANS
REPRESENTATIVE OF THE BEST WORK OF EIGHT LEADING BUILDERS, IN ALPHABETICAL ORDER.

The Groton organ, built by Aeolian-Skinner Organ Co. in 1935 and subsequently slightly amended since Mr. Gammons became music director in 1941, may be said to represent a synthesis of the classical and modern viewpoints. The acoustics of the chapel are ideal for organ and choral tone and the organ is especially magnificent for every aspect of the church service. The complete organ has two developed flue choruses plus a hooded 8' Bombarde in the open and the usual soft Flutes and accompanimental registers.

The Swell is also very complete with two mixtures, separate mutations, a Flute family, Strings, and an ensemble of three modified French Reeds. Unenclosed, in a small gallery stands the most effective Positiv organ, Mr. Harrison's first.

SPECIFIC EXAMPLES OF GOOD TONAL DESIGN

There is also an enclosed Choir organ with the usual flutes and quiet voices as well as imitative Reeds and a charming French Trompette.

As a foundation to the whole, the organ boasts a Pedal of eighteen ranks, including a full length 32' Contre Basse; a Principal group from 16' through mixtures; 16'-8'-4' Flutes and Reeds plus borrows.

The instrument stands as an example of Harrison's work at its best, and as long as Mr. Gammons remains at Groton it probably will be in process of development.

ST. JOHN'S CHAPEL, GROTON SCHOOL, GROTON, MASS.

AEOLIAN-SKINNER ORGAN CO. 1935

G. DONALD HARRISON, DESIGNER

PEDAL ORGAN: Unenclosed except for manual borrows. 5" wind pressure.

20 Stops—14 Registers—18 Ranks

32'	Contrebasse
16'	Principal
16'	Contrebasse
16'	Flute Conique
16'	Bourdon
10-2/3'	Grosse Quinte
8'	Octave (1)
8'	Violoncello
8'	Gedeckt
8'	Flute Ouverte
5-1/3'	Octave Quinte
4'	Superoctave (3)
4'	Klein Gedeckt
4'	Flute Harm.
III rks	Mixture (17-19-22)
III rks	Fourniture (22-26-29)
16'	Bombarde (3)
16'	English Horn
8'	Trompette (3)
4'	Clairon (3)

GREAT ORGAN: Unenclosed 3" and 3½" pressure. 6" to Bombarde

16 Stops—16 Registers—24 Ranks

16'	Sub-Principal
8'	Principal
8'	Diapason
8'	Gemshorn
8'	Flute Harmonique
5-1/3'	Grosse Quinte

4'	Principal
4'	Octave
4'	Flute Couverte (1)
2-2/3'	Octave Quinte
2'	Superoctave
1-3/5'	Tierce
IV rks	Full Mixture (3)
	(12-15-19-22)
IV rks	Fourniture
	(15-19-22-26)
III rks	Scharff (6)
	(22-26-29)
8'	Bombarde (7)

PROCESSIONAL ORGAN: (In Choir Room) 3½" pressure.

2 Stops—2 Registers—2 Ranks—Unencl'd

8'	Gedeckt
4'	Geigen (6)

POSITIV ORGAN: Unenclosed 2½" pressure.

8 Stops—8 Registers—11 Ranks

8'	Rohrflöte (3)
4'	Principal (3)
4'	Koppelflöte
2-2/3'	Nasat
2'	Blockflöte
1-3/5'	Terz
1'	Sifflöte
IV rks	Cymbel (6)
	(26-29-33-36)

Positiv organ in small projecting gallery below great organ.

SPECIFIC EXAMPLES OF GOOD TONAL DESIGN

CHOIR ORGAN: Enclosed 4¼" pressure.

11 Stops—10 Registers—10 Ranks

16'	Quintaton(3)
8'	Viola
8'	Dulciana
8'	Unda Maris
8'	Orch. Flute
4'	Lieblichflöte(2)
2'	Zauberflöte(2)
16'	English Horn
8'	Trompette Harm.
8'	Clarinet
	Tremulant
8'	Bombarde(7) (Great)

SWELL ORGAN: Enclosed, 4" pressure.

19 Stops—19 Registers—24 Ranks

16'	Flute Conique
8'	Geigen
8'	Viole de Gambe
8'	Viole Celeste
8'	Echo Viole
8'	Gedeckt
4'	Octave Geigen

4'	Fugara
4'	Flute Triangulaire
2-2/3'	Nasard(2)
2'	Flageolet(2)
1-3/5'	Tierce
III rks	Mixture(5)
	(15-19-22)
IV rks	Plein Jeu(2)
	(19-22-26-29)
16'	Bombarde(3)
8'	Trompette(3)
8'	Hautbois(5)
8'	Vox Humana
4'	Clairon(3)
	Tremulant

(1) Revised 1944
(2) Revised 1945
(3) Revised 1950
(4) New pipes 1944
(5) New pipes 1945
(6) New pipes 1950
(7) New pipes and chest in 1950. Gift of
   Dr. and Mrs. William H. Barnes

For Austin Organs, Inc. I wish to include the stoplist of an organ that this company is building for a church in Lodi, California. Their western representative, Mr. J. B. Jamison prepared the stoplist, and it has many unusual and interesting features. Mr. Jamison waxes eloquent in support of this scheme in a memorandum he has sent me. He entitles this "A minimum All-Purpose Organ". Curiously enough he considers thirty-four registers to be a minimum to accomplish all purposes, just as I did in the model stoplist that I discussed fully in the previous chapter. As is to be expected when two organ enthusiasts start and finish a project of this kind, Mr. Jamison's scheme and mine differ in many particulars. However, there are so many novel ideas expressed in Mr. Jamison's statement that I consider it a privilege to be able to quote his reasons for what he does.

In fairness, it should be said that Austin Organs, Inc. do not wish this to be considered typical of their work, and have submitted a typical scheme that is printed immediately to the right of Mr. Jamison's. It should also be said that some designers take violent exception to some of the ideas of Mr. Jamison. This is to be expected. Every new idea, whether good, bad, or indifferent, has violent objectors. My best ideas are embodied in the model scheme described in the previous chapter. They are more orthodox and will perhaps meet with general approval and acceptance. I would not care to put my "imprimatur" on all of Mr. Jamison's ideas until I have had much practical experience with them. They are interesting and convincing enough to warrant giving them in full in this book. If no new ideas are ever tried, we shall have no progress.

Mention has previously been made of the tonal accomplishments of Mr. R. J. Piper, tonal director for Austin. Their new work which I have heard is quite outstanding tonally. I am satisfied that the following stop-list, carried out by Austin will be something to make all organists and builders sit up and take notice.

A MINIMUM ALL-PURPOSE ORGAN

"The accompanying scheme represents an endeavor to list the fewest stops that will do justice to all schools and types of organ music. It has three manuals and thirty-four registers. Though a concert instrument it is first of all a church organ that will play any service throughout the church year and will equally well accompany boy or mixed choirs. There may be period music demanding other registers but it is not important enough to warrant enlarging this concept.

"The principle of inter-sectional contrast and inner-sectional blend is basic. The color-spread is as wide as blend and cohesion allow. Primary coloring is essential to inclusion of any register and from such the organist can make tints and discover new combinations after prolonged familiarity. The number of musical combinations approaches the mathematically possible number of groupings.

"Whereas the Schnitger system of ensemble subordinates climax to utility by regulating all voices to similar power, our pattern yields all the flexibility of the Schnitger (without its use of excessively high pitches) plus both reed and flue climactic tone. We eat our cake and have it. It also provides pianissimo tone. In scope and range it excels the classic plan. Though the bulk of the registers are of Mp-Mf power, every 8' and every 4' representative of the four classes of tone is different— decidedly so.

"The Great combines substance with brilliance. It does not emasculate the 8' stratum, nor does it provide an inadequate double. Each is there—in balance. You cannot get majesty without both,— and majesty is essential to the organ idiom. Time will laugh at Great 16' Quintatens and small scaled "Diapasons". They did all right in seventeenth century work but they cannot fit into a modern Great of impressive dignity.

"I believe a beautiful and cohesive chorus cannot be made from 'white' members. You can insert every practicable harmonic, made from 'pure' tone, and the chorus, if extended high enough, will remind you of a needle sticking out of a sponge. Every chorus member should have its proper share of innate harmonics. Thus is had the priceless quality of *warmth*,—the essence of organ charm, as elusive as it is obvious,—without which any organ is to me a dud—love's labor lost. R. J. Piper proved to me that warmth in big flue-chorus work stops short of 'hard' tone. Hardness comes from too-high innate harmonics. There is a happy mean that spells success.

"Notice should be taken of the current and almost universal violation of Great-Swell perspective, due to too-powerful Swell chorus reeds. This stems from another fallacy—the omission of a Choir Tuba. The name 'Tuba', strangely, connotes to many organists 'Tromba' timbre. (I wish we all were familiar with a real Father Willis Tuba. That would lay that ghost.) So a lot of otherwise fine organs fear the inclusion of a dominating reed and never reach climax or realize full emotional satisfaction. The correct power balance of Great-Swell is something like 100-75. If there is no major member of the trumpet family in the Choir, the Swell reeds must carry the reed burden and contribute enough reed quality to flavor full organ. That means they have to be loud. It follows that the gap in the build-up between the Swell flues and such reeds is wide. This provokes a jumpy crescendo and makes a difficult organ to play. It is all right if you do what IT wants to do, but all wrong if you ask it to do what YOU want to do. This chain-reaction in misfortune characterizes too many 1952 organs. I have tried some recent ones in which the excellent Swell Trompettes are twice as loud as full Great! This smacks of the farmer who played his aces first—frowned on in select bridge circles.

"The provision of a fiery Choir reed of big power permits the correct subordination of the Swell reeds to a point where they take over from the Swell flues in almost gapless fashion, and makes possible a two-stage reed crescendo that like a champion comes through in an unbelievable finish-climax—the mark of a real organ—or a real anything.

"So we have a noble, majestic Great, a Swell three-quarters as powerful, in which the flue-reed build-up *aids* us in every registration problem, and a Choir which has in it (though not of it) a climactic reed (as nearly as possible like the timbre of full organ up to that point) that extends full organ to satisfying fortissimo.

"Keep in mind that the Great has three stops enclosed with the Choir. They are Diapason Conique, Harmonic Flute and 4' Quintaten. The last acts as a tiny mixture and this group has harmonic texture.

"The Swell omits the conventional Geigen. Its place is taken by a large scaled Viola of rosiny timbre plus the Austin Innerbeard Flute. We often see, today, this deletion of the Swell diapason and its attempted replacement by a big string plus a stopped flute. No *stopped* flute can combine with a broad string to yield synthetic Geigen timbre as can a firm, open flute. This tactical blunder is so common as to justify mention. The Innerbeard-open-flute-plus-Viola 'Geigen' is so deceptive that a tuner once called out to me (when I had drawn the two) 'take that Octave off'.

"Where the organ is installed on both sides of the chancel the Swell can be somewhat larger, so Great-Choir on one side may be fairly well balanced in space by the opposite Swell. This is an additional reason for putting our mutations in the Swell, where they rightly belong, and where they have as many or more voices with which to combine as in the more usual Choir position. These authentic, ancient French type pipes are scaled and voiced to yield a cohesive Cornet (without which 18th century music cannot be adequately registrated.) They blend (in the true sense) with anything, because they have something definite to contribute. The pianissimo pair, Dolce and Celeste, are also in the Swell where they can accompany Choir voices.

"I am all for the versatile double Clarinet in the Swell. But to provide it at 16', only, is a mistake. This Clarinet is a sturdy stop whose upper end is two-thirds as loud as the Trompette's treble. It is exactly the right weight for the reed double. One of the worst American habits has been to make the Swell double reed too big. Then the unison has to be loudened, etc.,—and away goes Great-Swell perspective. The Clarinet avoids this and contributes a rich 16' that is ideal for the chorus. With 16' Clarinet, 8' Trompette and 4' Clairon we get the orthodox version, but with 16' and 8' Clarinet, 4' Octave, Mixture and super-coupler is had a chorus reedless reed chorus that is astonishing—the richest sound an organ can give out. The 8' is essential for this, so we unify it at 16' and 8'. The big 8' Clarinet goes admirably with flues, imparting a color impossible from any other source. The ordinary weak Clarinet will not turn this trick."

Now for the Schnitger element of automatic manual-pedal balance for polyphony, and sectional contrast for clarity of line.

"This scheme presents a new idea in the use of the Swell flue chorus as a polyphonic 'member'. Viola, Flute, Octave, Mixture. This Mixture is purposely low pitched (which incidentally permits coupling it and the reeds to Great at 4' as well as 8') and is scaled and voiced after the Father Willis 1890 manner, silvery and mild. The late Sir Walter Alcock called the chorus 'the most beautiful sound I have heard on this earth.'

"Omission of mutations from the Choir leaves that manual a Positiv-Choir division. It is a little flue chorus with a Stopped Flute unison, 4' and 2' Diapasons and a Cymbal. This Cymbal is higher in pitch and thinner in timbre than the Swell mixture. It stresses the off-unison ranks while the Swell stop accents the unisons. The two choruses are as far apart as Walter Pater and Elinor Glynn. Matching them in strength is the 16-8-4 Pedal Violone plus 17-19-22 Mixture. Here we have three 'lines' as distinct as red, white and green ribbons on a Maypole. No matter where a line goes it stands apart—proving that 'clarity' hangs on dissimilarity.

SPECIFIC EXAMPLES OF GOOD TONAL DESIGN

"We also have the Great secondary enclosed chorus—and what about the Swell Cornet? All are—or. can be made—approximately equal in what, for want of a better term we call 'power'. They impress us that way—subjectively. One has no mixture, one is all mixture, one is low mixture, one is high mixture. One is round and dark, one is medium pitch and silvery, one is thin and high, and one is trumpety! Four choruses of middle power, all balanced to the lovely, definite, musical Pedal Violone and its tierce mixture. You will have your choice of *several* ways of handling usually difficult situations. You will never be bored by this organ, and you will never have to go from New York to Chicago by way of New Orleans to registrate what you want.

"The Swell reeds are borrowed to the Pedal at 16' and 8' and as they are close to the Swell flues in power the reeds may be played on the pedal against the flues on the manual in perfect balance, through a wide dynamic range.

"I do not favor the completely independent Pedal. It is a waste of space and money. A properly scaled and voiced wood and metal 16-8-4 (56 pipes) Pedal Diapason cannot be .told from three good independent ranks. In octaves (I hear objection) one note drops out. Yes—but when pedal octaves are played it is likely full organ is drawn—and who could hear one pipe in full organ? The saving by. augmentation of this register almost pays for the Pedal Mixture. The Violone is a clean Great double of special scaling with an incisive low octave. It is equally balanced to Great and as a Pedal stop for polyphonic choruses. The Bombarde is a big reed with parallel shallots merging into a magnificent thrilling 8' Choir voice.

"To accompany a church service is the most 'romantic' task that an organ has to do. Note the three Celestes. Rich, sensuous tone. All organists will recognize what can be done with them. This organ will *really* play transcriptions—and what's wrong with a transcription if it is musically done! Whereas a mixed or men's choir can constitute the 8' line, and higher pitches of the organ be superimposed on this to yield a balanced voice-organ ensemble, boys' voices pose another problem. The timbre that goes best with this light, sexless sound is the dark, velvety Diapason Conique. In cathedral after cathedral, in England, France and Germany one hears this timbre in the chancel organs. Do not feature Mixture work with boys' voices. Let the organ supply the 8' line and the boys will take care of the upperwork.

"Thoughtful examination of this scheme will show it admirably fitted to Bach and Franck. It has everything each composer calls for. It will also play anything from Sweelinck to Reger, including Mendelssohn, Mozart, etc. It is magnificent for modern French music. But its main duty—the accompaniment of the church service—is the mould that shapes its form."

SPECIFIC EXAMPLES OF GOOD TONAL DESIGN

CHURCH IN LODI, CALIFORNIA (1952)
AUSTIN ORGANS, INC.

GREAT: (Unenclosed)
Major Flue

16'	Violone (pedal)
8'	Diapason
4'	Octave
2-2/3'	Twelfth
2'	Fifteenth
	(Mixture 19-22-26)

In Choir Box
8'	Diapason Conique
8'	Harmonic Flute
4'	Quintadena

SWELL: (Enclosed)

8'	Viola (52 scale)	W
8'	Viola Celeste 55 scale	
8'	Innerbeard Flute	W
4'	Prestant	WX
	Mixture 15-19-22	W
8'	Dolce (tapered)	
8'	Dolce Celeste	
4'	Chimney Flute	
2-2/3'	Nasard	X
2'	Flute	X
1-3/5'	Tierce	X

Double purpose MF reed chorus.
16'-8'	Clarinet
8'	Trompette
4'	Clairon
	Tremolo

POSITIV CHOIR: (Enclosed)

8'	Gedeckt
8'	Salicional (58 scale)
8'	Voix Celeste
4'	Nachthorn
4'	Principal
2'	Octave
	Cymbal 22-26-29
8'	Fagot
8'	Bombarde FF (pedal)
	Tremolo

PEDAL
16'-8'-4'	Diapason (24 wood, bearded, 32 metal)
16'-8'-4'	Violone 56 pipes
16'-8'	Gedeckt (Choir plus 12)
16'	Dolce (Swell plus 12)
4'	Nachthorn (Choir)
	Mixture 17-19-22
16'-8'-4'	Bombarde 56 pipes
16'	Clarinet (Swell)
8'	Trompette (Swell)

REPRESENTATIVE AUSTIN SCHEME

GREAT ORGAN

16'	Violone
8'	Diapason
8'	Diapason Conique
4'	Octave
2-2/3'	Twelfth
2'	Fifteenth
III	Mixture (19-22-26)
8'	Harmonic Flute
8'	Gemshorn
4'	Quintaten

SWELL ORGAN

8'	Geigen
8'	Melodia
8'	Gambe
8'	Celeste
4'	Fugara
4'	Chimney Flute
2'	Flageolet
III	Mixture (15-19-22)
16'	Fagotto
8'	Trumpet
4'	Clarion
8'	Oboe

CHOIR ORGAN

8'	Spitz Flute
8'	Bourdon
8'	Dolce
8'	Dolce Celeste
4'	Prestant
4'	Koppel Flute
2-2/3'	Nasard
2'	Doublette
2'	Block Flute
1-3/5'	Tierce
III	Mixture (22-26-29)
8'	Clarinet
8'	Bombarde (Pedal)

PEDAL ORGAN

16	Diapason	32 pipes
		(Great)
16-8-4	Violone	(Ch. 12 pipes)
16-8-4	Gedeckt	
8-4	Octave	44 pipes
III	Mixture (17-19-22)	96 pipes
16-8-4	Bombarde	56 pipes
16	Fagotto	(Swell)
8	Fagotto	(Swell)

W—Swell flue chorus, low pitched, silvery.

X—Cornet (4' Chimney Flute can also be used)

SPECIFIC EXAMPLES OF GOOD TONAL DESIGN

Casavant Freres of Ste. Hyacinthe, Canada, is a long established firm, that has built nearly all of the important organs in Canada over a period of many years, as well as a large number of organs for the United States. They have enjoyed an enviable reputation for building first class instruments of conservative design. They have done this consistently throughout a long period, and were less carried away by the Hope-Jones, theatre, influence (so strong thirty or forty years ago) than any of our American builders. On the other hand, at present our American builders are somewhat ahead of this firm in supplying more thoroughgoing classic instruments than Casavant. There are organists in this country who believe that no American builder can quite equal the work of Casavant. With this sentiment, I heartily disagree, even though I have a deep respect for what this firm has stood for in organ building throughout the years. Mr. Stephen Stoot of this company writes as follows: "Herewith a copy of the stoplist of one of our recent healthy two-manual organs, which was erected in a Presbyterian Church in one of the suburbs of Montreal. Although there was sufficient space provided in the organ chamber, the grille openings would not permit of two swell boxes. The enclosed scheme has thirty-five registers, and would normally be a three-manual, were it not for the peculiar chamber conditions. In discussing this matter with Mr. Henry Willis on his recent visit, he stated, 'It is unwise to proceed to the design of a three-manual unless an adequate two-manual has been laid down as a foundation.' "

I am quoting both Mr. Stoot and Mr. Willis, as both gentlemen should know about designing organs. However, I should like to point out that many other designers do not agree. Please note the Austin stoplist on page 310 consisting of one less number of registers and see that a healthy three-manual can be designed with this number of registers. It seems to me that there is much more variety in the choice of stops, and much more flexibility and ease of control in the Austin scheme, than in the two-manual Casavant, even though the latter is excellent for what it is. The healthy two-manual Casavant stoplist is as follows:

GREAT ORGAN		SWELL ORGAN		PEDAL ORGAN	
		8'	Geigen Principal		
		8'	Stopped Diapason		
16'	Dulciana	8'	Viola da Gamba	16'	Contra Bass
8'	Diapason	8'.	Voix Celeste (GG).	16'	Bourdon
8'	Melodia	8'	Aeoline	16'	Lieblich Bourdon 16'
8'	Rohr Flöte	4'	Octave Geigen	16'	Dulciana (Great)
8'	Dulciana	4'	Flute Triangulaire	8'	Octave (Contra Bass)
4'	Principal	2'	Fifteenth	8'	Stopped Flute
4'	Flute d'Amour		Mixture (12-19-22)	8'	Gedeckt
2-2/3'	Twelfth		-15th draws separately	8'	Dulciana (Great)
2'	Fifteenth	16'	Contra Fagotto	4'	Flute
	Harmonics (17-19-22)	8'	Cornopean	III	Mixture (10-15-17)
		8'	Oboe	16'	Trombone
		4'	Clarion	16'	Fagotto
			Tremulant	8'	Tromba

SPECIFIC EXAMPLES OF GOOD TONAL DESIGN

One of the oldest builders in America have just completed in the First Congregational church of Burlington, Vermont a fine example of a modern classic ensemble organ. Estey Organ Co. are the builders, and the stoplist, voicing particulars, and scales were furnished by Mr. Edward B. Gammons. It is a pleasure to reproduce this stoplist, as it might well be used as a model for an organ of this size. An interesting feature is the Pedal Bourdon. This breaks into an open flute at second E and thus is obtained the 8' Flute Ouverte in the Pedal. It is a very ingenious compromise for an open pedal Flute, and I can heartily recommend it. Even though the acoustics of the church are below par, the organ is a most effective instrument for all legitimate requirements of a church organ. It has a wealth of soft effects, as well as good characteristic ensembles on all manuals and pedal.

ESTEY ORGAN COMPANY, (1952)
First Congregation Church, Burlington, Vermont
Designed by Edward B. Gammons

GREAT (3½" pressure)

Gemshorn	16'
Diapason	8'
Hohlflöte	8'
Gemshorn	8' (from 16')
Octave	4'
Rohrflöte	4'
Super Octave	2'
Mixture	IV (12-15-19-22)
Chimes	
Tremulant	

SWELL (5" pressure)

Geigenprinzipal	8'
Bourdon	8'
Viole de Gambe	8'
Voix Celeste	8'
Geigenoctav	4'
Flauto Traverso	4'
Plein-Jeu	III (15-19-22)
Fagotto	16'
Trompette	8'
Fagotto	8'
Oboe Clarion	4'
Tremulant	

CHOIR (4½" pressure)

Dolcan	8'
Dolcan Celeste	8'
Koppelflote	8'
Violoncello	8'

Nachthorn	4'
Nasard	2-2/3'
Blockflote	2'
Tierce	1-3/5'
Clarinet	8'
Tremulant	

PEDAL: (6" pressure)

Acoustic Bass	32'
Diapason	16'
Sub-Bass	16'
Bourdon	16' (Swell)
Gemshorn	16' (Great)
Octave	8'
Flute Ouverte	8'
Gemshorn	8' (Great)
Bourdon	8' (Swell)
Choral Bass	4'
Super Octave	4' (from 8')
Posaune	16'
Fagotto	16' (Swell)
Trumpet	8' (from Posaune)
Clarion	4' (from Posaune)

ANTIPHONAL (5" pressure)

Principal	8'
Gedackt	8'
Kleinererzähler II	8'
Spitzflote	4'
Hautbois	8'
Vox Humana	8'
Tremulant	

SPECIFIC EXAMPLES OF GOOD TONAL DESIGN

The Kilgen Organ Company's latest cathedral organ is in the St. Louis Cathedral, St. Louis, Mo. Twenty years before, Geo. Kilgen & Sons built the organs in St. Patrick's cathedral. Mr. Eugene R. Kilgen, the youngest of the four Kilgen brothers is now head of the Kilgen organization, and he collaborated with Dr. Mario Salvador, organist of the cathedral, in the preparation of the stoplist.

Several recent Kilgens which I have designed, all of them of smaller size than the cathedral organ have all been musically satisfying. These organs in smaller churches with more normal acoustics give one a better opportunity to judge the work of this firm. The St. Louis Cathedral has so long a period of reverberation that it is impossible to tell how much of the effect is produced by the building, and how much by the organ. This instrument is, in any event, estraordinarily impressive, brilliant and thrilling.

ST. LOUIS CATHEDRAL, ST. LOUIS, MO.

Kilgen Organ Co. (1949)

GREAT (Enclosed in Chamber I)

16'	Spitzflute
8'	First Diapason
8'	Second Diapason
8'	Third Diapason
8'	Doppel Flute
8'	Clarabella
8'	Viola
8'	Spitzflute
4'	Octave
4'	Principal
4'	Hohl Flute
2-2/3'	Twelfth
2'	Fifteenth
V	Rank Full Mixture
	(12-15-19-22-26)
8'	Tromba

SWELL (Enclosed in Chamber III)

16'	Bourdon
8'	Diapason
8'	Geigen Diapason
8'	Rohr Flute
8'	Flauto Dolce
8'	Flute Celeste
8'	Salicional
8'	Voix Celeste
4'	Octave Geigen
4'	Flute Harmonique
2-2/3'	Nazard
2'	Wald Flute
IV	Rank Scharf
16'	Fagotto
8'	Cornopean
8'	Oboe
8'	Vox Humana.
4'	Clarion

CHOIR (Enclosed in Chamber IV)

16'	Dulciana
8'	Small Diapason
8'	Violin Diapason
8'	Gedeckt
8'	Concert Flute
8'	Flute Celeste
8'	Gemshorn
8'	Gemshorn Celeste
8'	Dulciana
8'	Unda Maris
4'	Fugara
4'	Suabe Flute
2-2/3'	Rohr Nazard
2'	Piccolo
1-3/5'	Tierce
1-1/7'	Septime
8'	English Horn
8'	Clarinet
	Chimes
	Harp

SPECIFIC EXAMPLES OF GOOD TONAL DESIGN

SOLO (Enclosed in Chamber II)

8'	Principal
8'	Gedeckt Pommer
8'	Violon Cello
8'	Solo Celeste
4'	Flute Ouverte
8'	Tuba Mirabilis XXX
8'	French Horn XXX
8'	Trompette XXX

XXX—12" pressure.

PEDAL (Enclosed in Chambers I, III, & IV)

32'	Acoustic Bass
16'	Diapason
16'	Violone
16'	Sub Bass
16'	Bourdon
16'	Spitzflute (Great)

16'	Lieblich Gedeckt (Swell)
16'	Dulciana (Choir)
10-2/3'	Quint
8'	Octave (Pad Drop)
8'	Principal
8'	Cello (Solo)
8'	Bass Flute (Boudon)
8'	Gedeckt (Swell)
8'	Spitzflute (Great)
8'	Flauto Dolce (Swell)
5-1/3'	Quint (10-2/3 Quint)
4'	Octave (8' Principal)
4'	Block Flute
2'	Doublette (8' Principal)
16'	Trombone
16'	Fagotto (Swell)
8'	Tromba
4'	Clarion
IVRk.	Mixture
VRk.	Mixture (Great)

I have chosen the organ in Trinity Methodist Church, of Youngstown, Ohio, as being typical of the more recent Moller designs.

Some fifteen years ago, the late Mr. Richard Whitelegg designed a complete Diapason Chorus, for demonstration purposes. It was set up in the Moller factory. In 1942 this chorus was purchased by Trinity Methodist. It is incorporated in the new Great organ, and the stops so incorporated are marked by a*. In looking through a good many Moller stop-lists of recent organs, this one seemed to embody to best advantage their thinking as to what a good-sized four-manual organ should contain.

GREAT ORGAN

*Violone, 16 ft.
*Diapason I, 8 ft.
 Diapason II, 8 ft.
 Hohlflöte, 8 ft.
 Gemshorn, 8 ft.
*Octave, 4 ft.
 Principal, 4 ft.
 Harmonic Flute, 4 ft.
*Octave Quint, 2-2/3 ft.
*Super Octave, 2 ft.
*Mixture, 3 rks.
*Cornet, 3 to 5 rks.
*Harmonics, 4 rks.

SWELL ORGAN

Lieblich Bourdon, 16 ft.
Geigen Diapason, 8 ft.
Rohrflöte, 8 ft.
Salicional, 8 ft.

Voix Celeste, 8 ft.
Spitzflöte, 8 ft.
Principal, 4 ft.
Fugara, 4 ft.
Flute Triangulaire, 4 ft.
Twelfth, 2-2/3 ft.
Flautino, 2 ft.
Plein Jeu, 3 rks.
Dolce Cornet, 3 rks.
Contra Fagotto, 16 ft.
Trumpet, 8 ft.
Oboe, 8 ft.

*ANTIPHONAL GREAT
(Playable from Great Manual)

Flauto Dolce, 8 ft.
Flauto Dolce Celeste, 8 ft.
Flauto Dolce, 4 ft.
Octave, 4 ft., 73 pipes
Fifteenth 2 ft., 61 pipes
Mixture 3 rks., 183 pipes.
Chimes

SPECIFIC EXAMPLES OF GOOD TONAL DESIGN

*ANTIPHONAL SWELL
(Playable from Swell Manual)

Muted Viole 16 ft., 73 notes.
Muted Viole 8 ft., 73 pipes
Viole Celeste 8 ft., 61 pipes
Fern Flote 8 ft., 85 pipes
Fern Flote 4 ft., 61 notes
Muted Viole 4 ft., 12 pipes
Fern Flote 2-2/3 ft., 61 notes
Fern Flote 2 ft., 61 notes
Trompette 8 ft., 73 pipes
French Horn 8 ft., 73 pipes
Clarion 4 ft., 12 pipes
Vox Humana 8 ft.,
Clarion 4 ft.,
Harp (from Choir).

CHOIR ORGAN

Dulciana 16 ft.
Viola 8 ft.
Concert Flute 8 ft.
Nachthorn 8 ft.
Dulciana 8 ft.
Unda Maris 8 ft.
Erzähler 8 ft.
Prestant 4 ft.
Chimney Flute 4 ft.
Nazard 2-2/3 ft.
Blockflöte 2 ft.
Tierce 1-3/5 ft.
Larigot 1-1/3 ft.
Sifflöte 1 ft.
Clarinet 8 ft.
Harp 49 bars
Celesta

SOLO ORGAN

Diapason 8 ft.
Doppel Flöte 8 ft.

Gamba 8 ft.
Gamba Celeste 8 ft.
Suabe Flute 4 ft.
Harmonic Trumpet 8 ft.
Cor Anglais 8 ft.

PEDAL ORGAN

Violone, 32 ft.
Contrabass, 16 ft.
Violone (from Great), 16 ft.
Gemshorn, 16 ft.
Dulciana (from Choir), 16 ft.
Bourdon, 16 ft.
Lieblich Bourdon (from Swell),
Quint, 10-2/3 ft.
Octave, 8 ft.
Bourdon, 8 ft.
Rohrflöte (from Swell), 8 ft.
Gemshorn (from Great), 8 ft.
Quint, 5-1/3 ft.
Super Octave, 4 ft.
Harmonic Flute (from Great), 4 ft.
Mixture, 2 rks.
Bombarde, 16 ft.
Contra Fagotto (from Swell), 16 ft.
Bombarde, 8 ft.
Trumpet (from Swell), 8 ft.
Clarion, 4 ft.

*PEDAL ORGAN (Antiphonal)

Bourdon, 16 ft.
Muted Viole, 16 ft.
Flauto Dolce, 16 ft.
Trompette, 16 ft.
Viole, 8 ft.
Flauto Dolce, 8 ft.
Fern Flöte, 4 ft.

Although the Reuter Organ Co. of Lawrence, Kansas, did not lead in the revival of the classic organ, they do excellent work, and their recent examples show them to be forward-looking. In fact, one of their recent organs in the First Christian Church of Columbia, Mo. is a classic design of such extreme severity that it actually out-Holtkamps Holtkamp in building this type of organ. But this organ is also capable of playing satisfactorily 19th century and contemporary music, so it is truly versatile.

The author has become very much interested in the work of this organization, because of their open-mindedness, in accepting new ideas, and suggestions, and incorporating them effectively in their organs. I have recently designed a number of organs which this firm are now building.

SPECIFIC EXAMPLES OF GOOD TONAL DESIGN

Rather than quote the Columbia, Mo. scheme, I prefer to reproduce one which I designed for the First Presbyterian Church of Wichita, Kansas, as being more truly representative of this firm's recent work. The stop-list as given below shows that here is a good sized three-manual organ with a modern, but not extreme design. It will undoubtedly satisfy all of the organ requirements of this large and important church for many years to come.

FIRST PRESBYTERIAN CHURCH, WICHITA, KANSAS (1949)

GREAT ORGAN

Violone, 16 ft.
Diapason, 8 ft.
Violone, 8 ft.
Clarabella, 8 ft.
Octave, 4 ft.
Violone, 4 ft.
Flute Harmonic, 4 ft.
Grave Mixture, 2 rks.
Cymbel, 3 rks.
Trumpet, 8 ft.
Tremulant

SWELL ORGAN

Flute Conique, 16 ft.
Geigen Diapason, 8 ft.
Chimney Flute, 8 ft.
Viole de Gambe, 8 ft.
Gamba Celeste, 8 ft.
Flauto Dolce, 8 ft.
Flute Celeste, 8 ft.
Geigen Octave, 4 ft.
Flute Triangulaire, 4 ft.
Flute Dolce, 4 ft.
Nazard, 2-2/3 ft.
Flautino, 2 ft.
Plein Jeu, 3 rks.
Contra Fagotto, 16 ft.
Trumpet, 8 ft.
Fagotto, 8 ft.
Vox Humana, 8 ft.
Clarion, 4 ft.
Tremulant

CHOIR ORGAN

Quintaton, 16 ft.
Viola, 8 ft.
Viola Celeste, 8 ft.
Concert Flute, 8 ft.
Quintaton, 8 ft.
Dulciana, 8 ft.
Unda Maris, 8 ft.
Rohrflöte, 4 ft.
Quintaton, 4 ft.
Rohrnasat, 2-2/3 ft.
Piccolo, 2 ft.
Clarinet, 8 ft.
Cor Anglais, 8 ft.
Tremulant

ECHO ORGAN

Echo Flute, 8 ft.
Dulciana, 8 ft.
Unda Maris, 8 ft.
Vox Humana, 8 ft.
Chimes
Tremulant

PEDAL ORGAN

Contra Bourdon, 32 ft.
Diapason, 16 ft.
Violone, 16 ft. (Great)
Bourdon, 16 ft.
Quintaton, 16 ft.
Flute Conique, 16 ft.
Quint, 10-2/3 ft.
Principal, 8 ft.
Octave, 8 ft.
Violone, 8 ft. (Great)
Bourdon, 8 ft.
Quintaton, 8 ft.
Flute Conique, 8 ft.
Super Octave, 4 ft.
Bourdon, 4 ft.
Posaune, 16 ft.
Fagotto, 16 ft. (Swell)
Posaune, 8 ft.
Fagotto, 8 ft. (Swell)

SPECIFIC EXAMPLES OF GOOD TONAL DESIGN

Five gentlemen bearing the name of Schantz, two of the older and three of the younger generation, collaborate with their artisans in building organs under the name of Schantz Organ Co. in Orrville, Ohio. In a quiet and unostentatious way, they have gradually improved their organs, until at present, this firm should rank as one of our leading builders. Mr. John Schantz has already been mentioned as having a particular aptitude for regulating and finishing organs so that they are truly musical. I won't say whether the fact that he is an excellent organist is a help or hindrance to him in this work. At least he knows from direct personal experience with playing organs, what it is that any good organist wants in an organ, and he sees to it that any organ bearing the Schantz name supplies this want.

The following stoplist is typical of their present day thoughts in regard to tonal design. Please note in the stoplist that the idea of an unenclosed Positiv division is not confined to Aeolian-Skinner or Walter Holtkamp. Indeed nearly all of our forward looking builders can and are supplying this type of organ on occasion, if not so frequently as these two builders.

CHRIST CHURCH CATHEDRAL, LOUISVILLE, KENTUCKY
Schantz Organ Co.

GREAT ORGAN (Unenclosed)

Quintaton 16'
Diapason 8'
Gemshorn 8'
Melodia 8'
Octave 4'
Flute Harmonic 4'
Octave Quint 2-2/3'
Super Octave 2'
Fourniture IV
Chimes
Trumpet 8'

SWELL ORGAN

Bourdon 16'
Diapason 8'
Stopped Diapason 8'
Salicional 8'
Voix Celeste 8'
Spitzflute 8'
Spitzflute Celeste 8'
Octave 4'
Flauto Traverso 4'
Flautino 2'
Plein Jeu IV

Contra Fagotto 16'
Trompette 8'
Oboe 8'
Vox Humana 8'
Clarion 4'

CHOIR ORGAN

Viola 8'
Quintadena 8'
Dulciana 8'
Unda Maris 8'
Octave 4' (Duplex)
Rohr Flute 4'
Nazard 2-2/3'
Piccolo 2'
Clarinet 8'

POSITIV ORGAN (Unenclosed)
(Playable from Choir and Great Manuals)

Gedeckt 8'
Principal 4'
Flute Ouverte 4'
Nazat 2-2/3'
Blockfloete 2'
Tierce 1-3/5'
Cymbale III

SPECIFIC EXAMPLES OF GOOD TONAL DESIGN

PEDAL ORGAN

Diapason 16'
Violone 16'
Bourdon 16'
Dulciana (Ch) 16'
Quintaton (Gt) 16'
Octave 8'
Bass Flute (Bourdon) 8'
Cello (Violone) 8'
Quintaton (Gt) 8'

Quint 10-2/3'
Super Octave 4' (Octave)
Flute 4'
Hohlfloete 2'
Double Trumpet 16'
Contra Fagotto 16' (Sw)
Trumpet 8'
Fagotto (Sw) 8'
Clarion 4'
Mixture III
Chimes

While the Wicks Organ Company have specialized for years in building small to medium sized, partly unified organs, this firm occasionally builds large organs, entirely straight, except for some Pedal borrows. The direct-electric action lends itself admirably to economical unification, and ordinarily the Wicks Company takes advantage of this feature of their system of building organs. In the case of their organ in St. Ita's Church, Chicago, it was much better not to do any unifying as a straight organ of this size is ample for playing adequately all styles of music. The church is excellent for sound, the gallery location with exposed Great organ is advantageous, and the results obtained are gratifying. This is one of the largest and most satisfying organs that Wicks ever built. It is an excellent example of the present day trend in organ design on all divisions, except the Solo. This division is reminiscent of the organs built in the 1920's. The Choir organ has many classic features, without calling the registers by the classic names. It might well have been unenclosed, with exposed pipes, like the Great, and have gained thereby.

WICKS ORGAN COMPANY
St. Ita's Catholic Church, Chicago

GREAT (Pipes exposed to view)		SWELL	
Diapason	16'	Lieblichbourdon	16'
Diapason I	8'	Diapason	8'
Diapason II	8'	Stopped Flute	8'
Gedeckt	8'	Flauto Traverso	8'
Hohlflöte	8'	Viola da Gamba	8'
Gemshorn	8'	Salicional	8'
Octave	4'	Voix Celeste	8'
Rohr Flute	4'	Octave	4'
Twelfth	2-2/3'	Violina	4'
Fifteenth	2'	Blockflöte	4'
Mixture	III (12-15-17)	Nazard	2-2/3'
Mixture	III (15-19-22)	Spitzflote	2'
Trumpet	8'	Scharf	IV
Clarion	4'	Contra Fagotto	16'
		Cornopean	8'
		Oboe	8'
		Tremulant	

SPECIFIC EXAMPLES OF GOOD TONAL DESIGN

CHOIR

Dolce	16'
Geigen	8'
Melodia	8'
Harmonic Flute	8'
Viola	8'
Dulciana	8'
Unda Maris	8'
Claribel Flute	4'
Dulcet	4'
Nazard	2-2/3'
Flageolet	2'
Tierce	1-3/5'
Septieme	1-1/7'
Clarinet	8'
Tremulant	

SOLO

Stentorphone	8'
Gross Flute	8'
Viole d'Orchestre	8'
Viole Celeste	8'
Octave Viole	4'
Orchestral Oboe	8'
French Horn	8'
Tuba	8'
Tuba Clarion	4'
Chimes	
Tremulant	

PEDAL

Principal	16'
Diapason	16' (Great)
Violone	16'
Dolce	16' (Choir)
Bourdon	16'
Lieblichbourdon	16' (Swell)
Quint	10-2/3'
Octave	8'
Flute	8' (Pedal Bourdon)
Gedackt	8' (Great)
Flute	8' (Choir)
Cello	8' (Swell)
Dulciana	8' (Choir)
Twelfth	5-1/3'
Super Octave	4'
Blockflote	4' (Swell)
Mixture	III (17-19-22)
Bombarde	16' (Exposed)
Contra Tuba	16' (Solo)
Contra Fagotto	16' (Swell)
Tuba	8' (Solo)

CHAPTER 18

SUGGESTIONS *for* PURCHASERS

GENERAL REMARKS

The experience which the author has had for the past thirty years in advising committees in the purchase of organs has proved to him that such committees are nearly always at a disadvantage in making a satisfactory choice. The purchase of an organ is usually an unique experience; it happens only once in a life time. Unlike purchasing an automobile or a suit of clothes, or even a new house, with which nearly every one is at least familiar, the selection of an organ must be approached with no previous experience as a guide.

The customary selection of an organ committee, made by nearly all churches, consists of two or three of the leading business men in the church, one of whom is usually the chairman of the building committee (if a new church); the pastor and the chairman of the Ladies Aid Society; and probably the organist, if the church happens to have the latter. Such a committee frequently has no one thoroughly competent to advise it. Organists, as a rule, know surprisingly little concerning the instruments they play, either mechanically or from the standpoint of tonal design, with a few happy and notable exceptions. Hence their advice should not always be followed.

To increase this knowledge among organists and interested laymen has been the chief purpose of this book. Congregations nearly always employ a competent architect to design and supervise construction of their buildings. It would simplify matters greatly for those interested in the purchase of an organ, were they able to go to a disinterested adviser, and get just the vital information necessary to make sure they were doing the right thing.

Unfortunately, the majority of so-called organ architects are either incompetent, or have an axe to grind of some sort, or may actually be dishonest in trying to collect a commission from the church that employs them, (a perfectly legitimate practice if the fee is commensurate with the services rendered) and also another fee from the builder to whom the contract is awarded. Organ builders have grown to distrust organ architects and to consider them unnecessary and a nuisance generally. This is to be regretted, as a competent and honest adviser may make himself of great advantage and assistance to both the church and the builder.

On the other hand, it happens that not all builders have representatives competent both to sell organs and to design them scientifically to suit the building, the acoustics, and the purpose most in mind. Here is where a disinterested adviser may be invaluable. Assuming, however, that such a person is not available to the committee, I am endeavoring to furnish them with the following suggestions that have been found to be of advantage.

320

SUGGESTIONS FOR PURCHASERS

When an amount of money not in excess of thirty thousand dollars is available a different procedure should be followed from the one I suggest when a greater amount than this is provided. A fair way to arrive at a reasonable amount to spend for an organ is to divide the cost of the church building by ten. Ten percent of the cost of the church itself usually is a fair average price for a suitable organ. A minimum allowance should be one pipe in the organ for each seat in the church, though double or triple this allowance is better. If a church costs two hundred thousand dollars, an organ of minimum requirements may be bought for fifteen thousand dollars and it would be unjustifiable, except in rare instances, to spend more than thirty thousand dollars; a fair price would be a little less than mid-way between these two figures. When a church costs more or less than suggested above, the allotment of funds for the organ should be correspondingly increased or decreased.

As a general rule, the organ is the last thing to be considered when a new church is under construction and it is frequently found that so much of the available money is already spent that there is no adequate provision for the organ. In such cases, preparations may be made in the console for future additions when more money can be obtained to complete the plan.

It is a poor practice, but one frequently followed, for the organ committee to write a number of organ builders, stating that it has a given amount of money to spend for an organ. The builder is then invited to submit a specification which he will build for this amount. This inevitably results in the committee receiving a different specification from each builder, some good and some bad. It is usually impossible for the committee to analyse the bids received or to make comparisons in price per stop; and by the time the representative of each builder has called and stated that his company undoubtedly builds the best organ, at least for the money, the committee begins to realise that it is out over its head, and needs some disinterested advice. I have been called in on numerous occasions of the sort. I have found it more helpful to proceed from the first along different lines.

The organ committee should itself send the builders a carefully considered specification that will cost approximately the amount they desire to spend. The difficulty here lies in procuring such a scheme. Nearly all organists think they can draw a good specification for an organ. In reality a good many cannot. For this reason I do not suggest that an organist be permitted to draw the scheme unless his knowledge and experience is unquestionable.

In the chapter on Specific Examples of good Tonal Design, I have there listed a number of schemes of various sizes (of tested and proved merit) which cost from a few thousand to twenty-five or thirty thousand dollars. When more than this amount is available I suggest that the organ matter be placed in the hands of one of our recognized leading builders at the very start, and that his advice be accepted implicitly. This course cannot be so advantageously followed when the more usual appropriation for an organ is made, as in such cases it is most important that the maximum value be received for each dollar spent.

The committee should bear in mind that an organ costs from a thousand up to twelve hundred dollars for each set of pipes, depending on the builder selected, with a fair average of eleven hundred dollars. They may then multiply the number of sets of pipes listed in the examples given by eleven hundred dollars, to arrive at an approximate cost on any of those schemes. Then selecting a specification likely to cost the amount the church plans to spend, the identical scheme should be submitted to various builders. In that manner a direct comparison of the prices of each builder may be readily obtained. These prices are those in effect for 1952. Prices have doubled and tripled since 1945. No assurance can be given than they will not go higher.

After the prices are received, the committee should next hear representative organs (of the approximate size under consideration) of each builder. In this manner, a much more intelligent opinion may be formed as to whether the committee feels it advisable to pay ten, fifteen or fifty per cent more for A's organ as compared with B's or C's. I have known prices to vary greatly on the same specification, so committees need not be surprised at wide deviations in price.

It must again be pointed out that if the same specification was built by a dozen different builders, a dozen different organs would result, ranging in quality from excellent to quite the reverse. We may assume, to take an example with which all are familiar, that the general specifications of a Buick automobile are the same, both with regard to wheel base, motor size, etc., as a Cadillac. Yet no one would expect to get Cadillac quality for the price of a Buick. People can see this readily in respect to automobiles, with which they are familiar, but frequently fail to see this with organs, concerning which they know much less.

For the comfort of those committees with limited funds, it should be noted that many of the lower priced builders give excellent value, the same as many lower priced automobiles will perform in general like those of much higher price. Certain refinements and subtleties are the chief distinguishing features of the higher priced product in either case.

Having settled on a builder, he should be informed of all particulars with regard to size of church, its general acoustical conditions, type of service, whether liturgical or otherwise, and his suggestions should be followed as to placing the organ and the openings required. If he has then any real suggestions to make as to modifying the scheme slightly to suit his factory methods, whereby it is evident the church and perhaps the builder will benefit, such suggestions may be carefully considered.

322

Nothing but confusion will result in listening to such suggestions before the builder is actually decided upon. In such a case the whole purpose of asking each builder to bid on an identical scheme would be defeated, and the same uncertainty would exist as with the customary procedure.

LOCATION AND SPACE REQUIREMENTS OF THE ORGAN

One of the problems that the designer of an organ (usually the builder) nearly always encounters is that of getting the proper amount of space and the most advantageous location for the organ. As a rule, architects are glad to co-operate with the organ builder by providing adequate space for the organ, but unfortunately many architects do not know what is required. Frequently, the plans of the church are completed before the organ builder is called in, or any other person sufficiently versed in organ matters to advise with the architect of the church. In such cases, it is nearly always found that inadequate provision has been made for the organ and it frequently becomes difficult to make changes that could easily have been made had the architect been advised in advance. It is always desirable for those contemplating the building of a new church or other building in which an organ is to be placed to secure a competent adviser early in the proceedings to consult with the architect of the building as to just what is necessary. A great many mistakes and a good deal of unnecessary expense can thereby be avoided.

Having assisted in the design and layout of some 200 organs over a period of years, I can speak from considerable knowledge of this subject. I find that many architects are inclined to think that space that can not be used for any other purpose in the general layout of the church, not even for wash rooms, or preacher's study, choir rooms, or any other conceivable *useful* purpose, is assigned to the organ. Attic space, or space of awkward and irregular shape is frequently provided, that causes a great amount of difficulty to the organ builder in assembling the parts of the organ. This also causes very undesirable cramping and crowding of the speaking parts. After all, if an organ is worth building and worth paying for, it certainly seems only proper that it be given an opportunity to sound at its greatest efficiency.

Undoubtedly one of the most ideal locations for an organ is that in which the instrument stands in the auditorium entirely open on all sides. Formerly, such installations were frequently encountered, either in a rear gallery location, (almost the invariable practice in Roman Catholic churches) or spread out across the front of the church in the case of many Protestant churches.

Such an open location is essential for the low pressure classic style of organ, now becoming so popular. Certain portions, if a gallery location, may well be bracketed over the gallery railing. It is, however, merely theorizing to talk about such desirable locations for the organ, when congregations, ministers, and architects have become so enamoured the past thirty years with the so-called Episcopal style of chancel. If this style be adopted, the organ is usually placed at one or both sides of the choir stalls, and in chambers.

I can see why those who consider church worship from the liturgical view point should wish to make the altar or communion table the central point of interest of the chancel of the church. It has logic and common sense to recommend it. But I fail to see why so many Protestant churches should slavishly copy the style of chancel adopted by parish churches in England who wished to ape the cathedrals. Cathedral churches had reasons for having choir and clergy stalls in the chancel. Ordinary parish churches do not have such reasons. Of course, this arrangement of choir stalls facing each other, with the basses seated, in some cases forty or fifty feet distant from the tenors is the worst possible arrangement for getting good musical results from a choir. But it is popular, nonetheless, and it is surprising how many Protestant churches have been rebuilt to conform to this fad. In a city like Evanston, Illinois, for example, the First Methodist, First Presbyterian, and First Baptist have each of them rebuilt their chancels in this style within the past twenty-five years. And the majority of present day Protestant churches are still being built along these lines. You ask what have I to offer that is better?

Ideally, a rear gallery location for both organ and choir is better. It has been the invariable custom in Roman Catholic churches for centuries. The Episcopal style of chancel does not even have the force of centuries of tradition behind it, being a comparatively recent innovation, not a hundred years old.

Many congregations like to see their choir, to see them march down the aisle, and to see them sing, without turning to the gallery of the church. I don't have the answer to this problem, and I have been unable to find anyone who has. But it must be emphasized once more that the rear gallery or open location for the organ must be used if the low pressure, unforced type of voicing is to be effective. And this is what many organists want more than anything else about the organ at present.

In spite of many disadvantages both to choir and organ, I am being realistic when I assume that a great many Protestant churches are going to continue to be built with the Episcopal style of chancel, and the organ will therefore of necessity have to be disposed in one or more chambers at the sides of the chancel. If the church isn't too long, there is a possibility of placing the organ in the gallery, and placing the choir and console of the organ in the chancel, thus getting the favorable open location for the organ at least. The inevitable difficulty here, made worse if the church is long, is that the listeners seated near the gallery end of the church hear more organ than choir, and listeners near the choir don't hear the organ. The choir itself doesn't hear the organ unless it is played too loudly.

This matter of location of organ and choir in the Episcopal style of chancel presents some insuperable problems. At present, it must end in compromise. The organ must be placed in chambers, for such an arrangement of choir and chancel. Extremely low wind pressures are then definitely impossible, if the organ is to be in any way effective. With the organ already enclosed in chambers, there is no real reason why it should not be entirely under the expression control of the swell shutters. The disadvantages of enclosure are already present. One should at least make full use of the advantages. The disadvantages may be minimized if the following statements are fully observed by the architect when planning the chambers.

The best conditions, for this placing of the organ, are to have a shallow chamber of considerable width, and a large amount of height. An organ chamber of this general shape allows the instrument to be assembled so that no portion of it obstructs any other. When great height is available, one or more divisions of the organ may be placed on top of the other, perpendicularly, the Swell over the Choir, and Solo on top of the Swell Organ (in the case of a four-manual organ).

This is not the most desirable arrangement, however, and should be avoided if possible. For the best results, all divisions of the organ should be on the same level, in order to avoid difficulty with tuning. It is almost impossible to keep the various sections of the organ in tune together when they are on various levels. The temperature of the church does not remain even, particularly in the winter time when the upper portions of the church heat more rapidly, causing these sections of the organ to be sharper in pitch than the lower sections, unless the organ happens to have been tuned under exactly the same conditions, which is not apt to be the case. When all pipes in the organ are on approximately the same level, they are usually found to be reasonably in tune with each other, even though the temperature is considerably above or under the point at which the organ was tuned. The ideal shape of an organ chamber is, "twice as wide as it is deep and as high as it is wide."

It is generally unwise when an organ is placed in a chancel location to open the side of the chamber towards the transept, particularly if the organ is divided on either side of the chancel. If this is done, people seated in a side gallery or transept will inevitably hear one side of the organ out of balance with the other, with very unpleasant effect. A divided organ should properly speak into the chancel from opposite sides, and allow the tone to have an opportunity to mix before it reaches the ears of the congregation. In any event, the best results from the organ are always obtained when its tone is directed towards the singers, so that the voices and organ tone are blended together, and do not come from disjointed and several removed locations.

The tone of an organ can be made to go around corners and follow devious paths, but all such obstruction and interference with the direct egress of the sound creates considerable loss in volume. This can be partially compensated by higher pressures and excessively loud voicing. The results are never so satisfactory as when the tone can proceed more freely and with more normal speech of the pipes.

Another matter that should be considered by architects in regard to organ chambers is the material which is to form the walls of the chambers. Whether part of the organ is to be left without expression, or whether all the pipes in the chamber are to be enclosed behind shutters, is immaterial to the consideration that should be given to the walls themselves. Under ordinary conditions, walls made of hard patent plaster are quite successful in sound reflecting properties. Where a greater amount of reflection is desirable, Keene cement is sometimes used. In no event should rough or sand-finished plaster be used, as particles are apt to drop off into the pipes by vibration of the organ and such a surface is not so good a reflector of sound. Hard wood walls are sometimes desirable in a basement location, particularly as they will absorb part of the dampness. Hard surfaced wallboard may also be successfully used, such as tempered "Masonite."

The wall surfaces should preferably be as smooth and free from obstructions as possible. Some builders prefer to make the corners concave, thereby avoiding sharp angles. This does not appear to be of great importance, ordinarily. It is, however, very important that the openings shall be free to practically the top of the chamber in order that a very undesirable tone pocket shall not be created above the opening. This will cause an appreciable loss in the amount of sound which will issue from the chamber. Unlimited height above the pipes is not desirable but simply enough for adequate speaking room.

Regarding the *Space Requirements*. One dimension of any organ chamber (in plan) must be at least 9 feet. The standard length of a 73-note windchest is 8 feet 6 inches. Some builders make this dimension as much as 10 feet and a half. Nine feet is the least that should be allowed for even the smallest organ. If the organ is to be placed all on one level, 13 feet in height is ample, especially if there are to be no full-length 16' pedal or manual stops. Twenty-one feet in height will permit of double-decking the organ. Each set of pipes will average 9 inches in width on the windchest, and allowance must be made also for passage boards, offset and pedal chests, relays, reservoirs, tremolos, and so forth.

For a thirty-stop organ (a fair sized three-manual) two chambers located on either side of the chancel, each 20 feet long by 8 feet deep by 17 feet high will be found to be ideal. The same organ may also be conveniently disposed in two chambers 10 feet square, by double-decking it.

326

Twenty-one feet in height will be necessary for this lay-out. Similarly, a fair sized two-manual of fifteen registers may be housed in one of the chambers whose dimensions are given above. Any builder's space requirements should be met by these dimensions. They are ample and adequate. It is possible to install the sized organs mentioned above in smaller chambers, but this would cause crowding of both speaking and passage room, and make the organ difficult to service. The high prices prevailing for organs in these days make it unlikely that the church will want to buy enough organ to overcrowd any reasonable sized chamber.

3 pipes per person

Thirty stops should be adequate for a church seating 600 people. Fifteen stops for one seating half that many, although any good organist would want more. These are reasonable, average sized organs for the seating capacity given. The suggested sizes are by no means invariable, and in fact may vary 50% in either direction from the average sizes given.

The musical requirements as well as the ability to pay for them vary greatly in different churches. I am merely setting forth some more or less normal figures as a guide.

Chambers less than 11 feet high will necessitate more mitering of the pipes than is desirable, although an organ may be squeezed into 9 feet, if there is no more height available. Compared with electronics, it must be admitted that organs do take up a considerable amount of room but they are worth it. The same thing may be said of a church tower or spire. The latter appeals to the eye and the former to the ear. If our senses are going to be really satisfied, there must be more space allowed in planning a church edifice than merely enough space to seat the congregation. An auditorium 10 feet high might have ample seating capacity for 1000 people, but no inspiration whatever. Similarly an electronic substitute can be installed in a church which has no organ chamber, but what does the church have then? Neither organ chamber, organ or musical inspiration. Good organ chambers are as necessary a part of the construction of the church sanctuary as the chancel, narthex, aisles, or any other part of the building. I am arguing this point, because I have found that some church architects have advised that there is no need to spend money for organ space now-a-days with electronic organs available. A church doesn't need a slate roof either. A tar-paper roof will keep the rain out. It doesn't need a spire or other decoration, except for one reason—to help create an inspiring atomsphere in the services. It needs adequate organ space and a good organ for precisely the same reason, only more so.

SUGGESTIONS FOR MODERNIZING OLDER ORGANS

Another problem frequently confronts churches that have an organ built twenty-five or thirty years ago. The organ may be modern so far as console and action are concerned, but may need releathering.

SUGGESTIONS FOR PURCHASERS

One of the unfortunate characteristics of the modern organ is that the pouches or pneumatics must be made of leather that is perishable. This lamb-skin (employed as the most suitable leather) lasts only from twenty to thirty-five years, depending upon the atmospheric conditions and use of the organ. In a smoky city location, if the organ is much used, twenty years is an outside limit of life for these pneumatics. In a country or small town location, where the atmosphere is cleaner, the leather may last thirty-five or forty years. In any event, sooner or later in any modern organ, all leather on all the pneumatics must be renewed and replaced. This is a fairly expensive process in these days of high prices for both material and labor.

It should be said that if it is done properly, the organ is restored to many years of additional service, as good as when the organ was first installed. If it isn't done, the organ gradually becomes unplayable, as one pneumatic after another gives out. All the leather in an organ never fails all at one time, but gradually over a period of some years. The weaker skins may be renewed first, and the renewal process continued by easy stages, if it happens to be more convenient to do it in this manner.

It has happened in some cases, however, that the music or organ committee of a church is persuaded to buy some sort of electronic organ when they learn the cost of releathering.

Ordinarily to releather an organ averages about $2.00 per pneumatic. With the primaries, switches, and pipe valve pneumatics, a medium sized organ will cost from $4000 to $5000 to releather at today's prices. An electronic organ may be purchased for this amount. As compared with the musical capabilities of the church's old organ, when properly restored, the advantage is all on the side of the old organ by ten to one. But some churches have succumbed to the glib talk of the electronic salesman, and have actually thrown out a good organ, rather than spend the necessary money to restore it. This seems wicked and extremely stupid to me. Such churches were surely in need of some disinterested advice.

One thing should be made clear at this point. Churches should not be misled into thinking that an electronic will require no servicing nor up-keep. With the possible exception of the Hammond, all other electronics require servicing, and in the case of some, a great deal of attention. I want to emphasize this point, as there is a good deal of misapprehension.

At the time it becomes necessary to releather and restore the old organ it is good to know that it is not only possible but comparatively easy to make tonal changes as well. If a church has an organ built twenty-five or more years ago when the theater organ influence was at its height, the Diapasons, upper work, and Chorus Reeds, may all be lacking in sufficient harmonic development. Upper work may also be lacking altogether. By substituting Diapasons, Octaves, and Chorus Reeds of proper harmonic development, and adding one or two mixtures III-IV Rk. to the Great and

328

Swell, the organ may be transformed tonally into what is considered to be a first class organ today. It is amazing what the changing of two 8' Diapasons, two 4' Octaves, and even one 8' Trumpet, and the addition of two Mixtures will do for an organ which was formerly dull, tubby, and foundational and with no brilliance nor upperwork. These changes may be made for a small amount compared with the cost of a new organ.

To be specific: I have in mind now the First Congregational Church of Battle Creek, Michigan. This church had an organ of about thirty stops built by one of the early twentieth century builders, Lyon and Healy. It was built in the days when the builder thought he was being honest, and giving the church its money's worth by providing large scale Diapasons, thick Flutes, honkey Reeds, and negligible upper work. The idea was to impress by sheer weight of tone, rather than by brilliance, texture, ensemble, and cohesion. This organ had been releathered and a new Austin console added only ten years ago. The church acquired a young, ambitious organist, who was very unhappy about the tonal results he was able to accomplish with the instrument. Even though it was mechanically sound and modern enough, it was unsatisfactory tonally by present day standards.

Two representatives of two of our leading builders called on the church and stated there was nothing worth saving about the old organ. They advised that it be discarded, and that their firms would be happy to build a new organ of the same size for $35,000.00.

Upon being called upon for advice, I suggested the tonal modernization plan outlined above, which was carried out by F. C. Wichlac & Son of Chicago, at a cost of just 20% of that for a new organ. Excellent satisfaction was the result, so far as the organist, the church, and myself are concerned.

As I am writing this, I have been engaged in planning the tonal modernization of the Reuter organ in the Moody Church in Chicago. The organ was built in 1928, during a period in tonal design when builders were still under the Hope-Jones, theater influence. This is a large organ, and it needed a good many tonal changes to bring it up to present day ideas. But even so, the cost of all of these changes plus releathering of the entire organ plus a new console amount to only a third the cost of a completely new organ.

I quote these two recent instances in my experience as being representative of what may be done.

With our leading builders, now having commitments to build new organs for a year and a half to three years ahead, it is small wonder that they do not wish to disturb their factory routine by doing such rebuilds and repair work.

There are, however, in many cities of this country good, honest, competent organ service and maintenance men, who are capable of doing this work, and who may obtain good, well voiced pipes from a number of trade pipe makers.

It should be mentioned in passing that when the 8' Diapasons are replaced, they need only be replaced from 4' C up, as the bottom octave is of comparatively small importance, and costs as much as all the rest of the stop. The important part of the stop for ensemble purposes is from Tenor C up. This is a worthwhile saving.

Ordinarily it would be the most desirable for the original builder of the organ (if still in existence) to do such tonal and mechanical work. But some of these, because of pressure of new work are unwilling to do so. Three years ago, when the rebuilding of the Reuter organ in Moody Church was first discussed, the Reuters were so crowded with work that they could not undertake the contract. Now they see their way clear to take this work on, and are about to do so. If and when conditions in the industry get back to normal, all builders will be interested in doing this rebuilding work, particularly of their own organs. Organ committees should certainly know about the possibilities outlined above. They should not be misled by the zealous electronic or organ salesman whose chief ambition is to sell a new organ or electronic, and collect a good commission for so doing. The last thing some of these salesmen wish to consider is the ultimate good of the church.

REQUIREMENTS FOR GOOD CHURCH ACOUSTICS

Another matter (which seems to be as little understood by the average building committee of a new church as the organ is by the organ committee) is the acoustical requirements of the new church auditorium. This is a problem of greatest importance if the best musical results are to be expected from the organ. The success of the instrument depends at least half on the acoustical conditions of the building in which it sounds. Some one has said that "the soul of music is in the Gothic cathedral, the organ is its voice". How true this is! The average church in America today, or for that matter, at any time in its history, has never been like a Gothic cathedral. The present day cost of a carved stone and ornamented building is so great, as to make it prohibitive, except in rare instances. Some form of colonial, neo-classic, or frankly "contemporary" style is usually adopted today. As a matter of personal taste, I should like to say that the "contemporary" has little to recommend it except that it is "functional" and economical. These are two worth-while considerations, to be sure. But why a building has necessarily to be ugly in order to be functional, is a fair question also. Be that as it may, we are dealing with present day churches as they are being built, and I do not set myself up to sit in judgment on their style.

With all the vehemence and eloquence that I can command I do wish to protest most emphatically the absurd, and I should almost say criminal lengths that the acoustical engineers have gone in many of these buildings to make them acoustically inert, and to "sterilize" the acoustics. The buildings are acoustically "dead".

No one likes a bad echo in any building in which he is trying to listen to either a voice or music. This is agreed by all, I believe. But reverberation period (the time required for a sound to completely die out, after it is discontinued at the source) is being cut down to practically nil by the acoustical engineers. So that in many modern churches, the acoustical conditions are similar to those found in an old-fashioned broadcasting studio, or boudoir. Even the radio engineers discovered eventually that there must be some reverberation for effective broadcasting or recording. A considerable reverberation period is essential for the best effect of music in a large room.

I suppose there may be such a person as a disinterested and competent acoustical engineer. I have never encountered one. Nearly all represent some sound absorbing material company, directly or indirectly. Apparently their one object is to sell as many square yards of acoustical material as possible, be it acoustic plaster, hair, felt, cork, lumber waste, or some other material of similar purpose. Now, a limited and reasonable amount of any of these materials may be highly desirable and beneficial in cutting down a disturbing echo, but when four times the proper amount is used then every sound suffers, whether it be the voice of the organ, the choir, or the minister's. The live, vibrant, buoyant quality of sound has been completely obliterated, leaving the music only half effective, and the minister having to work twice as hard as should be necessary to make his voice carry to the back of a moderately large room. Usually it is found necessary to install a public address system in order that the minister may be heard properly. Then we have completed the full circle of becoming the victims of the engineers and so-called science. The church pays to kill the sound of the minister's voice by overpadding the walls and ceiling, and carpeting the floors, and then pays to build up the sound of his voice again by means of radio tubes, so that he may be heard. Absurdity could go no further. Unfortunately this sort of practice has become increasingly prevalent for the past twenty-five years. It is high time someone like myself called attention to it. I have repeatedly gone into a new church where I have been told that the acoustics are "perfect". Upon testing, I have discovered the reverberation period to be close to zero. Somehow, the people of these churches have been sold a bill of goods, of very shoddy character. They have been told that "perfect" acoustics means no reverberation.

It should be mentioned that there is a disparity in acceptable reverberation periods which are best for speech and music. The obvious result will be a compromise, between ideals, in so far as the acoustical properties of the worship room are concerned. This compromise must be understood and accepted by all related group factors. But let it be a true compromise. If the ideal reverberation period for the sound of music in a given room be four seconds, and for speech two seconds, let the reverberation period be three seconds—a little too long for speech, a little too short for music. Do not compromise at two seconds, or one second or none at all, as is too frequently done.

Symphony Hall, Boston; the Auditorium, Chicago; the Tabernacle, Salt Lake City; are three large concert rooms where the acoustics are generally considered ideal for music. They have no acoustical treatment whatever. They were built before the days of the acoustical engineers, except Symphony Hall, on which room, the late Professor Wallace Clement Sabine, the first of the physicists to take up serious study of acoustics as related to buildings, made some suggestions. That was long before the acoustic treatment of buildings had become a "racket", and I mean no pun here.

Years ago, Mr. Ernest Skinner suggested that no acoustical treatment be applied to any building until it was finished up to the painting and decorating. Then if it was discovered that there was an annoying echo somewhere, acoustical material should be applied to that particular portion of the building (usually a rear wall). The science of acoustical treatment of buildings is by no means exact, and the indiscriminate and wanton application of square miles of acoustic plaster, hair felt, or wood fibers in advance of the actual testing of the building results in so many auditoriums with wretched acoustics.

The nephew of Professor Sabine mentioned above, Dr. Paul E. Sabine, has a booklet entitled "Theory and Use of Architectural Acoustical Materials", which may be secured from the Acoustical Materials Association, 59 East 55th Street, New York 22, N. Y., which gives information largely for laymen. I am bold enough not to agree with many of of Dr. Sabine's conclusions about the best reverberation periods for church auditoriums, as he prefers a much shorter period than I think is proper. We have had many debates about this in years past. Certainly his distinguished uncle, Professor Sabine, preferred a much longer period of reverberation, as demonstrated in Symphony Hall.

Eventually, the proper acoustical treatment of buildings may become a science worthy of respect. I sincerely hope so. Up until now, it has consisted largely of mumbo-jumbo and greatly over-padding of buildings when acoustical engineers are called in. The minister is assured that he may be heard more easily by his congregation, if the auditorium is padded indiscriminately and too much. Actually, the reverse is the case. Perhaps not in a small auditorium, but in a large one, the voice is so absorbed by too much acoustic treatment along the way of its travel, that very little of it reaches the back of a long building, such as the University of Chicago Chapel. This room had the ministrations of Dr. Paul Sabine. In this chapel, we have what is common to all over-acoustically treated rooms, viz., the well-known bass-drum effect from the organ when heard from half way to all the way back in the building. All bottom and no top. The low notes of the Pedal organ are tremendous when heard from the rear, but the brilliant upperwork which this organ actually has, when heard from the console, nearly disappears in the interstices of the acoustic tile ceiling. The acoustic treatment of this large building for both the sound of music or speaking has been overdone, in my opinion. But compared to some small auditoriums where the acoustical engineers have done their worst, this chapel is fairly good acoustically. Large buildings normally present much greater problems for the acoustical engineer, it should be said in fairness.

Ray Berry, of Colorado Springs, Colorado, in a pamphlet published by the American Guild of Organists says in part:

"Acousticians, and makers of acoustical products, must become aware of the *quality* of sound, rather than restrict their thinking, design and products merely to the control of sound. The author could not do better than quote a letter from organbuilder Charles McManis, who wrote in part:

" 'I should like to suggest the close relationship between the acoustical "feel" of a sanctuary and the quality of religious feeling. It is interesting to note that the cathedralesque night clubs in New York have quietly died a natural death. The successful clubs are the low-ceilinged, acoustically padded rooms where each little party can feel secluded even in the wildest sort of hubbub.

" 'Now then, dealing in opposites, the purpose of public worship is to knit individual worshippers into a unified congregation where the individual loses his identity in the "church universal." When he sings or joins in the liturgy he must not feel isolated and self-conscious about participation. His voice must join with the others to transcend individual limitations. With acoustical treatment absorbing a large part of congregational (as well as choir and organ) sound, the effect is precisely that of the intimate night club where each party is secluded by sound absorption.

" 'True, bothersome *echo* must be eliminated from the sanctuary, but *reverberation* the aliveness of the room, must be retained if any high quality of worship is to be obtained. No group can lift its voice in joyful song if 50% of the tone is absorbed by acoustical "improvements."

" 'Another item: low frequencies beget crying-in-the-beer emotions; high frequencies lift the spirit to higher things. It is a well-established fact that most acoustical materials absorb much more of the high frequencies than the low. So—the damning indictments from a religious point of view seem to add up to: (1) isolationism of the worshipper, and (2) bringing out of the lower emotions—self-pitying sadness rather than inspiration and aspiration.' "

Another recognized authority, organbuilder G. Donald Harrison, furnished both architects and acousticians food for thought when he wrote the author:

"The relationship of height, distance and space generally to the music is of paramount importance, and what the eye sees in terms of space and dimension, the ear must receive in terms of its treatment of sounds. If there is a great deal of hard looking material in a building, the sound must behave as though it were hard material. The great, statuesque organ literature was neither conceived, composed or performed in buildings which behave acoustically like bedrooms."

If controlled sound in a worship room is to maintain a spiritually uplifting level, acoustical materials must receive and act upon all frequencies—high, medium and low—at approximately the same rate of absorptivity. This applies to both speech and music, since today one hears both the male and female speaking as well as singing voice. The frequency range of the female voice, in both conditions, must be taken into account. The frequency range and complexity is enlarged in choral sound. Range and complexity are magnified many times in the organ, which has the greatest tonal range and complexity-in-sound factor of any musical instrument.

It is today perfectly possible for acoustical experts to design, and manufacturers to produce, absorbents and reflectives to suit any given need or wish. If the quality of sound is made the determining factor, acoustical environment for the Church can be effected which will enhance rather than detract from both musical sound and speech. Proper acoustics for music and speech can be planned, but not by technicians who understand only the details of one of these and are oblivious of the meanings of both in the Church.

What then, is the perplexed building committee of a church to do? At present my advice would be, if the church architect insists on an acoustical expert, to discount the amount of acoustic treatment he says the room needs by 50% to 75%, and the church is then quite likely to come out about right. For smaller churches, let ordinary plaster be used, or brick and stone or wood on the walls and ceilings with no acoustic treatment of any kind. An auditorium such as this (especially if there are exposed roof trusses) when more than half filled with worshippers, will not have excessive reverberation, and should also be acoustically about right for music and speech.

SUGGESTIONS AS TO ORGAN CASES AND GRILLES

It is also important for the committee to decide early in the proceedings whether it is wise to spend at least eight to ten per cent of the cost of the organ for a case. From this minimum allowance, cases may cost as much as the organ itself. When funds are limited it seems much wiser to put all the money into the organ and (instead of attempting to purchase a makeshift case) to use some form of grille.

Such a practice has come into general favor the past twenty five years, due in part no doubt to reasons of economy, but more to the fact that organs are now usually placed in chambers, where no case work is necessary. Such treatment of the exterior of the organ is probably better than the typical organ builder's front, or perhaps what might more accurately be called the organ committees' front. When so little money is allotted for a case that it consists merely of some dummy pipes and some cylinders behind them, which look like tomato cans (to create the effect of additional pipes), even this expenditure is unwise; rather no attempt at an organ case than such a one. The money would be far more usefully spent for additional pipes in the organ.

When ample funds are on hand to purchase a suitable case, it is possible to enhance greatly the beauty of that portion of the church where the organ is located, if it is treated architecturally in a congruous manner with the church interior. Best results will be obtained in this event, by employing the architect of the church to design something suitable and appropriate.

This book contains photographs of several outstanding organ cases. They are included both because of their inherent beauty and also as suggestions for the design of others. The author feels competent to offer only these suggestions concerning the design of casework. With full appreciation of the value of beautiful organ fronts, he nevertheless feels that grilles are preferable to a cheap and ugly conglomeration of display pipes.*

Several of our builders are advocating the exposure of part of the speaking pipes in lieu of casework or grilles, or a combination of the two examples of such treatment of the facade of the organ as shown on pages 113, 229, 235. This treatment is especially valuable for the best musical results from low pressure pipework.

One more very important matter should be mentioned. Those who have read the chapter on Voicing of Organ Pipes will know the extreme importance I place on the final finishing of every organ. Readers are referred to this chapter for details as to what this finishing comprises. It is

---

*After all, we shall have to admit that "Beauty is in the eye of the beholder." Visiting the University of Chicago Chapel recently, which contains a large Skinner organ, with one of the most beautiful organ cases in this country, and the building itself the last design of Bertam Brovenor Goodhue, the author heard an illuminating conversation.

Droves of tourists are being shown through the chapel every day during the Century of Progress Exposition. At the back of one such group, a couple, who were probably a farmer and his wife, engaged in the following comments: "Well, there isn't anything to see here, John." "Well, anyway, it's a good fireproof building," John answered. This should take its place among high architectural criticism.

the most difficult matter for builders to supervise, as they are generally dependent on the finisher they employ, without any factory supervision. A church should in all possible cases secure the services of an organist or person qualified to judge, to pass on the final finishing. This will be of advantage both to the church and the builder. They will both have a better organ. The builder should be glad to cooperate and thus have the assurance that this vital matter has been properly carried out.

Finally, it is a pleasure to record after long experience with organ builders, that honest and conscientious builders are in the large majority, and that they strive to do the right thing and frequently do more than merely fulfill their agreements.

ELECTRONIC INSTRUMENTS
SUPPLEMENT

The present chapter describes in outline form, some of the more important electronic instruments that have been placed on the market during the past fifteen years. No attempt will be made to go into all of the technical details of construction or to elaborate unduly upon the theories of synthetic and oscillating radio tube tone production. A sufficiently complete statement of general principles and descriptions of the various examples will be given to enable the interested reader to gain a fair idea of what is involved in these mechanisms.

The author originally had some misgivings about including this chapter, and it might well be questioned as to whether a discussion of electronic instruments has any place in a book devoted to organs and organ building. There is this to be said, however; all electronics have the following qualities in common with the organ:

1. The tone may be sustained indefinitely.
2. The tone may be increased or decreased while being sustained, at the will of the performer.
3. The range of tone volume from soft to loud is entirely comparable with organs.

These three characteristics make the sound of electronics sufficiently like the sound of organs to the uncritical ear of the casual listener so that it has been possible to sell many thousands of them as substitutes for organs. It seems obvious then, that descriptions should be given and comparisons made of their relative musical merits with those of organs. At present the musical results possible with electronics differ from those obtainable from organs in the following respects:

1. Many qualities of tone, common in all good organs, have not to date been successfully imitated. More important still, the chorus or ensemble effects of an organ (except with the largest electronics) are only feebly suggested.
2. The attack and release of the tone is very different from that of an organ in many of the electronics.
3. The tone must invariably be heard by means of one or more loud speakers.

With these few general statements, we shall proceed immediately to our description of electronic instruments, and to a more detailed explanation of their musical similarities to the organ, as well as where and why they differ from that instrument.

ELECTRONIC INSTRUMENTS

DR. LEE DE FOREST—THE VACUUM TUBE

In 1906 a basic patent was granted to Dr. Lee De Forest on a vacuum tube containing three electrodes. Hardly a field of industry is left which the vacuum tube has not influenced. It was to be expected that sooner or later the field of music would be touched. All electronic instruments depend on vacuum tubes (or as they are commonly called "Radio tubes") as an indispensable part of the mechanism for amplifying the initial sound impulses which are normally practically inaudible without such magnification.

MR. LAURENS HAMMOND—"THE HAMMOND ORGAN"

The electronic instrument invented by Mr. Laurens Hammond of Chicago is first described as it was first in the field with a commercially successful substitute for an organ.

It works as follows: The essential part of the Hammond mechanism begins with a revolving tone-wheel, which is not circular, but has humps on it, as shown in the accompanying drawing. The complete tone-producing assembly consists of this tone-wheel, a permanent magnet, and a coil around the magnet. The tone-wheel is about two inches in diameter and revolves at fixed speed; it does not touch the magnet point; it merely passes close to it. Each time a hump on the tone-wheel "passes the permanent magnet, a change of magnetization occurs within the magnet." This causes an impulse to be induced in the coil. If this happens 440 times a second we get 440 impulses and "if a pair of head-phones were connected to the terminals of the coil, a tone would be heard" giving the note A. There are 91 tone-generating elements in the Hammond, each supplying a different pitch. All are geared together. The instrument can never get out of tune, although the pitch of the entire instrument may rise or fall, in accordance with the speed of the driving motor. Ordinarily this speed is practically constant, as the tone-wheels are driven by a synchronous motor which has a constant speed determined by the frequency

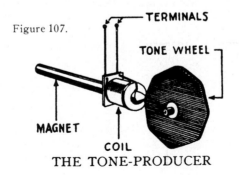

Figure 107.

THE TONE-PRODUCER

of alternation of the current supply. Mr. Hammond's organization has made millions of electric clocks driven with synchronous motors, so that this feature of the instrument is not new, but has many years back of it. The tones thus generated are amplified by a radio tube amplifier and sent out over one or more loud speakers.

The initial tone is the familiar flute-like fundamental, a simple tone devoid of partials to enrich it. If no other quality of tone were available than this, the instrument would be impossibly dull and monotonous. Fortunately, much more can be done, by making use of a series of upper pitches, easily available, (by means of switches and wiring) similar to the way they are obtained from a unit stop in an organ. There is this difference between the pitches higher than the unison available on any one key on the keyboard of the Hammond and a unified organ stop. On the Hammond the relative intensities of the upper pitches may be varied. Let us take for comparison, the familiar dull toned Stopped Flute, an organ stop whose tone most closely approximates the fundamental tone of the Hammond. This stop is frequently unified in organs. If the octave of the unison be drawn with the unison, both pitches are equally loud. Similarly with the Twelfth, Fifteenth, Seventeenth, and Twenty-second.

In the Hammond, these same pitches may be obtained, not by means of stop tongues or knobs, as is done in organs, but by a series of drawbars or slides. The slides have a handle provided, by which they may be drawn out from the name board above the top keyboard, through a series of eight positions. The first position of the slide, being about ½'' out from the silent position, and each of the other eight stages may be obtained by progressively drawing the bar farther forward. When fully drawn out, the tone of the particular pitch which the drawbar controls is at its loudest, (about 64 times as loud to the ear as position 1) each position from position 1, representing a logarithmic increase in tone. Thus if the unison drawbar is set at position 8, (its loudest position) and the drawbar next to it, controlling the octave pitch is set at position 4, with all the other drawbars set at 0 (or silent position and a note is played, we will get a tone with considerable more fundamental pitch than octave. By pulling the octave pitch drawbar out to position 8, the resulting tone, when a note is played, will sound the unison and octave pitches with equal strength. Each of the drawbars provided may be adjusted to any one of its eight positions. The possible theoretical combinations run into figures like 257 millions. Practically, one would need an acute ear to recognize perhaps 50 different combinations distinctly. The most distinctive and frequently used combinations are set on "pre-set" keys by means of which certain qualities are instantly available.

I have purposely used the term "higher pitches," rather than harmonics of the prime tone in referring to the function of the drawbars, because only the octave pitches obtained in this way are true harmonics.

The 12th, 17th and 19th being equally tempered intervals (and while approximations to the pitch of true harmonics,) are anywhere from 1 to 10 beats per second flat or sharp of the true pitch of the natural harmonics. The fact that the so-called harmonics in the Hammond are out of tune as compared with natural harmonics, (which are those inextricably bound up and associated with the natural sound of an organ pipe, for example) has been urged as a chief reason for the unsatisfactory musical results of that instrument. At least this point must be considered to be a debatable one. Mr. Hammond insists that this fact is not important, and has built elaborate apparatus to prove that tempered intervals and true intervals sound equally well to the majority of musical ears. Perhaps this point has been overstressed in some discussions of the instrument. The chief defects as well as virtues of the Hammond are listed later in this article.

It will be evident from the preceding description that with this series of drawbars, it is possible to add to a simple unison tone, from one to eight other so-called harmonics or partials of the prime tone in *varying degrees of intensity*. This is the important and essential difference between the Hammond and the typical unified Stopped flute in an organ.

The whole series of pitches (so-called harmonics) available on the Hammond at present, expressed in pitch-length, would be—

16'–10 2/3'–8'–4'–2 2/3'–2'–1 3/5'–1 1/3'–1'.

In other notation, the series would be—CCC-GGG-CC-GG-c'-e'-g'-c2. It should be clearly understood that each of the harmonic draw-bars brings on a tone which is exactly like all the others, and each in turn has exactly the same strengths available through the eight positions into which each slider may be drawn.

Helmholtz made the statement and it is still considered to be true by present day scientists that "Tones of complex qualities have various strengths." It follows from this statement that if we can generate a fundamental and a series of higher pitches or overtones, and are able to vary their relative strengths in any way we wish, we can theoretically produce any tone quality we wish, *provided that particular tone quality does not require any more overtones than we have available.*

But right here is the first limitation of the Hammond in its present form. There are too few so-called harmonics provided. The fact that it uses only the fundamental plus six of its first seven overtones, is the reason why it is unable to reproduce correctly any but the purest organ colors, the flutes. (The sub-harmonics are not in the harmonic series, unless the tone which it is wished to imitate is set up and played an octave higher than normal). The tone of many organ pipes, especially of the Trumpet and String families would require twenty, thirty or even more true harmonics to reproduce them to the point of the illusion of identity.

And now we come to the second important defect of the Hammond in simulating the sound of the organ. The tone comes on in the Hammond with a perfect sforzando onset of tone, due to the instantaneous response characteristic of electronic reactions, whereas the organ probably does not supply air to all of the pipes at precisely the same instant. Furthermore even if it did, some of its sources speak more rapidly than others. The result is a very rapid crescendo, almost instantaneous, but not quite. Even more of what Mr. Wilmer Bartholomew calls an "agogic fringe" is present in the release of organ tone, where some pipes, by virtue of their hard walls, or other characteristics, remain in vibration longer than others.

Mr. Bartholomew in an article entitled "When Is an Organ Not an Organ?" published in the Peabody Bulletin for December, 1936, says:

"To summarize: the lifeless, dull, dead, hooty, tubby quality of the Hammond as now built, even when using its more complex colors is due to (1) its use of too few partials, and none of them particularly dissonant ones, such as number 7, and 11 in the harmonic series, which would add considerable color. (2) Its lack of any pitch fringe; and (3) its lack of any temporal or agogic fringe.

"The improvement of (1) would (if expense permitted) eventually give the complete illusion of identity with the various organ colors. The improvement of (2) and (3), (if possible) would add the illusion of the typical organ ensemble, and the illusion of the typical sluggish response and cut-off. The charm of the pitch fringe and the agogic fringe both stem from the aesthetic principle of uncertainty, plus the unconscious realization of the incongruity of organ tone (traditionally associated with great instruments, dignified liturgies, and extremely reverberant cathedrals) being able to limit itself to dead level pitches, or being able to stop, start and cavort with all the agility of a xylophone."

Objection (2) has been partially overcome by installing two additional sets of tone generators from about C up, one set rotated slightly faster and the other slightly slower than the speed necessary for normal pitch, so that a celeste or beating effect is established, without having the effect of raising the pitch, (about four beats per second in the middle range). These additional generators are not very successful in loud passages, any more than a celeste of Diapasons or Trumpets would be in an organ, but for softer playing, they add very materially to the illusion of uncertainty in pitch, which within certain limits, as Mr. Bartholomew so well observes, is an aesthetic principle of great importance. The fact that the instruments of an orchestra are never dead in tune with each other gives the live, interesting quality to the sound of the full orchestra. However, there is nothing mathematically correct about out-of-tuneness of an orchestra.

In the past few years, Hammond has abandoned the "chorus generator," in favor of a new type of vibrato device, which at least is cheaper to manufacture, if not better than the "chorus generator" in producing a pitch uncertainty.

ELECTRONIC INSTRUMENTS

Now let us turn to the good qualities of the Hammond.

1. Portability; weight under 300 pounds, moved as easily as an upright piano and merely plugged into a lighting socket.

2. Stays in tune. The instrument cannot get out of tune with itself.

3. Enormous range of dynamics from soft to loud. By means of a foot lever, equivalent to the organ expression pedal, the power on the amplifiers may be increased so that the tone from being barely audible may be gradually augmented to the full power of the radio equipment. This range is probably 10 times as great as that afforded by a good expression chamber on any organ.

4. Instantaneous response. This is both a virtue and defect, as has been previously pointed out. For church playing it is a defect, for accompanying a jazz orchestra it is valuable. Many orchestral conductors consider this feature more important than any other.

5. Practically no limit to the volume of tone (not referring to quality of tone) which may be obtained, by adding more loud speakers, and amplifying apparatus.

6. Requires less service than any other electronic.

7. During the past fifteen years, several improvements have been made in the larger models of the Hammond. As noted later on in this chapter, in 1938 Mr. Hammond invented an oscillating tube instrument, which he called the "Novachord". For a description of this please see page 345. The simplified version of the "Novachord" was the "Solovox", a short keyboard device for playing melodies, when attached to a piano, electronic organ, or organ. A few years ago, an adaptation of the Solovox was made available as a special pedal attachment to the Hammond organ. This gives a much more versatile and better pedal, which may be played at 32' — 16' — 8' — 4' — 2' pitches. The attack is more that of the normal organ attack, and it is a great improvement on the earlier Hammond pedal which was too reminiscent of the theater organ Diaphone to be used in church. For jazz playing the earlier Hammond pedal was good. Diaphones are happily a thing of the past in church organs, and this effect is also no longer necessary in the Hammond, with this improved and extended pedal attachment. The 32' part of the compass is good down to low A, (the bottom note of the piano) and from there to low CCCC it is some sort of resultant tone. Tones lower than low AAAA will not come through on any but the largest and special type of loud speaker.

Improvements have also been made in the loud speakers employed and in the various types of vibratos which may be obtained, by means of a new type of vibrato mechanism.

ELECTRONIC INSTRUMENTS

Another ingenious device is one for producing artificial reverberation. In acoustically "dead" rooms this attachment creates the illusion of some resonance and is definitely valuable for this purpose.

FREDERICK ALBERT HOSCHKE—THE "ORGATRON",
NOW THE "WURLITZER"

The late Mr. Frederick Albert Hoschke, of South Haven, Michigan, was the inventor and developer of the "Orgatron" (a shortening of the words organ and electronic.) His instrument uses an amplifier and loud speaker also. However, the initial tone is produced by free reeds, in the same manner as is done in the case of a melodeon or harmonium. In fact the mechanism up to this point is the same as in our old fashioned, lowly friend, the reed organ. But from here on, the analogy ceases. Instead of permitting the reeds to produce the sound directly, and thereby creating the nondescript tone, typical of free reed instruments, the reeds simply vibrate without producing an audible sound. By means of a "tone pin," or "tone screw" adjusted with great nicety above each reed, (though not touching the reed itself) various selected harmonics produced by the vibrating reed are picked up, transmitted to an amplifier and sent through one or more loud speakers.

It should be noted that the harmonics used are natural harmonics and are associated naturally with the fundamental tone, and in inextricable relationship to it. Several sets of reeds can have a greater or lesser number of harmonics used in varying degrees of intensity. The physical characteristics of the reeds themselves (thick or thin, wide or narrow, greater or less curve, etc.) enable the position of the tone pin with relation to the vibrating reed to be varied, and thereby it is possible to create real differentiation in quality of tone. There is also an ensemble, when several sets of reeds are played at once.

In 1946, the manufacture and sale of the Orgatron was taken over by the Rudolph Wurlitzer Company with Mr. Zuck in charge of development. A number of refinements and improvements have been made without changing the basic characteristics of the instrument as described above. The present Orgatron is now called the Wurlitzer.

Another electronic made in England was invented by Mr. Leslie E. Bourne—"The Compton Electrone." The tone is produced by engraved sine-waves on fixed insulated discs. Tone is picked up by motor driven exploring electrodes. Those who have heard this electronic, speak most highly of it, as being the best substitute for reproducing the sound of a good organ heard to date.

Several other electronic organs were described in the third edition of this book. During the past ten years they have either fallen by the wayside, or else they have never progressed beyond the laboratory stage, or have died at birth. It would serve no practical purpose to describe these instruments in the detail given to them ten years ago, when their ultimate possibilities were yet to be proved. Among these instruments should be mentioned the following:

1. Mr. Morse Robb, Belleville, Ontario—"The Wave Organ," built with twelve iron cylinders, geared together, running in an oil bath at a speed necessary to produce the correct pitch, with progressively smaller bands on each cylinder for each octave higher. Lost out, because of expense being too great to build.

2. Richard H. Ranger, Newark, N. J.—"The Rangerton." First in the field with an electronic instrument, where twelve tuning forks, a semi-tone apart, were the tone generating basis. Fallen by the way.

3. Mr. James H. Nuthall of Los Angeles and Mr. Ivan Ivanovitch Eremeef of Philadelphia—"The Photona." These devices use the interrupted light beam and photo-electric cell. Nothing has been heard of this system for the past ten years.

4. Mr. Edwin Welte, Frieburg, Germany—"Welte Phototone." Here we have an instrument which uses tone discs upon which are drawn or printed in circles, a series of a dozen or more outlines which represent tone qualities. Photo-electric cells are used in connection with the tone control. Not commercially available to this day.

5. Rada-reed: Like the Wurlitzer, the source of the tone was free reeds, modified by a radar-inspired development. Evidently the inspiration wasn't sufficient to keep the firm from discontinuing manufacture.

For more complete information on any of the above instruments, the reader is referred to the third edition (pp. 355-362.) Even "Who's Who in America," has another book called "Who Was Who in America" for those who have died, but who were formerly listed in current editions, while still alive. This summary treatment of some of the electronic experiments, is necessary for reasons of space. They seemed promising enough at the time, but, following the history of all new developments, did not measure up, for one reason or another with their competitors. The space thus saved will now be used to describe a whole new series of electronics which have great promise and present accomplishment. In the author's opinion, the instruments now to be described, each of them a development of the past fifteen years bid fair to be the leading electronics of the future.

They are the Oscillating tube electronic organs. They are made in all sizes, up to three manuals with many sets of tone generators, amplifiers, and speakers, and the larger models really do simulate an organ ensemble with greater fidelity than any other type of electronic. But first let us have some history.

OSCILLATING RADIO TUBE ELECTRONIC INSTRUMENTS

In the year 1938, Mr. Laurens Hammond introduced to the public, an entirely different type of electronic musical instrument, which he termed the "Novachord." The sounds are produced by means of oscillating radio tubes.

Mr. Hammond had in mind, when he invented this instrument, not a substitute for an organ, which he already had, in the Hammond organ, but an entirely new type of instrument. Something which would take the place of a piano, harpsichord, string quartette, trumpet, and various other instruments. As a consequence, it was equipped with only one manual, like a piano keyboard, and a sustaining pedal, and various other controls to alter the tone quality and the attack and release of the tone.

While the instrument had many novel and interesting features, and to my mind was much more musical than the Hammond organ, it was never a commercial success. The salvage from this invention was incorporated in a much simpler device, called the "Solovox," where the same principles were used, but with a much simpler method of wiring, so that only a single note could be played at any one time. The Solovox was provided with a short compass keyboard with short keys which can be attached in front of the keys of a piano or organ and played along with, and as an adjunct, to, these instruments. The "Solovox" had a wide sale and great popularity before the war, and since.

The principle of the oscillating radio tube, as demonstrated, by Mr. Hammond to be a practical way of producing sustained tones, similar to to those of an organ, immediately engaged the attention of other inventors and manufacturers. Possibly some were working on the idea before Mr. Hammond.

OSCILLATING RADIO TUBE ORGANS

By applying the principles demonstrated by the "Novachord", a whole series of electronic organs have been developed in the past ten or fifteen years. In these organs the only things that move to produce music are electrons. The electrons are caused to oscillate at various frequencies in accordance with the pitch of the tone desired. These oscillations give complex harmonic waves, and therefore do not require any form of synthesis for the production of various tone qualities. The harmonics produced are comparable in complexity with those produced by a vibrating free reed.

It is possible to "filter out" as few or as many of these harmonics, as are desired by means of suitable filtering circuits. Tones of very foundational character may be produced, or tones with considerable harmonic development at the top of the series, or tones rich in harmonics at the fundamental or ground-tone end of the harmonic series. By this means, various tone qualities may be produced from one set of oscillating tubes. Naturally there must be a tube for each pitch desired. Compound tubes which will produce two pitches from one tube are now being used by all oscillating tube organ manufacturers.

ELECTRONIC INSTRUMENTS

By appropriate wiring between the key contacts and the oscillating tubes, the whole compass may be played from 16' C to top C. Then by means of stop controls, various tone filters may be introduced into the circuit which control and modify the sounds from the tone generators. As soon as the instrument is turned on, all of the tubes are warmed up, and are then instantly available for use. It would be quite impractical to have the tubes only come into action when the keys were played, if they were not already warmed up and ready for immediate use.

Apparently the principles involved are much simpler than their practical development into an "organ" which can actually be manufactured to sell for a comparable price to the Hammond organ or the Wurlitzer. In fact, only the smallest ones do sell for as small an amount as the Hammond.

At the time of writing the revision of this chapter, there are at least five, and possibly more, builders of electronic organs, who use the oscillating tube principle. They are the Allen, Baldwin, Connsonata, Haygren and Minshall-Estey organs. All of them are available commercially and are either sold through dealers or travelling representatives. All of them are normally two-manual and pedal instruments, but the Allen and the Haygren occasionally build three manuals, costing as much as $15,000.00. Both of these latter instruments are more or less custom made and are much more complete and satisfactory than the smaller models. Several models of various sizes are available from all of the oscillating tube electronic manufacturers. All have consoles fairly close to A.G.O. standard measurements, and in fact the Allen and Haygren both use standard organ consoles, and place the electronic parts in an adjacent room or basement.

My recommendation to any intending purchaser is to hear them all, if possible. All the big cities have dealers which sell both the Connsonata and the Baldwin. The Allen has sales representatives and many organs available for demonstration throughout the country. Minshall-Estey has some sales representatives in various cities. Haygren has so far confined their sales to the mid-west, but are expanding their territory.

Developments are taking place so rapidly in this field, that any statement of preference by me might easily become out of date. Therefore, for tactful reasons, as well as for reasons of not being sure of what the facts might be at any given time, I shall make no statement of preferences. The Baldwin organ has resistances placed under the keys which delay the attack and permit it to give about the normal attack of an organ. It is also possible to obtain an accent, because of the resistances. The Allen and Haygren have the normal attack and release of an organ.

It should be remembered that the number and quality of the loud speakers and amplifiers, as well as the auditorium or room in which the instrument sounds, all affect the quality of tone the listener hears, on *any* electronic, be it a Hammond, Wurlitzer or any one of the oscillating tube organs. A room with a good resonance, and fairly long period of reverbera-

346

tion is a great help to any electronic, even as it is to organs. But electronics are even more sensitive to accoustical conditions than organs.

The Allen has developed a special type of speaker, called the "Gyrophonic projector". Two loud-speakers are mounted opposite each other on a disc about three feet in diameter. The large disc may be rotated by means of a motor, and with ingenious contact devices, the speakers are supplied continuously with the signals coming from the amplifier. By rotating the large disc at a speed of about one revolution per second, a non-directional and doppler effect is obtained from the speakers, that is much more pleasant to listen to than when the speakers are fixed permanently. Faster rotation (four or five revolutions per second) produces a pleasing vibrato effect.

ELECTRONIC ADDITIONS AND SUPPLEMENTS TO ORGAN TONE

It is possible to place microphones in the organ chambers and reproduce the sound of the organ at distant points in the church. There is, of course, nothing new in this idea. It has been done for years in picking up the sound of organ chimes by means of a microphone, and greatly increasing the sound (by means of amplifiers and loud-speakers) in the tower of the church. With proper equipment, the sound of the organ chimes can be made to carry for a mile or more.

Mr. Frank C. Wichlac of Chicago, and Mr. Alfred G. Kilgen of Los Angeles, both organ men of many years experience, have each independently of the other arrived at similar results in amplifying and transferring the sound of organ pipes by electronic means. Mr. Wichlac has found that a special type of amplifier is required of more than ample power, and one which filters out all of the electronically-produced clicks of the organ magnets. With this amplifier, a pair of good ribbon microphones (one in each chamber) and a pair of good 15" Jensen speakers, with concentric "Tweeters" the tone of the organ in the gallery may be satisfactorily transferred to the chancel of a long church. The practical application of this is obvious, if one wishes to accompany a choir in the chancel, one hundred fifty feet distant from the organ. By adding two expression pedals, to control the volume of the amplifier separately in each chamber, the volume may be increased on the speakers in the chancel, and the shutters closed on the organ in the gallery, or vice versa. Antiphonal effects of great interest can be produced, as well as making it possible to play the organ so softly in the gallery as barely to be heard in the chancel, and still effectively accompany a chancel choir by means of the sound from the speakers.

Fortunately, the pitch of the amplified sound is identical with the original source, so there are no pitch problems as there frequently are in divided organs.

ELECTRONIC INSTRUMENTS

Mr. Kilgen's application of this principle has been made in connection with a small organ in a large church. The full organ was inadequate for the church. His amplifier control is attached to the organ expression pedals and when the amplifier is turned on, as the volume of natural tone from the organ increases, when the swell shoe is opened, the power on the amplifier is also increased. There are, of course, musical limits to electronic amplification. But an inadequate organ can be made to have double or more volume by this means. It is essential, to the success of this use of amplification that the amplifiers, speakers, and microphones all be adequate and correct in power and efficiency. Neither one of these gentlemen have invented anything radically new. They have been patient in doing the necessary experimenting with well-known electronic equipment to produce satisfactory musical results in amplifying the sound of an organ for the first time in my observation.

The implications of this are quite large. Processional or pitch organs, to give the pitch to the choir for processionals, are now totally unnecessary. Widely separated choirs can now hear the organ equally well. Small organs may be made to sound much bigger than they actually are. Both of these men are so saturated with organ lore and tradition, as is the author, that they could never be satisifed with an electronic organ, but can be satisfied to permit of electronic amplification of a real organ, when it is well done.

Mr. John Hayes Hammond, Jr. of Gloucester, Mass., has also developed a system of electronic amplification of the organ in the chapel of his castle in Gloucester. This amplification makes possible a continuing increase in the tonal volume, after the swell shutters are fully open, to any degree of volume desired. When reducing the volume of sound to softer effects, the electronic amplification is first gradually discontinued, and then the swell shutters are closed. The result is that an extension of a crescendo is made possible to much greater limits, and conversely, a much longer and more extensive diminuendo. I am not sure that this sort of amplification is desirable or especially practical. It is hailed by the local newspapers as a marvellous accomplishment. I would say that an organ in a comparatively small chapel such as Mr. Hammond's with some 150 stops, needs no electronic assistance. My recollection of the organ is that it had more than ample volume for all musical purposes. Perhaps the invention will be useful when applied to smaller organs, to give them greater flexibility and dynamic range.

THE ELECTRONIC ENSEMBLE

The Haygren Organ Company have made commercially available during this past year, a small edition of the Haygren organ, without console, which is attached directly to the junction board of one of the manuals of any small organ. This is called the Haygren Electronic Ensemble.

They are just now making a pedal section of this attachment. With one or both of these units (or auxiliary organs) it is possible greatly to expand the tonal variety of a small organ.

An ingenious tuning device makes it easy to adjust the pitch of the Haygren units to that of the organ, which latter will vary in pitch, according to the temperature conditions in the organ chamber.

A four stop unit organ, for example, with Diapason, Flute, String and Trumpet, and one pedal stop, extended from the Flute, can be made quite attractive. Such an organ will have much more flexibility and variety with the Haygren units added to it. Various kinds of solo voices are easily obtained, and more grades of tone in the Pedal and an improvement in the ensemble. The Haygren units may be played separately, the organ may be played separately, or the two may be combined in any way desired. Here is something that I have been looking for ever since the first electronic appeared—a happy combination of both organ and electronic. I believe that Messrs. Richard Peterson and Solomon Haytow, the indefatigable engineers and experimenters for Haygren, have really done something with this development that has importance for many small churches. The church may not have the financial resources to buy an adequate organ, but its congregation may be musically discriminating enough not to be satisfied with either a four rank unit organ, or an ordinary electronic. Inasmuch as these attachments are relatively cheap, compared with the price of either of the above, it is possible to add the Haygren units to a small organ and still keep the price under that of all of the larger electronics, and have something better. I hail this invention as a real contribution to the solution of the perplexed organ committee's problems.

ELECTRONIC CHIMES AND HARPS

For a description of these special tonal effects, see P. 109.

CONCLUSIONS

The author will not attempt to state at this time what the ultimate development of the electronic instruments may be. The whole field is still new, and the refinements and improvements which have already taken place in fifteen years, are so numerous that it is impossible to say at present as to what may be accomplished facts in electronics ten years from now.

Considering the matter of the relative merits of electronics and organs in the year of grace, 1955, the author is still of the opinion that small churches would probably do better were they to spend the same amount of money that an electronic would cost on one of the three or four ranks of pipes, unified organs, available from nearly any builder in the country. I realize that this statement is debatable. I give it as my considered opinion. This statement has been, and is being, debated by many churches with limited funds to purchase musical equipment. Claims and counter-claims are made by both electronic and organ salesmen. What to do? So far as the four stop unit organ goes, it leaves much to be desired. Unfortunately, so does any electronic. A final answer to this question must wait for future developments.

One thing should be noted. It is almost essential that any of the small unit organs must contain a chorus Reed as one of its stops, to be considered an organ at all. It is amazing the effect that a well-voiced chorus Reed will have on the ensemble of a very small organ. Granted that such small organs are by no means ideal, and that the millenium has not yet arrived, whereby it is possible to buy the equivalent of a $20,000.00 organ for $5,000.00 or less from any organ builder; neither is it possible to do so from any builder of electronics, at present.

If I were spending my own money to secure the best musical equipment for a small church at minimum cost, I would first buy a four rank unit organ, and then add the Haygren units described on page 348. It seems to me that for a very modest expenditure, better musical results would be obtained in this way, than to do anything else with the same amount of money. The church would then have the nucleus of a traditional organ, plus the soft "pretty-pretties," in which effects nearly all electronic instruments are very satisfactory.

After all, the primary purpose of a church organ is to create a religious atmosphere in church. In my opinion, the combination above described will do this better for a small church, than anything else that a small church can afford to buy.

For use in funeral parlors, or in one's home, all electronics are probably very suitable. They are also, especially the Hammond, adapted to restaurants, night clubs and other distinctly secular places in conjunction with a jazz orchestra, or where portability is important, as well as low cost. The Wurlitzer and all of the oscillating tube electronics are better adapted for use in church. Of course, a more or less standard console is almost a necessity to make electronics useful for organ practice purposes. Several of the electronics have such consoles, and the Hammond now has available at additional cost, one which is more like an organ console than their earlier models.

Personally I prefer to hear voices or instruments directly, rather than over a loud speaker. Inasmuch as all electronics are dependent upon amplifying and loud speaking equipment, until these are greatly improved from their present stage of development, I am going to be satisfied only for a limited range of effects with the musical results possible on any electronic. It is no doubt unfair to blame all the shortcomings of the musical results of electronics on the amplifying and loud speaker mechanism. It should be carefully noted that a series of loud speakers will provide better results than one, as they can then be used with moderate power. This adds to the cost, but is distinctly worth while, rather than to overcrowd the capacity of a single speaker.

Allen's gyrophonic projector is a real advance in loud speaker equipment, as are also some of the speakers employed by several other manufacturers. Haygren, especially have made a deep study of combining various types of speakers, using a special speaker for reproducing the sound of a trumpet very successfully.

Nearly all musicians and those who have good musical judgment, who have heard electronic instruments, are agreed on the statement that the softer effects are much pleasanter to listen to than the louder. In other words, the sound will stand only a limited amount of amplification or magnification, after which it becomes increasingly unpleasant, until the effect is positively devastating, when played at the full capacity of the loud speakers in the system. This defect is minimized but not overcome, when many speakers are used as suggested above.

Certainly the larger models of the Allen and the Haygren succeed in getting full ensemble effects (when the acoustical conditions of the building are favorable) that are quite remarkable. But these models cost up to $15,000.00 and an organ costing this much, is preferable, in my opinion.

It will have been observed from the descriptions which have preceded, that the inventors of electronic instruments are located in widely separated parts of the U. S. A., as well as Canada and Germany, and much work has also been done in England by John Compton and others.

The field is wide open. Developments and improvements are taking place continually that make it impossible to state what may be accomplished in the next ten years.

FAMOUS OLD ORGANS IN HOLLAND DENMARK AND GERMANY
SUPPLEMENT

CHAPTER 20.

In Chapter 15, "A History of Tonal Design" (starting on page 228) I made the statement that my first hand knowledge of 17th and 18th century European organs was limited. The information that I was presenting had been ferreted out from historians and other writers who have made first hand observations of the organs of this period and who have put in writing what they saw and heard. Since my tour of famous organs in Holland, Denmark and Germany, in the summer of 1955, I can now add a supplement to Chapter 15.

My first concern in writing this book, has properly been to describe American organs. However, the interest in classic European organs continues to grow in America. Even though I do not expect all of my opinions and conclusions (which are personal) about these organs will be shared by all American organists and builders, I am nevertheless stating them. They are at least the observations and opinions of an experienced organist and organ expert. Many parts of Chapter 20 have appeared in the October and November, 1955 issues of the "Diapason." Letters and comments received from many sources since publication in the "Diapason," have caused me to revise a few statements, and I believe that this Chapter is now a fair summary of these famous old organs.

In the "Odyssey of an Organ Enthusiast and his Wife," which I wrote in 1932 after a European trip, I quoted a statement of one of my old army friends. He says "My chief objection to war is, that it makes so many veterans, and they are all — liars." So it is that one might object to his friends making a trip to Europe, because they will come home and talk about it.

I am well aware that many of the organs that I am going to discuss here, have been previously described in the pages of the "Diapason," "The American Organist," and "Organ Institute Quarterly," both recently and during the past twenty-five years. Mr. E. Power Biggs has recorded many of them. I believe it was Emerson Richards who twenty-five years ago first called attention to many of the famous German organs, notably at Weingarten, Ottobeuren, Ochsenhausen and elsewhere in southern Germany. In spite of what has previously been written by American as well as European writers, I still feel that many ideas about these old organs need clarifying and summarizing so that our earnest American students of the art of organ building will have a clearer idea of what these old European organs are actually like. Their virtues as well as their many limitations will be described.

FAMOUS OLD ORGANS IN HOLLAND, DENMARK AND GERMANY

Mr. Arthur Howes, who directed the tour of European organs during the month of July, 1955, has this to say: "The true purpose of our tour (lest any mistakenly feel that our interest in these organs and in articles by European authors implies disparagement of our own culture) is to ascertain whether the old organs there (we have none in our own country) and the contemporary organs (quite different from our own) possess virtues that ought to be incorporated into modern American organs." I believe that this is an excellent statement of the purpose of the tour, and that most of the thirty-five men and women, including Mrs. Barnes and myself had this purpose in mind, and did not approach these old organs with too many preconceived notions. I know that I was open-minded, particularly with regard to the organs in the Netherlands and Denmark as I had no previous experience with them.

A word about the tour party. The members ranged in age from under twenty years old to over sixty. Organists with forty years experience were mixed with those in the early student stages. Four practical and experienced organ men from M. P. Moller were among the most interested and intelligent of the observers. I was able to discuss all of the organs that we heard with this varied group of observers, and get their reactions, as well as my own. I also had a long talk with Mr. G. Donald Harrison immediately upon my return to New York City. Mr. Harrison had just completed (on his own) a very similar trip. I was particularly interested to find that his impressions and opinions coincided with mine on nearly all the essential points regarding the organs heard. My observations and deductions may not be identical to those of all of our party (there is no reason why they should be). I am satisfied that they are in substantial agreement with the more mature and experienced members of the party.

Before describing some of the famous organs in detail, some general observations should be made, these apply to all organs of the classic period.

1. Practically all of the classic organs were located in a completely open position on the rear gallery wall. A few smaller organs were occasionally located on the side wall of the nave of the church. There were usually subsidiary to the main organ in the gallery. The case (usually highly ornamented, and invariably with all display pipes being speaking pipes) was not, and is not considered today merely ornamental, it was essential to the focus and blend of the tone. The particular type of voicing, often spoken of today as "ancient or classic" depended in part for its success upon the enclosure of each separate division in its own specially built case, or box, that just fitted around the longest pipes in each division. In reality each section of the organ was enclosed in a kind of swell box, only there were no shutters in front, only display

speaking pipes. These enclosures (sides and roof) were only a half inch or less in thickness, and therefore did not prevent the escape of tone through the walls of the box. They served to reflect and direct the tone forward.

The action of all old organs was, of course, direct mechanical, or tracker, with channel and slider windchests. This also had a large influence on the speech of the pipes, and permitted a type of voicing, almost unknown, except by those builders of today who are making as nearly as possible, direct copies of old organs.

This style of voicing consists of making all pipes with wide open toes, and adjusting the amount of wind that the pipes receive at the windway, between the lower lip and the languid. The languids either are not nicked at all, or very lightly nicked at wide intervals. This kind of voicing is only practical with low wind pressure, 3" or less, and normally around 2-1/4" or 2-1/2". Later Schnitger and Silbermann organs had 3" wind pressure, but the earlier organs considerably less. It is also more successful on the barred or channel windchest, where the wind pressure builds up gradually in the channel to cause the pipes to speak gently at first. Modern, individual valve windchests do not encourage unnicked voicing, without causing a great deal of "chiff" or transient noise in getting the pipes to speak their true musical note. Modern examples such as the Nason Flute have been introduced into American organs by the Aeolian-Skinner Organ Company and other builders. For special effects, and for playing staccato music, the sharp "chiff" and attack of the tone can create a quite charming effect. But for playing sustained, legato music, such transient noises in getting the pipes to speak are distressing, and it is quite impossible to play so that the music sounds legato. In the big churches on the European continent, this "chiffing" isn't heard at any distance from the organ. In some modern small churches where this style of voicing has been adopted in so-called modern organs after the classic models, the "chiffing" was quite disturbing and to most American ears highly undesirable. Here again, we are dealing with matters of taste, and previous training in listening.

Even though this style of voicing may have been adopted primarily for tonal reasons, it did have another important advantage, in that the pipes so voiced are remarkably efficient in the use of wind. To supply enough wind for a good sized organ, was always one of the chief problems of the organ builder before the days of the electric blower. So efficiency in the use of wind was a great advantage. Also the 16' pedal stops were very lightly winded with little foundation tone. Even the bottom octave of all the 8' stops was generally so lightly winded that little power and weight was present.

FAMOUS OLD ORGANS IN HOLLAND, DENMARK AND GERMANY

Nearly all of these old organs have now been furnished with some type of electric blower. The ardent believers in the ancient organs are not pleased with such modern improvements. Mr. Harrison told me that he remarked facetiously to one of the curators of ancient art objects, including old organs, that it was too bad to modernize them with electric blowers. He was startled to be taken seriously, when the gentleman replied, "Yes, there was a certain unsteadiness to the wind when blown by several sweating men, that gave a great charm to the tone, unobtainable with a modern blower." He evidently believes like Dr. Glenn Dillard Gunn, who used to irritate any group of organists he could find together, with the statement, "When the hand blowing of organs was given up and the electric blower substituted, they took away the last human contact with the instrument."

In one of the largest old organs of over 50 stops, we found it adequately blown by two 3/4 H.P. blowers. Modern American organs of that size would require five times that power, even on low pressure. Obviously the pipes of the old organs were efficient in the use of wind. Then, of course, there was no wind required for the action or for the many reservoirs introduced in modern organs, all of which take power.

The classic organ was limited to two classes of tone for all practical purposes.

1. The penetrating, principal tone, with fairly narrow scales, and wide, low mouths, called the male element in the tonal spectrum.

2. The milder, larger scaled pipes with narrower mouths, called the female element, or flute tone.

Both kinds of tone were represented in the larger organs at all pitches, from 16', 8', 4', 2-2/3', 2' and on up through ten to twenty ranks of Mixtures to the highest pitches that it is practical to make, tune or hear. All of these ranks were of very nearly equal power. No preponderance of unison tone ever.

Larger organs had some examples of the most unmusical Reed stops that can possibly be imagined. A Regal, or early version of the theater organ Kinura was quite common. Such a buzzing, thin, distressing voice seems to have little musical purpose. The Schalmei reeds were equally bad, but did add something to the ensemble that was interesting in a large church. The so-called Trumpets were thin, uncertain, out of tune, examples that certainly were better omitted. The truth is, of course, that whatever the virtues of low pressure, unnicked flue pipes, there is no virtue in very low pressure reed pipes, as the tongues must be so thin that there is little stability or musical character possible in such pipes.

I am speaking of wind pressures of 2-1/4" or anything lower than 3". With 3" wind pressure some good free trumpet tone is possible, as the Silbermann brothers amply demonstrated. So little servicing or tuning is done on the majority of these old organs, that what reeds they have are normally out of tune and out of regulation. Some exceptions can be noted, to be sure.

For all practical purposes therefore, we have the two classes of tone as outlined above. There is nothing in any classic organ that remotely resembles string or viol tone in any way. No softer, subtler voices such as Dulcianas, Gamshorns, Spitz Flutes, or anything resembling a modern solo reed or chorus reed, so these occupy a role of minor importance in the tonal scheme of old organs, even if such voices exist at all. One exception should be noted. The 16' Posaune or equivalent 16' reed in the pedal was frequently quite good, and very useful in giving some weight and solidity of tone to this division. The flue 16' registers were invariably so soft that they urgently needed some support.

Right here I would like to speak about something that shocked me on our trip — the great gulf dividing classic European Pedal Organ specifications on paper and the actual tonal output, with the great lack of independence and tonal distinction. To be sure, the old Dutch and German pedal organs are independent but they usually sound like another manual division, for the simple reason that the 16' ranks do not stand our sufficiently to give adequate foundation to the elaborate tonal sonorities of the manuals. I missed the firmness of really adequate 16' reeds especially in the larger instruments where they are most needed. My reaction was simply this: These pedal organs actually are not 16' sections as they should be. We speak of the Great as 8', the Rück Positiv as 4' or 2' in pitch, and certainly the pedal organ should center around 16' pitch. Here again the problem of securing sufficient wind is doubtless to blame.

The best modern builders are not guilty of this lack. Flentrop, Harrison, and Holtkamp all seem to build pedal organs with a 16' center. On paper the 17th and 18th century pedal organs look well in tonal foundation — they seem to be genuine 16' sections — but their upperwork destroys this in actual sound, or else the 16' ranks are just not sufficient for all they should support. Whatever criticism one may make of the French pedal organs (and there are several weak items in their make-up) certainly they are really 16' sections in no uncertain terms and they add a grandeur that I find missing in the Dutch and German antiques.

Why are these old organs so effective when used for their primary purposes which were and are:
1. Accompanying congregational singing,
2. Playing contrapuntal music of Bach and earlier composers?

The reasons resolve themselves into a combination of various answers. In the first place, contrapuntal music was written to be played on this type of organ. The organ with all of its limitations, had the very positive virtues of being capable of playing contrapuntal music and supporting congregation singing supremely well. This was brought about by:

1. The voicing treatment as above described;
2. The placement of the organ and its specially designed cases;
3. The mechanism;
4. The acoustics of the magnificent stone buildings, often 90' to 140' high, with highly reflective surfaces. Even with the tracker action consoles, where the player must of necessity be near the pipes, the effect in a big church is one of remoteness. Majestic repose and dignity are the words to describe its effect. In smaller buildings this effect becomes more energetic, and sometimes a little brash and rugged for the ears of those who are not such old organ enthusiasts.

The Flentrop Organ Company of Zaandam, Holland, as well as the Frobenius Brothers in Copenhagen, and Von Beckerath and Kemper in Hamburg, some of whose factories we visited, are all building slider chests and tracker actions, with the tonal design as nearly a copy of the old organs as it is possible to make.

Each of these builders, I found to be idealists, and they honestly believe that there have been no improvements in organ building in the past 200 years, if not longer. Therefore, any voices introduced or any mechanical improvements in the action and console conveniences that have been made since 1750 are ignored. I noticed that all of these builders did have modern woodworking machinery in their factories, and made much use of plywood, masonite, bakelite and other modern materials in building organs, but otherwise just as they were built 200 years ago.

The large firm of Walcker in Ludwigsburg build nearly all of their organs that are for home consumption, as tracker organs. Just about half of their organs are exported to other countries, where modern organs are required. They even have to build a modern radiating, concave pedal board for their organs shipped abroad. All of these other builders use the flat, old fashioned pedal board by request of the resident organists. It is just 100 years ago that the Willis pedal board was first used (St. George's Hall, Liverpool, 1855).

Walcker also builds slider chests and tracker action organs with electro-pneumatic machines to move the sliders, thus making the stop control something more than brute force. Enough brute force is required to put down the keys on the old organs, as well as the new ones built in the same style. Mr. Flentrop states that "the direct advantage of a good mechanical action lies in the tactile connection afforded to the player between the key and the pallet under the pipe. Not only does the finger control, to a degree, the speed of opening the pallet and its closing (which if electrically controlled is invariably instantaneous and very snappy) but it feels the action of the pallet. This gives the player more control over timing than is possible with electric action. A further ad-

357

vantage of mechanical (tracker) action is implicit in the manner of voicing the pipes. While voicing with little or no nicking was certainly the
technique of the builders of yesteryear, and was discarded during the
19th and 20th centuries, this technique should not be called the "ancient" or "classic" manner of voicing. It is another of those features
or organ building which defy fashion or style. For if an organ builder
will make an instrument with tracker action, he will discover that the
pipes must be voiced in the way that is most advantageous to the key
action and to the musical requirements."

Th. Frobenius & Co. of Copenhagen handed me this memorandum
of their conception of organ building, which states the case for making
mechanical (tracker) organs in the year 1955, as well as I have seen it
stated anywhere, and in all fairness, I quote it in full:

"In one way the art of building organs is in a unique position in
modern times. It tends to renounce the solutions provided by the general
technical progress.

"The old mechanical organ was followed by the pneumatic, and a lot
of new technical facilities were added: general pistons, crescendo
pedal, etc.

"Then the electric organ followed the pneumatic, and the new technical advantages were further elaborated: the free placing of console
and pipes, etc.

"And after the electrical organ came — the mechanical!

"The FROBENIUS—Organ which will be demonstrated to you here
in Soborg Kirke is a mechanical organ, based on the ancient, simple
principle of levers, comprehensible to everybody from a physical point
of view.

"What is the explanation of this turning back to the original (and
over a long period abandoned) principle of organ building? Is it a kind
of escapism from the current technical confusion, or is it a result of
profound historical analysis? It is neither the first one nor the other,
to tell the truth.

"The answer is simply that the mechanical organ with all its limitations compared to the pneumatic and the electric organs holds one
advantage, and this advantage is to be found on the artistic level. We
are thinking of a quotation from Igor Strawinsky's "Poetique Musicale":
The more pressure one submits to, the more one is released from the
chains, which restrain the spirit.

"The mechanical organ with sliderchests puts much restraint on the
organ builder: The number of stops on each manual is limited, the
distance between the different windchests is limited, the wind pressure
has to be kept down, etc.

"The low pressure of wind brings forth the old method of intonation.
The pipes are voiced with "full wind sypply" (big holes in the pipe

feet) and without nicks. Through this method the pipes will produce important harmonics and non-harmonics, and the attack is precise and characteristic. But it should be noticed that the pipes without nicks require an extremely sensitive way of voicing. The voicer has to learn patiently the very restricted conditions of intonation required by this kind of pipes.

"All these difficulties thus forced on the organ builder mean that the organ will turn out successfully, only when the design of the front, the specifications of stops, and the voicing form a synthesis. If you ask, why we build mechanical instruments, the answer — in shortest form — will be, that this method gives us a chance to achieve something artistic. Consequently we gladly take the trouble.

"And we are convinced that the organist having once realized the artistic possibilities secured through the mechanical organ — the vital and acute performance, the beautiful sound and individuality of the stops — will always favor this kind of instrument. It is true that some parts of the organ literature will not get an adequate performance on the mechanical organ. But this sacrifice is worthwhile considering, because the main part of the most valuable music for the organ will sound absolutely true to style and character.

"But, of course, we have many problems to face, some of a more "spiritual" nature. It gives great satisfaction to build instruments on which the huge classical literature is brought forth in accordance with the great traditions. But we would feel that we have confirmation of our principles and thoughts concerning our work, if the young composers would realize the inspiration the mechanical organ offers them."

Why all of these very serious limitations should be listed as advantages, I can't see, unless one gets himself into a 17th century mood, and believes like Elijah "I am not better than my fathers." If one really believes that perfection was reached in organ building 250 years ago, then why try to improve on perfection?

The many keen minds that have tried to improve on the old masters during the past two centuries, both with regard to obtaining more tonal variety and in ease of control, have wasted their time and effort so far as these organists and builders are concerned. They glory in the fact that the old organs as well as the ones they build today, are very difficult to play, and that the mind of man has never conceived any more awkward or unwieldy means of stop control than are on the old Dutch organs. They are like the automobile of 50 years ago, with one cylinder, no self starter, no power steering or brakes, and that take brute force to operate, or even to start.

The tracker organ built in America, upon several of which I was brought up, at least had the stop knobs in terraces immediately adjacent to the keyboards; they also had some combination pedals to move a fixed group of stops in and out quickly; to be sure, with a considerable amount of clatter, like a girl going down steps with a load of kindling dropping some on each step. The clatter of moving stops is present in these old organs, even when only one stop is moved at a time, so that anyone sitting in the middle of the church is well aware that something is going to be changed in the registration, before hearing the sound of the pipes. The knobs of the old organs were placed on the casework, as far away from the organist's reach as possible. They would be more accessible if placed on the choir stalls. No wonder organists didn't attempt any registrational changes, other than that provided by changing from one manual to another during the course of a movement or a variation. Then everything comes to a complete stop, a grand clatter ensues, and the next movement is ready to be played. French organs have antiquated stop controls also, but with their system of ventils and combination pedals, rapid changes are possible, where they are quite impossible on the old organs in the Netherlands, Denmark and Germany.

No one need worry about the registration being restless or kaleidoscopic.

Certainly Walcker has a compromise on all this when he builds slider and pallet windchests, with modern stop control for the sliders. I can subscribe to this compromise especially in smaller organs. I agree that for the lower notes, from middle or 2' C downwards, the pipes speak better on channel, barred chests, than on individual valves. Mr. Donald Harrison and I are both agreed that for the pipes smaller than 2' long, there is no advantage in the barred chests. Inasmuch as about 95% of the pipes on these old organs are smaller than 2' long, if one counts all the pipes in the mixtures, none of which are as much as 2' long, one wonders what all the excitement is about for having tracker organs. The effect of the tracker action on the player is certainly more subjective, psychological and physical, rather than having any objective effect on the listener. In other words, the organist may imagine he hears a difference in sound when he depresses a key rapidly on a tracker organ, as compared to when he presses it slowly down. Actually there is no difference. Mr. Harrison says that if by some miracle it was possible (overnight) to substitute modern pitman windchests for the old tracker chests on any of the old, much admired organs, and plant all the old pipes from 2' and up on the new wind chests, he doubts that any of the experts would ever know the difference in the sound of the organ. If on top of this, a good modern console were substituted for the absolute curiosities that pass for consoles on the old organs, everyone would be happy, except the antiquarian, who worships the old because it is old, not because it is good or worth keeping.

Two other points about the old organs should be mentioned. (1st) — they were nearly a whole tone sharp in pitch as compared with the present standard. The old organ CC pipe was about the same length as our DD pipe. A 16' low CCC need only be 14' 3" long. This was a real saving in material and cost. It might make it difficult for singers to reach the top note, without transposing a whole tone, but it was the custom. (2nd) — all manuals and pedal keyboards were invariably of short compass as compared to our modern compass. Thus CC to F3 (54 notes) was an extreme compass, more often CC — C3 49 notes. The pedal compass was CCC to D (27 notes). Toward the close of his life Bach had an organ with the pedal board going to F. No old organ has a longer pedal range than this.

These old organ enthusiasts who carefully measure the diameter of the old pipes at various Cs will find their measurements to be two scales out when applied to the scaling of pipes with modern pitch (A 440). This is something they perhaps hadn't realized unless in attempting to reproduce the old pipes they maintain the old high pitch as well.

One very commendable feature of the old organs was their relatively steady wind. The wooden wind trunking was not large, nor the wind chests oversize, and yet with modern blowers, the wind is reasonably steady. Much more so, than the wind was found to be on a number of recent copies of the old tracker organs. Maybe the old masters knew something that the present builders haven't learned about obtaining steady wind. All old organs at least were strictly custom built, and the voicing of the pipes was done in the church by the builder himself, to get the best results in the particular accoustical environment. This is something manifestly impossible for modern builders except in special instances. True, the tone regulating is done in the church, but this is not the same thing as what the old builders did.

A lifetime output for an old builder was forty organs. This is the number Arp Schnitger is credited with, perhaps one organ a year. Some of our present builders turn out as many organs in a year as Schnitger did in a life time.

I think that enough has been said about the classic organ in general, and that it is now proper to take up some specific examples —

OLD ORGANS IN THE NETHERLANDS AND CONTEMPORARY ORGANS COPYING THE TONAL AND MECHANICAL CONCEPT OF THE OLD ORGANS

It was a privilege to have Mr. Hennie Schouten, the eminent Dutch organist and expert on Dutch organs as our guide throughout our trips to the old organs in many cities in the Netherlands. No one better qualified could have been found, or one more sympathetic to these old organs.

Starting in Amsterdam with the organs in "The 'Old' Church" and the 'New' Church, the "New" church being built only in 1560, not quite 400 years ago. The organ in the "Old" church, built by Christian Vater in 1724-26 has 46 speaking stops, three manuals and pedals with a magnificent case, in the late baroque style. The stops were almost equally divided between the four divisions, with the customary stop list of Diapasons (Prestants) and flutes, and 16' and 8' Trumpets on the Great, similar diapasons and flutes and their octaves and a few poor solo reeds on the other two manuals. A complete stop list of the Schnitger organ in Steinkirchen is given on page 245. It is typical of the classic organ at its best.

We attended services at the "New" church on Sunday and had an opportunity to hear just how the big organ there is used for its chief purpose. There is no choir in any of these large Dutch churches, in fact there is no room for one in the rather cramped organ galleries. The organist and his visitors must plod their weary way up dozens of the most rickety and devious of steps to the organ gallery.

The organist plays a prelude, inevitably a composition of Bach or his precursors, and then before each hymn or choral, he plays an extended, elaborate and brilliant improvisation on the hymn about to be sung. Then he settles down to the key of the hymn, and the congregation take the hymn from there in good, sturdy fashion, supported by a solid and brilliant organ, played in strict harmony with the parts the congregation are singing. At the close, there is no amen, but rather a quieter improvisation, based on the hymn just sung, fading to the point where the Minister can again be heard, and the service continues. Used in this manner, it seems to me that these old Dutch organs are well suited for their purpose. They more than adequately support and encourage congregational singing and of course are ideal for playing contrapuntal music. For accompanying a choir flexibly, for playing the greater part of 19th Century and later organ music, for quiet, meditative places in a service, they would be ill adapted.

Other journeys were to Alkmaar, where there are two old organs in the St. Lawrence Church. Originally, the organs were by Galtus — Garmer and Jacob Galtus Van Hagerbaer, in 1639-45. The big organ has been no less than six times restored, once by Franz Casper Schnitger in 1723 and the last time by D. A. Flentrop in 1949. Another most interesting morning was spent at the little village of Maassluis. Surprisingly enough this small town's central feature is a great church, with an organ by Garrells, 1732, recently restored, and one of the fine organs of Holland. The ladies of this church had gathered together a collation for us, and we were most warmly welcomed. It was truly a most gracious gesture.

The Pieterkerk in Leyden has an organ built by Germeer Baltassen in 1639, several times restored. This is the church which welcomed the Pilgrims from England, and there is a memorial to John Robinson, Pastor of the English church in Leyden: "His broadly tolerant mind guided and developed the religious life of the Pilgrims of the Mayflower."

The organ known best in Holland to many of the older generations of Americans, from reading about it in "Hans Brinker and the Silver Skates" is the Müller organ in the Bavo church in Haarlem (1730). The group heard this organ really played on two successive evenings. The church was nearly full with those who had paid admissions. Interest in old organs is shared by the public in Holland. The first evening five organists competed in an improvisation contest. The three times winner of these annual improvisation contests, Piet Kee, a young Dutch organist, can now permanently retain the Silver Tulip given as a prize. The next evening, the three judges played, ostensibly to prove that they knew as much as the contestants the night before, but also because they were on hand after traveling considerable distances as this was an international contest. The Bavo church organ is scarcely big enough in sound to fill this large church, but it is intensely brilliant, and the reeds are somewhat better than average. I don't know how much assistance the various players had with changing stops, but there were some fairly rapid changes made, that one man alone could not possibly make, these were accompanied by the usual amount of clatter and noise. The effect is nevertheless noble and dignified, even if not thrilling, in this great church.

A third night in Haarlem was spent first in listening to a fine rendition of a Bach Cantata, with the recitatives done with organ rather than harpsichord. There seems to be considerable debate and difference of opinion about how the recitatives in the cantatas should be accompanied. A brilliant concerto for organ and orchestra was an added feature. But the culmination of the evening was to go to the City Hall (Rathaus) where the party had received engraved invitations to attend a reception given by the burgomaster and city council to a select group. Here, a number of the string players from the orchestra we had just heard, played a Haydn concerto for organ and string orchestra. The hundreds of candles in the magnificent brass chandeliers were all lit, casting a warm glow on the 400 year old room with its fine old Dutch portraits. We were transported indeed to the 18th Century, both with the music and the whole environment. This was one of the high points of the entire trip. We reached our hotel at Amsterdam at 1 A.M.

St. John's Church, Gouda has an organ by Moreau (1736). We reached Gouda just after the famous cheese market had closed. The organ was not unlike many of the other Dutch organs we had heard. There is a great similarity between all of the Dutch organs built between 200 and 300 years ago. This is only natural as there were the strictest rules for the layout of the organ due to the tracker action and to the tonal appointment in general. Rück positive in its own little enclosure at the

FAMOUS OLD ORGANS IN HOLLAND, DENMARK AND GERMANY

gallery rail, Brustwerk, immediately in front of, and a little above the head of the organist. Hauptwerk above the Brustwerk, and Pedal disposed in two side cases, usually connected in the case work to the two main divisions, but sometimes separated in the case work, as well as being separated behind the case work. The larger metal pipes of the Pedal and Hauptwerk were invariably in the case and were of course both ornamental as well as useful.

A recent Flentrop "Modern" tracker organ, built along the old lines was heard in a truly "modern" church at Amstelveen, a suburb of Amsterdam, the Kruiskerk. While only containing 20 registers, it was entirely adequate in volume for this rather large church. Another suburb of Amsterdam, Zaamdam, is where Flentrop's factory is located. This was visited, and all could see for themselves how 17th century organs are being built in 1955. The anachronism of this proceeding does not trouble Mr. Flentrop, who has a zeal and love for the old work. I don't quarrel with his enthusiasms, only I believe they are misdirected.

At Zaandam, the burgomaster, made a speech of welcome and we were served refreshments, presented with souvenir spoons, and copper organ pipes by Mr. Flentrop, and treated royally. One of the pleasantest memories of the trip was the cordiality shown to us by the Dutch people. Mr. and Mrs. Schouten had a reception for us in their home and everywhere we were treated as honored guests.

FAMOUS OLD ORGANS IN DENMARK

By plane to Copenhagen, where we arrived around three in the afternoon. By the time that the party had got "bedded down" in the hotels, it was nearly five. We looked at four organs, in widely separated churches before dinner that night. In Copenhagen alone there are many instruments in which modern adaptations of old principles of construction, action and voicing have been incorporated into modern organs. Actually there is little modern adaptations of the old principles. The old principles are just copied, more or less successfully. The case work, while having the same layout as the old organs, is treated considerably more simply for the obvious reason that the expense would be prohibitive in trying to do the elaborate carving and gilding at today's cost of labor. Marcussen, and Frobenius are the two present day Danish builders whose work was examined. I was much impressed with the work of Frobenius in two examples, Van Löse church and St. Jacobs Church in Copenhagen. I believe that Frobenius has really caught the spirit and technique of the old masters to a greater extent than any of the contemporary builders, who are copying the old organs. The Frobenius Brothers are truly artists in their own right, and they do not need the past to support them.

Fredericksburg Castle, has a Copenius organ from 1615, on which Mr. Finn Videro, who joined the tour at Copenhagen played a series of

364

variations. This is said to be one of the oldest organs in existence that is still playable. It too has been restored. Bellows leather, and many of the trackers, and their connections will last only so long. Every 50 to 100 years, a restoration of all old organs is essential if they are to continue to play tunes. If the restoration does only this, and a century's accumulation of dust is knocked out of the pipes, and the pipes otherwise are left alone, except for tuning, one can hear the sound very much as it was originally. Organs, unlike violins, do not improve with age. The pipe metal becomes softer, and if it originally wasn't of sufficient richness in tin, the toes of the pipes settle into the holes, and the pipes generally deteriorate.

Roskilde Cathedral, where the Danish kings are buried, was having work done on its organ, so no one was able to "toodle" it, a pleasant relief. Kronberg Castle was visited the same day, even though there was no organ there in playable condition. Magnificent view of the sea from all rooms of the castle. How could Hamlet have been melancholy amid such surroundings?

FAMOUS OLD ORGANS IN GERMANY

Again by plane to Hamburg. Here we started our study of German organs, though not in the city itself. There are many interesting organs, not far from Hamburg, but since the great Walcker in St. Michael's Church was destroyed, the most interesting organ in Hamburg is probably the Arp Schnitger in St. Jacobi's Church. This church was partly destroyed and the organ is temporarily set up in a very bad position on the floor of a roofed-in aisle. Here again Schnitger's work of 1688-1693 was restored by H. H. Jahnn in 1928 and by Kemper of Lübeck. I strongly suspect a considerable amount of change has taken place, since Schnitger built this 60 stop, 4 manual organ with 12 bellows (12 men to blow it in the old days). It is difficult to judge what this organ might sound like in its original gallery location. At present it certainly lacks the great distinction of the recently restored Schnitger in Steinkirchen (Altesland), about 20 miles southwest of Hamburg. Von Beckerath of Hamburg did the restoration here and from this restoration and other work of this builder, I rank him as one of the great builders of Europe and a true artist. In this small church, this organ has the sound of a cathedral organ, and it is truly thrilling. If anyone is ever to become enthusiastic about old organs, this is the one for him to hear. The 28 ranks are disposed as shown on page 245, and the supplementary information is as follows:

Compass: Manuals, CC-C3, with no C#, D#, F# or G# on
      low octave.
    Pedals CCC-D with no CC# or DD#
1955 pitch about one semitone above present standard. Two

pairs of small bells, about a major and minor third apart, attached to a wheel rotated by wind. Two golden stars in the case revolve. The device was used appropriately at Christmas time.

Another Schnitger close to Steinkirchen was visited at Neuenfelde. This organ was somewhat larger, but unfortunately it was so out of tune that it was impossible to form a fair judgment of its true musical character. This organ also has been greatly admired by connoisseurs such as Mr. Robert Noehren and I have no doubt when it is in reasonably good tune that it measures up to Steinkirchen. But my vote goes to the latter.

Mr. William Leslie Summer's series of articles in the "Organ Institute Quarterly" gives full details of the scaling of all the stops, and the composition of all the Mixtures in the Steinkirchen organ. Those who are interested in knowing all of the details of this outstanding organ of 260 years ago may find them here. I presume that they were obtained from Von Beckerath when he restored the organ. They could hardly be obtained otherwise, but they are certainly worth having. If one must build organs like the old masters, this is a choice one to use as a model.

Trips to Lübeck and Lüneberg took one day. The Jacobi-Kirche organs were played (15th Century Stellwagen). The one in the transcept was surprisingly effective for its size as compared with the gallery organ. Recently restored by Kemper. The organ in the Marienkirche was disappointing, although located in a magnificent building. Lübeck is one of the most charming and quaint old cities of Germany. Lüneberg's St. Johanniskirche has just another German organ of no great distinction.

Traveling by plane once more, the party stopped only for luncheon at Frankfurt, where we met the bus that had driven over from Amsterdam to meet us there, accompanied by a driver and a most intelligent and interesting guide by the name of Mr. Van Beek. He was invaluable to the tour. From then on, our travels were entirely by this bus. On the one-night stands, which we made for the most part, it was something to get 70 suitcases piled on the roof in the morning and down again at night.

We drove through Heidelberg, and settled in what was termed the Swallow's Nest, ten miles out of town on the Neckar River. This is a muddy stream, that holds a fascination for the Germans, and they make full use of it by riding bicycles, scooters and small cars along the adjacent highways and camping on its banks. Sunday morning was spent walking the streets of Heidelberg and looking at the interesting shops and University buildings, which are spread out in various parts of the city. Two Steinmeyer organs were heard. Sunday afternoon produced a long bus ride to Amorback, where the organ in the Abteikirche was played (P. & H. Stumm, 1782), being interrupted from time to time by services, and ten bus loads of German tourists.

FAMOUS OLD ORGANS IN HOLLAND, DENMARK AND GERMANY

Next day, on our way to Stuttgart, we stopped at Ludwigsburg, nearby, to visit the factory of Walcker. This is probably the largest organ factory in Germany. Herr Walcker-Mayer, fifth generation of Walckers was on hand to meet us, and several of his assistants showed us through the oldest buildings I have ever seen. The work turned out in the factory, however, was superior. I have previously described the various types of organs that are built here, both ancient and modern, and a combination of the two styles.

The Lake of Constance was just as beautiful as advertised. We piled out of the bus in a pouring rain to hear the organ in the Minster at Constance. The original 1518-22 organ has been replaced with a modern organ, that sounded very well. Even the modern electro-pneumatic German consoles, have only two to four "free" combinations that do not move the stops, but merely cancel the rocking tablets and establish the combination that is on the button that is pressed. The crescendo pedal is in the form of a large roller or "walze." These are the only registrational controls on even large German modern organs. Obviously the consoles are much cheaper to build than American consoles, but they seem to satisfy the requirements of the German organists.

By ferry across the Lake of Constance where the night was spent in the charming town of Überlingen. The next morning, our first stop was at Weingarten Monastery. We were all amused by the priest who attempted to demonstrate this famous organ by Joseph Gabler (1735). He was interested only in letting us hear the cuckoos, the cymbal stars, and the toy counter of this organ. Mr. Howes was beside himself to get the priest off the bench, so that he could demonstrate the pipes of the organ. The Principals here were particularly noble and pervasive even though the total effect of the full organ left something lacking. Four manuals, with the most amazing collection of trackers in the back of the organ, running to the various sections that have ever been put together. That the organ can be played at all is a marvelous achievement. Along with the myriad trackers, two small cables run to two sections, high on either side gallery with (of all things) electro-pneumatic action. This is, of course, a recent desecration of this great monument, the ultimate in tracker organs. Then on to Ochsenhausen Monastery where another Joseph Gabler organ, Opus 1 (1727-1729) was heard. This was not as good as Gabler's masterpiece at Weingarten.

Later in the afternoon some of the party went to Ottobeuren Monastery where another of the famous baroque organs was visited. The rest of us went on to the Cathedral at Ulm, one of the greatest Gothic churches in Germany. A Steinmeyer organ here, proved to be interesting. Finally we arrived at Augsburg. Another group went to see the famous Laukuff factory in Würtemberg. Laukuff has 350 employees and is the

FAMOUS OLD ORGANS IN HOLLAND, DENMARK AND GERMANY

largest builder of organ pipes and parts in Europe, with a world-wide trade. Three men to translate correspondence.

From Augsburg to Nuremburg, by way of the charming town of Dinkelsbuhl, where some of the party discovered more organs. If any one should try to retrace our trip on a map of southern Germany, he will see that we traced our steps many times, but it was all interesting.

The morning was spent in Nuremburg looking at a new Steinmeyer organ in a suburban church, that is typical of modern German work. The sections of the organ were divided at a great distance, and, it was quite a far cry from the classic German organ but successful in its own way.

Bayreuth in the afternoon for the opening performance of the Wagner Festival. Tannhauser was the opera, and it was done in a way to make Wagner turn over in his grave, with Hollywood touches, and almost complete lack of lighting.

We reached Munich by one o'clock Sunday, where the party were greatly entertained in the afternoon by playing and hearing all of the ancient musical instruments in the famous German Museum. Harpsichords, clavichords, organs and a real ancient Regal with striking reed pipes with small resonators. The curator was most cooperative and every one had a wonderful time. Two big Steinmeyer organs were heard. One in the concert hall of the German museum and another 1932 Steinmeyer spread out across the rear gallery of an octagonal shaped church. These are both good examples of present day German organ building, as was the large Walcker on which Finn Videro played a broadcast at Stuttgart in the broadcasting hall.

Arriving at Salzburg in time for luncheon, the afternoon was devoted to shopping and that evening came the musical high point of the trip. Mozart's "Magic Flute" done in the outdoor section of the Festspielhaus. Here was heard musical perfection - singers, orchestra, staging, conductor, and most of all, Mozart. The Salzburg Mozart Festivals are justifiably famous.

Innsbruck, like Salzburg is another picture-book Austrian city that is a tourist's paradise. Here we had a truly modern hotel with full plumbing conveniences, something very much lacking in all the other hotels.

Zurich, from where we flew back to New York City with stops at Frankfurt, Shannon and Gander, is a beautiful Swiss city. We had only time for a sightseeing tour here, where Mr. Franz Herrenschwand, the organ expert from Switzerland, who had joined our group in Amsterdam, really came into action, telling us of the Swiss organs we had missed seeing. There is always, we hope, another time. As it was, the count of organs visited ran to 54.

What conclusions may we draw from this trip? Let us go back to Mr. Howe's question as to whether or not these old European organs and the modern organs made in the ancient pattern have features that should be incorporated in modern American organs. The answer is that the best features of these organs have already been incorporated in many fine American organs built in the past ten years by a number of our builders. The "chiffing" Nason Flute, the Rohr Schalmei, the Krummhorn, the unenclosed Choir organs, with complete mutations (Rück Positiv) are all American adaptations of the classic organ.

Also we have learned the great advantage of an open position for the organ, with ample space around and above the pipes. Many new American organs have all of the pipes of the Great organ and Positiv organ completely out in the open. They are actually better located than the classic examples.

The new organs have Great, Pedal, and frequently Positiv with full flue choruses at all pitches. Besides this, we have a complete Swell division with an enclosed Choir organ, giving us the advantage of two expressive divisions, something completely lacking in the classic organ. Even though we grant that because of the long reverberation period of the magnificent European churches, the organs in these churches do not call for expressive divisions so urgently as do our typical American churches, such expressive divisions are valuable anywhere.

When all of these tonal features are combined with the ease of control of our modern consoles, and the many additional voices developed during the past 200 years, we not only have all of the best features of the classic organ but a great deal more besides. Let no one say that the present day American organs aren't the best in the world. They are two centuries ahead of the European organs, generally speaking. The best of the modern organs in England and Scotland must be excepted from this statement, but not those on the continent. By all means let us learn from the past, and adopt worthwhile features of organ building from the past, but let us also learn about and use, the tonal and mechanical improvements of the past two centuries.

A SELECTED BIBLIOGRAPHY *of the* ORGAN

*Indicates works referred to in the text. All are illustrated.

HISTORY AND CONSTRUCTION

*Audsley, George Ashdown.
    The Art of Organ-Building. New York, 1905. 2 vols.

*Bedos de Celles, Francois.
    L'Art du Facteur d'Orgues. Paris, 1766-78. 4 parts. (Reprint in two-thirds size. Kassel, 1934-36. 3 vols.)

Cellier, Alexandre.
    L'Orgue, ses Elements—son Histoire—son Esthetique. Paris, 1933. 254 p.

*Clutton & Dixon
    "The Organ", Grenville, London, 1950, 172 p.

Dufourcq, Norbet.
    Esquisse d'une Histoire de l'Orgue en France du XIIIe ^{au} XVIIIe Siecle. Paris, 1935. 508 p.

Ellerhorst, Winfrid.
    Handbuch der Orgelkunde. Einsiedeln, 1936. 850 p.

Goodrich, Wallace
    "The Organ in France"

*Hopkins, Edward John *and* Rimbault, Edward Francis.
    The Organ, Its History and Construction. 3d ed. London, 1877. 160+ 636 p.

*Hunt, Noel Aubrey Bonavia.
    The Church Organ. London, 1920. 108 p.
    *The Modern British Organ. London, 1947. 267 p.
    "The Organ Reed", 1950. J. Fischer & Bro.

*Koch, Caspar.
    "Gradus ad Parnassum", 1945, J. Fischer & Bro., 80 p.

*Leet, Leslie Norman.
    An Introduction to the Organ. Cranford, N. J., 1940. 160 p.

*Lewis, Walter *and* Lewis, Thomas.
    Modern Organ Building. 3d ed. London, 1939. 247 p.

*Miller, George Laing.
    The Recent Revolution in Organ Building. 2d ed. New York, 1913. 191 p.

Prick Van Wely, Max Arthur.
    Het Orgel en zign Meesters. 's-Gravenhage, 1931. 317 p.

BIBLIOGRAPHY

*Rupp, Emile.
   Die Entwicklungsgeschichte der Orgelbaukunst. Einsiedeln, 1929.
   467 p.

*Skinner, Ernest M.
   The Modern Organ. New York, 1917. 48 p.

Töpfer, Johann Gottlob *und* Smets, Paul
   Lehrbuch der Orgelbaukunst. 3. aufl. Mainz, 1936-48. 4 vols.

Van de Muren.
   "Het Orgel in de Nederlanden".

Westbald, Gösta.
   Kyrkoorgeln, Handbok for Organister och ovriga Orgelvanner. 2. uppl.
   Stockholm, 1941. 248 p.

Whitworth, Reginald.
   The Electric Organ. 2d ed. London, 1940.

*Wicks, Mark.
   Organ Building for Amateurs. London, 1887. 287 p.

ORGAN STOPS, TUNING AND VOICING

Audsley, George Ashdown.
   Organ-stops and their Artistic Registration. New York, 1921. 294 p.

Mahrenholz, Christhard.
   Die Orgelregister, ihre Geschichte und ihr Bau. 2. aufl. Kassel, 1942.
   329 p.

Smith, Hermann.
   Modern Organ Tuning. London, 1902. 120 p.

*Wedgwood, James Ingall.
   A Comprehensive Dictionary of Organ Stops. 8th ed. London, 1935.
   189 p.

ORGAN BUILDERS

*Flade, Ernst.
   Der Orgelbauer Gottfried Silbermann. Leipzig, 1926. 161 p.

Cavaillé-Coll, Cecile *et* Cavaillé-Coll, Emmanuel.
   Aristide Cavaille-Coll: ses Origines—sa via—ses oeuvres. Paris, 1929.
   183 p.

Wörsching, Joseph.
   Der Orgelbauer Karl Riepp (1710-1775) Mainz, 1940. 327 p.

BIBLIOGRAPHY

ORGAN CASES

Hill, Arthur George.
  The Organ-cases and Organs of the Middle Ages and Renaissance. London, 1883-91. 2 vols.

Kaufmann, Walter.
  Der Orgelprospekt in Stigeschichtlicher Entwicklung. 2 aufl. Mainz, 1939.

Servieres, Georges.
  La Decoration Artistique des Buffets d'Orgues. Paris, 1928. 228 p.

PERIODICALS

*The American Organist, New York.
*The Diapason. Chicago.
 The Organ. London.
 L'Orgue. Paris.
 De Schalmei. Amsterdam.

BIBLIOGRAPHIES

Burn, John Henry.
  "Bibliography of the Organ" *in* Dictionary of Organs and Organists. 2d ed. London, 1921. p. 99-134.
Ellerhorst: p. 824-830.
Cellier: p. 249-250.
Kaufmann: p. 104-106.
Leet: p. 125-145.
Prick Van Wely: p. 310-312.
Wedgwood: p. xiii-xv.

This is not an exhaustive bibliography. Its purpose is to act as a guide to further reading on various phases of organ history and construction. Many good works, as well as poor ones, have been omitted from the list. Likewise many languages are not represented. Books on the organ are known to exist in at least thirteen languages of which only five are represented here. An attempt has been made to include the best books in each classification irrespective of whether or not they are still in print. Where more than one edition exists only the latest has been given. It may be wondered why Sweden and the Netherlands are represented in such a short bibliography designed principally for English speaking people. The Scandinavian countries have taken an interest in the organ for centuries, and their literature dates back to the 18th century. While the literature is not extensive, it has appeared bit by bit down through the years. A quick glance at the Dutch literature will reveal an enormous output for that small country, and for including only one item an apology should be given.

372

BIBLIOGRAPHY

ORGAN MANUFACTURERS INCLUDE:

Aeolian-Skinner Organ Company, Inc.
Boston 25, Massachusetts

Austin Organs, Inc.
Hartford, Connecticut

Casavant Brothers Limited
Saint Hyacinthe, Quebec, Canada

Estey Organ Company
Brattleboro, Vermont

Hillgreen, Lane and Company
Alliance, Ohio

Holtkamp Organs
Cleveland 9, Ohio

Keates Organ Co., Ltd.,
Lucan, Ontario

The Kilgen Organ Company
4632 W. Florissant Avenue
St. Louis 15, Missouri

M. P. Moller, Inc.
Hagerstown, Maryland

J. H. and C. S. Odell and Company
18 Belmont Avenue
Yonkers 4, New York

The Reuter Organ Company
Lawrence, Kansas

Schantz Organ Company
Orrville, Ohio

Schlicker Organ Co.
1530 Military Road,
Buffalo 17, N.Y.

Standaart Organ Co.
Suffolk, Va.

Tellers Organ Co.
Erie, Pa.

The Wicks Organ Company
Highland, Illinois

Felix F. Schoenstein & Sons
San Francisco

ELECTRONIC ORGAN MANUFACTURERS INCLUDE:

Allen Organ Company
~~Allentown~~, *Macungie* Pennsylvania

Baldwin Piano Company
Cincinnati, Ohio
Address: Organ Division

Connsonata
Elkhart, Indiana

Hammond Instrument Company
4200 West Diversey Avenue
Chicago 39, Illinois

Haygren Organ Company
2212 East 75th Street
Chicago, Illinois

Minshall-Estey Organ
Brattleboro, Vermont

Wurlitzer Organ Company
Tonawanda, New York

In addition to the above list of builders, there are probably a hundred organ service and maintenance men throughout the country who occasionally build an organ from old and new parts. The names listed are those regularly engaged in building new organs as their main business.

Errors

160   172   182